Rehabilitation:

A COMMUNITY CHALLENGE

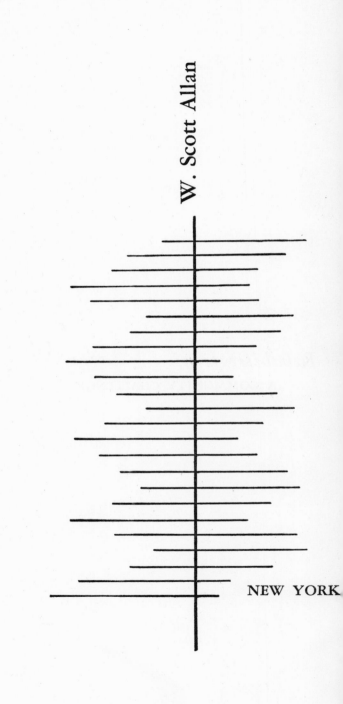

W. Scott Allan

NEW YORK

Rehabilitation:

A COMMUNITY CHALLENGE

JOHN WILEY & SONS, INC.

London · Chapman & Hall, Limited

Dedicated to the memory and the pioneering

contributions to rehabilitation of Bell Greve.

Foreword

WITHIN ONE GENERATION THE PHILOSOPHY OF rehabilitation of the physically disabled has become widely accepted and understood. This same period has been a time of rapid development of techniques in the broad range of medical, psychological, social, counseling, and employment services needed to enable the disabled person to develop independence and become self-sustaining. The rehabilitation movement has gained momentum particularly in the decade following World War II in which such dramatic success was achieved in the physical restoration of injured servicemen. Times are changing rapidly. No longer are there only a few dedicated individuals and a small group of rehabilitation specialists who are concerned. The general public, voluntary health agencies, government, and organized medicine have awakened to the challenge.

The magnitude of the concept of rehabilitation and the wide variety of agencies which at the present time are engaged in extensive activity in one or more of its aspects have brought us to a point where we need to assess seriously the means by which knowledge of techniques and principles can be translated into community action, to bring the vast potentialities of rehabilitation to greater numbers of disabled persons.

For example, the current thinking of organized medicine on these matters, as reflected in the following excerpts from a recent report of the Committee on Rehabilitation of the American Medical Association, is pertinent:

> There is need for increased utilization of the many ancillary personnel such as physical therapists, occupational therapists, clinical psychologists, and others who work under direct medical supervision. The physician also

vii

needs to become aware of the great amount of work already done in the
fields of education, sociology, and vocational counseling and placement. . . .
Every individual physician can and should assume responsibility for the
rehabilitation of his patients. Accomplishment does not depend so much
upon the rehabilitation center as it does upon the mobilization, integration, and provision of rehabilitation services. The physician should
ascertain what rehabilitative, community, and specialized medical services
are available, and direct his patient to them as necessary. Although both
federal and private national organizations are interested in rehabilitation,
actual service is provided to the individual at the local level.

In the context of these times of rapid developments and concern for
the future, *Rehabilitation: A Community Challenge* appears most
propitiously. The author's grasp is extensive, and he has thoroughly
penetrated his subject. A marked clarity of vision has enabled him
to project an orderly development of rehabilitation services that would
make the most of community resources.

Reasoned consideration of how to reach the greatest number of
handicapped persons with a program of rehabilitation almost inevitably would lead to the conclusion that rehabilitation services must
be community-oriented. This is where the disabled individual must
be reached, and this is where the interest and financial support must
be generated to initiate and sustain the necessary services. There
may be differences of opinion on the details of how this can be
accomplished, but with the basic concept there can be no quarrel.
Among the voluntary health agencies, particularly those that have
a program both national and local in structure, there is a growing
recognition that close, effective interagency working relationships are
essential. There is no proper place in the community for a self-
centered agency that pursues its preferred course without consideration of or relation to those other agencies having similar or related
interests.

Mr. Allan instills new meaning into the well-worn expressions
"coordination" and "integration," and neatly distinguishes between
the more easily achieved harmonious adjustment or functioning of
parts which is signified by the first, and the much deeper process of
identification of aims and objectives of parts within a united whole,
which he conceives to be the meaning of the second. It is to be hoped
that full integration of services can be achieved without loss of the
very real values inherent in the present widely diversified pattern of
agencies composed of volunteers dedicated to particular problems.

Illustrative of Mr. Allan's firm grasp of the issues is his chapter
Social Laws and Rehabilitation, which touches upon the delicate subject of legislation on behalf of the disabled. Many workers in

rehabilitation have been concerned that legislation dealing with such problems as public assistance, social security, workmen's compensation, and veterans, be designed to aid in the process of rehabilitation rather than to provide a financial reward for continued disability.)

Mr. Allan's vision of a perfect community organization for rehabilitation of the physically handicapped is probably utopian. As a master plan, however, it is inherently flexible, and many compromises with the detail could be accomplished without diminishing the validity of the basic outline. It deserves careful attention, and should contribute greatly to enlightened planning of rehabilitation services for the physically handicapped in communities throughout the country.

Dean W. Roberts, M.D.
Executive Director
National Society for Crippled Children and Adults, Inc.

Preface

THE BASIC CONCERN OF REHABILITATION IS NOT
professions or disciplines, not facilities or techniques, not agencies
or programs, but people. Human beings do not live as isolated individuals, neither do they suffer in isolation. This means that restoration of the handicapped person to a fuller existence, a greater
opportunity, does not happen by chance but neither is it the particular
province of any one profession or group. It is rather the responsibility of the community—it calls for community planning, action,
and support.

We are in the throes of a change from the acceptance of dependency,
with appropriate public responsibility for custodial and supportive
measures, as being the lot of the handicapped, to a new insistence
upon independence, through maximum physical or mental restoration, social acceptance, and vocational opportunity, as the right of
the disabled. The comparatively recent growth of the rehabilitation
idea and the fact that it has been the product of many individual
and group activities have resulted in a scattered, complicated, and
sometimes controversial series of ideas, aims, methods. It has become
increasingly difficult for any planning group to readily gather together
significant facts which will support prospective and collective action
toward new or improved rehabilitation programs or facilities. Education, in this field of rehabilitation which involves so many different
aspects and encroaches upon so many areas of professional or technical training, has been erratic and confused, by reason of the multiplicity of material and data in professional journals, association
proceedings, and the minds of knowledgeable people but a relative
paucity of definitive literature, especially in book form. This book is

intended to draw some of this material and these ideas together to form a source of reference and guidance for all those interested in the field, particularly those at the planning level of community activity.

The focal point of the book is that more governmental bureaus, more specialized programs for selected categories of activity, more associations for this or that particular disease, are not the long-range answers to effective rehabilitation. The real solution lies in the incorporation of basic principles and tested methods into our existing medical and therapy facilities; public and private community programs; health, welfare, and social agencies; industrial operations, insurance practices, and social laws, so that the job is done not piecemeal or by category but by coordinated effort and integration of the rehabilitation idea as basically sound for all disease and injury classifications—for all disabled, regardless of the cause of their disability. Successful rehabilitation must be broad in scope, practical in purpose and integrated in practice. It cannot go forward without general participation; it requires the respect and confidence of all those concerned.

The vista of rehabilitation planning may be as broad as sensitive imagination and careful planning can make it. It should not be dominated by individual interest, by single disability concern, by agency publicity desire. Rehabilitation is the best practical demonstration of one's faith in his fellow man. As such it calls for the highest sort of dedication, confidence and cooperation. The community can effectively translate the wide range of individual effort into a meaningful plan for the best advantage of the disabled in its area. Although all in this fascinating field of activity become impatient at apparent delay, at frustrating lack of communications, at stifling shortcomings in enthusiasm and cooperation, tremendous gain has already been made. Considering the inertia of human thought and established practice, the broadening scope of rehabilitation has been little short of startling. Our continued dedication to community, national, and international improvement in the opportunities for the disabled cannot fail to achieve even more significant gains in the years ahead.

The book is not intended as a "how-to-do-it" manual of detailed scientific or technical information. It is rather a broad approach to the several aspects of rehabilitation, stressing key facts and general principles rather than particular plans or methods, many of which can be more readily obtained from supplemental reference data or from research into existing programs, services and facilities. It is aimed at the general reader, the student and the professional worker in the field who are interested in a review of the development of rehabilitation concept and methodology; current services, facilities and personnel involved, and the interpretation of the community pattern and emphasis which seems the surest guarantee of effective rehabilitation now and in the future. No attempt has been made to include individual case histories to illustrate particular points; they would add materially to the length of the book and any agency or worker in the field could supply scores of equally dramatic and inspiring accounts. Statistics and tabular computations have been held to a minimum.

Verbiage of the field has been somewhat of a barrier in the development of understanding of rehabilitation by the general public and, together with the concentration of material in the professional and technical publications, has possibly accounted for the marked lack of definitive literature on rehabilitation for the general reader and student. An attempt has been made, in this presentation, to avoid confusing terminology such as "frame of reference," "rationale," "client," "dynamic"; any medical language which would need much interpretation to the lay reader, and even such words as "problem." I suspect few of us, including the handicapped, relish the thought of being referred to as a "problem."

If the facts and ideas presented succeed in stimulating individual or community thought and action toward more realistic and effective rehabilitation services, the hope and aim of the author will have been realized.

Space would never permit the proper acknowledgement of all those who have helped the author in this effort. Many have assisted over a period of several years by encouragement, by interest in speeches or articles, by suggestions for content, by even the contribution of a thought on some small area of comment. It would be remiss, however, to omit particular mention of the advice, help and interest of Stanwood L. Hanson, Bell Greve, Roy E. Patton, Willis C. Gorthy, Mary E. Switzer and her staff at the Office of Vocational Rehabilitation, especially Henry Redkey; Alfred L. Frechette, Donald Wilson, Dean Roberts, Ruby Oscarson, Eugene J. Taylor, Esther Walther, Howard Johnston, Kenneth N. Palmer, George Sawyer and Lindley M. Branson.

Special thanks is due to Miss Mary C. Schmitz and Miss Elizabeth Nelson for their patient and rewarding assistance in the typing of the manuscript and the research for useful material.

W. SCOTT ALLAN

Scituate, Mass.
January, 1958

Contents

"Men who are occupied in the restoration of health to other men, by the joint exertion of skill and humanity, are above all the great of the earth. They even partake of divinity, since to preserve and renew is almost as noble as to create"

VOLTAIRE 1694–1778
A Philosophical Dictionary

"That everyone shall exert himself, in that state of life in which he is placed, to practice true humanity towards his fellow-men; on that depends the future of mankind"

ALBERT SCHWEITZER 1875–
Out of My Life and Thought

CHAPTER 1

The Concept
of Rehabilitation

REHABILITATION IS A BIG WORD WITH A BIGGER purpose. The term had its origin in the civil or canon law of a feudal society in the Middle Ages. Its common meaning at that time was the restoration to a baron or knight of a former right, rank, or privilege which had been lost or forfeited, often through the whim or disfavor of his liege lord. A somewhat later and broader definition included the restoring to good repute by the clearing of unjust or unfounded charges, a re-establishment of one's good name. Joan of Arc, for example, was formally rehabilitated in 1456.

With the advent of modern social thinking and practice, the word has come to mean principally the restoration of a person to his former capacity, most often his physical or mental capacity. However, the term "rehabilitation" has been loosely applied to theories and practices which range from penology to public housing. In the minds of many, rehabilitation includes also what perhaps may be more properly called "habilitation," which is not restoring but achieving independence, self-care, and work potential in the first instance; as, for example, in the child born blind or with cerebral palsy. If we are to define rehabilitation properly in the light of its objectives rather than applied services, rehabilitation is making a person aware of his potential and then providing him with the means of attaining that potential.

In its more commonly restricted application, as used and explained in this book, it refers to a combination of disciplines, techniques, and specialized facilities which are intended to provide physical restoration, psychological adjustment, personal and vocational counseling, job training, and placement. The National Council on Rehabilitation in 1942 issued a definition of rehabilitation which is still widely quoted and used: "restoration of the handicapped to the fullest physical, mental, social, vocational and economic usefulness of which they are capable."[1]

Dr. Leonard Mayo has aptly referred to rehabilitation as being first, a philosophy, second, an objective, and third, a method. In that sense, perhaps rehabilitation began with the first time that historic man concerned himself with the welfare of his fellow human. The broad concept is certainly not a completely new one in philosophy, medicine, or the social sciences. In the fascinating account of Marco Polo of his travels to the Mongol empire of the Great Khan, he describes the watchmen patrolling the streets who, if "they notice any person who from lameness or other infirmity is unable to work, they place him in one of the hospitals, of which there are several in every part of the city, founded by the ancient kings, and liberally endowed. When cured, he is obliged to work at some trade."[2]

Yet it must be admitted that, for many centuries, man's inhumanity to man was most evident in the treatment of those who were afflicted by physical or mental incapacity. The killing or banishment of the deformed or weakling child or incapacitated elder was rife among earlier civilizations; in still later times, the congenitally malformed or those crippled by accident or illness were deemed to have been cursed by the devil, to be actually a witch, or to have been the victim of the "evil eye." Abandonment to beggary and ridicule was the rule rather than the exception. It is not by chance that the court jester was a misshapen creature, forced to gain favor by capitalizing on his own misfortune. There was a fatalism or literal acceptance of the will of the Almighty which acted as an effective barrier to any efforts at changing or improving the lot of the crippled or the deranged.

Since physical and mental handicap have been the objects of derision, fear, discrimination, and even hatred, from the earliest cultures until very recent time, it is not difficult to appreciate why vestiges of the belief that the crippled are in some way connected with sin and evil, that they are to be avoided and feared, still cast a shadow upon our whole approach to the question of the handicapped in a modern society. In this sense of vital concern for the individual, particularly the person disabled by disease, illness, or injury and the comprehensive

[1] National Council on Rehabilitation, "Symposium on The Processes of Rehabilitation," Cleveland 1944, p. 6.

[2] *The Travels of Marco Polo,* revised and edited by Manuel Komroff, The Heritage Press, N. Y., 1934, pp. 326–327.

planning for improvement of his lot, rehabilitation is a late-comer on the stage of man's social progress. It is probable that the two principal factors in the gradual development of such concern were Christianity and democracy. The Christian teachings of brotherhood, of charity, of the dignity of human life and man's essential worth, together with the individual rights and freedoms, the mutual dependence and trust of democratic practice, formed the roots of our mounting concern for the medical, social and economic welfare of our fellow man which has characterized the latter half of the nineteenth and first half of the twentieth centuries.

From the earliest forms of the healing art, through the wise counseling and individual patient relationship of the nineteenth-century horse and buggy doctor, to the present age of medical specialization, the physician has always recognized and utilized some aspects of rehabilitative therapy. But rehabilitation today is more than merely the palliative or curative treatment for injury or illness which medicine has always provided. It is a concentration upon the crippling after-effects of disease and injury which were formerly regarded as hopeless and as the expected consequences by doctors and laymen alike. The conviction that forces, both lay and medical, can be marshaled to prevent these disabling complications is the true significance of rehabilitation and its real distinction from preventive or curative treatment.

Pioneers in the fields of psychology and social work, whether concerned with illness, alcoholism, or slum housing, knew and practiced rehabilitation. But again, the development of concentrated medical and therapy techniques for maximum physical and mental restoration, of counseling and guidance toward specific adjustment and performance goals, of specialized facilities and equipment, of guided training to develop work skills, of testing, analysis and placement methods—these are the contributions which have made rehabilitation a focal point of private and public endeavour in our own day and age. The wide range of its present application, involving many disciplines and diverse humanitarian and economic factors, has awakened public interest and resulted in legislative action, community planning, and education for specific service in the several aspects of rehabilitation.

Rehabilitation, in its practical conception, is not only the services and techniques of functional restoration but also the organization of all the efforts of all the people involved, as well as the end result or goal of those efforts. It is individual adjustment and reintegration which involves the acceptance of the program designed to accomplish maximum restoration. While necessarily patient-centered and oriented, there is a positive quality to rehabilitation activity which implies not coercion but active attempts to counsel, to lead, to demonstrate the value of the services to be rendered, to convince the patient that his acceptance and cooperation are vital to the complete fulfillment of the objective; namely, his return to self-sufficiency.

Time-wise, successful rehabilitation starts with the onset of disability, not after the patient leaves his hospital bed or after some crucial point of ineffective living has been reached. Practically all those concerned with the development and operation of rehabilitation programs agree that, if it is to be truly effective, rehabilitation must start early—that each passing month results in greater fixation of disability and reduces the opportunity for maximum restoration of physical, mental, social, and economic function.

From the point of view of its location, rehabilitation services are provided in many places, running the gamut from hospital to vocational school and industrial plant. Its personnel are varied and form a cross section of the professions, the technical trades, the volunteer lay public, and government service. More than those who directly work in the field and provide some aspect of service, rehabilitation activity is peculiarly intermingled with almost every aspect of our daily living and may involve all manner of persons from the physician and the educator to the business executive and even the man next door.

Why has rehabilitation rather suddenly become such an important subject and activity in our modern existence? Partly because of the spiritual and social concern for human welfare which is the mark of our age, but also because of the economic pressures of the times. In a highly industrialized culture, with increased urbanization, constant striving for better standards of living for all and the staggering national production rate which goes with that ambition, and with our new responsibility for world conditions, we cannot, as a nation, any longer afford the luxury of a large segment of handicapped and nonproductive people. The growing burden of their continued support by public welfare or private charity, the loss of their potential work skills, is completely out of step with our burgeoning economy. There is likewise an indefinable challenge to all our modern knowledge and creative talent in this task of removing or markedly lessening the effects of disability. Our professional people, our educators, our technicians, our labor leaders, our industrialists, yes, even our politicians, are struck with the necessity of conquering this blight on human enjoyment and fulfillment.

Yet, fundamentally, although all these pressures are felt and recognized as stimulating forces for rehabilitation activity, it has gained its momentum from the fact that people like to be involved. It has great personal appeal and satisfaction, a sense of accomplishment that reaches deeper into our hearts and minds than almost any other human endeavour, with the exception of the practice of medicine and nursing or the spiritual guidance of the clergy. Unlike those specific professions, however, rehabilitation is a philosophy and practice in which all kinds of people, professional or layman, can and do share. Whatever the reason for the contact with rehabilitation programs, there are few satisfactions which can compare with that of having had a part, however modest, in the lifting of a human mind out of despair and the restoring of a crippled body to full activity. To the Christian, Moslem, Hebrew, or Buddhist—to any real believer in the great religious faiths of the world—there can be no greater accomplishment than the salvation of the individual, the restoration of his worth, his dignity, his sense of accomplishment in the eyes of his God. In this lies the strength and the promise of rehabilitation as a concept for our time and for all people.

CHAPTER 2

Rehabilitation Comes of Age

INCREASING POPULATIONS LEAD NATURALLY TO broadened interest in and responsibility for social welfare. The rise of public interest in the need of rehabilitation services in the community is no exception to the rule. When social life and even much of the work in the United States was centered in the home, there was less of a problem in caring for the crippled child or the mentally deficient adult. If home care by relatives or friends was impractical, asylum or custodial care of some sort was the accepted practice. With the social and economic pressures of our great urban populations of today, relegating the handicapped to home confinement or to a lifetime in an institution is both morally and financially unsound.

Interestingly enough, some of the earliest efforts in the direction of what we now term rehabilitation were made by private interests or groups, frequently in one specialized area of disability. Around the turn of the century, the work with crippled children involved restorative procedures and exercises carried out by orthopedists as well as by nurses and therapists. The Shriners and other associations or agencies sponsored and supported the development of specialized hospitals as well as individual programs of care, maintenance, and education on a national, state, or community level. Organizations such as the National Tuberculosis Association began to emphasize total bed-to-job care of the patient and this soon became one of many programs devoted to one particular kind of handicap. Much of the thinking and action was directed along lines of physical restoration, was often limited in scope and diversional in character.

The beginnings of that unique facility which has come to be called "a rehabilitation center" were seen during the same period. In 1889 the Cleveland Rehabilitation Center had its inception in a program for crippled children which was gradually oriented toward the problems of the disabled adult as well. The Institute for the Crippled and Disabled in 1917 and the Curative Workshop of Milwaukee in 1919 were other pioneering ventures in this new field. Here were the positive results of an idea that rehabilitation needed something more than principles and techniques; that it needed also a special place to carry out a definitive program.

The first nation-wide public effort in rehabilitation was the vocational training program begun in 1918 under the Smith-Sears Veterans' Rehabilitation Act. Individual states such as Massachusetts and New Jersey enacted rehabilitation laws for the vocational training of disabled civilians and by 1920 a dozen states had such laws. In the same year, Congress passed the Vocational Rehabilitation Act which provided for federal grants to each state for the purpose of providing vocational training, counseling and job placement for disabled civilians. The programs were to be administered by a state vocational agency usually operating within the framework of the state division, commission or board of education. The original appropriations were considered to be on a temporary and experimental basis. Federal and state expenditures were matched on a 50–50 basis. Succeeding years found the Congress extending the program and rehabilitation, at least in its vocational aspects, had become a real concern of the American taxpayer.

About this same time, schools of physical therapy and occupational therapy began to develop their programs and curricula along lines which recognized the value of an early rehabilitation program, both in the general hospital and in the specialized workshop or center. Social workers, particularly medical social workers, began to recognize and follow the counseling and home care concepts which were later to become so important in the development of a comprehensive rehabilitation program.

In 1935 the vocational rehabilitation program was established nationally on a permanent basis under the provisions of the Social Security Act. The federal act had been administered first by the Federal Board of Vocational Education and later by the Office of Education. The Office was a constituent unit of the Department of Interior until 1939 when it was transferred to the Federal Security Agency. The National Health Survey conducted in 1935–1936 by the U. S. Health Service attempted an estimate of the total number of persons in the United States who were disabled by chronic disease, injury, or congenital impairment. This survey dramatized the scope of the rehabilitation problem and emphasized the need of developing our national thinking and action in the direction of a comprehensive attack upon all types of disability rather than helping merely those who were vocationally handicapped.

Development of modern rehabilitation programs was given its greatest impetus during World War II. Professional and public interest and concern was stimulated by several significant developments: (1) advances in surgical technique and drug therapy, (2) armed forces and Veterans' Administration medical care and rehabilitation programs, (3) interest in the job placement of the returning veteran, (4) expansion of the federal–state program, (5) increased use of handicapped workers by industry, (6) growth of rehabilitation facilities, and (7) development of physical medicine as a medical specialty.

Military casualties during World War II were greater than any war in which the United States was previously involved. Coincident with this great problem of medical care came significant advances in the use of highly skilled surgical "teams," immediate transportation by air from front-line first-aid stations to well-equipped military hospitals far behind the lines or even across the seas, and the use of the new "wonder drugs" to combat surgical shock, infection, and other post-injury complications. This kind of attack upon the medical problems of battle casualties made it possible for most of these cases to survive the early critical phases and to become long-term problems of medical handling and rehabilitation. Injuries to the spinal cord resulting in complete or partial paralysis, multiple amputations, severe burns of the body surface, or sucking wounds of the chest no longer died within days or months of the injury as the result of shock or other complications. The survival of these severe disability cases presented a challenge to those interested in salvaging something of social and economic value from this generation of "lost" young men.

The reconditioning and rehabilitation programs set up by the medical and paramedical personnel of the armed forces and the Veterans' Administration made a significant contribution to the development of greater knowledge of the effectiveness of rehabilitation methods. Early exercise, reconstructive surgery, early ambulation, improved prosthetic devices and individual fitting and training in their use, and psychological counseling, all under competent medical supervision, proved eminently successful. Many disabled service men were returned to active duty, but many more were discharged back to their communities in a physical and mental condition which would enable them to more easily adjust to active and useful civilian life.

Interest in the more effective job placement of the returning veteran of World War II was a continuation and expansion of the philosophy and practice which followed World War I. Public Law 16 of the 73rd Congress, passed in 1943, made provision for increased vocational rehabilitation opportunities for the disabled veteran. At the same time, veterans' associations, public agencies such as the state employment services, business groups, and insurance associations carried on programs of education which bore fruit in increased job opportunities for the veteran, disabled or not.

The amendments to the original Vocational Rehabilitation Act provided for in the so-called Barden–LaFollette Act, or Public Law 113 of the 78th Congress taking effect in July 1943, significantly expanded and improved the vocational program for civilians. The basic changes were liberalized fiscal provisions and broadened scope of the services to be furnished. Physical restoration was to be utilized as well as training and counseling to accomplish the end result. Medical examinations and treatment, limited hospitalization, and corrective surgery were authorized as necessary concomitants of the vocational rehabilitation process. Such practical adjuncts as the cost of training supplies, tools and equipment, licenses, necessary travel and maintenance during training were added to the individual pattern for making the handicapped person employable. Fixed ceilings on the grants-in-aid to the states were removed and total annual expenditures of both federal and state funds began to move up toward the thirty-million mark.

Manpower needs of industry, during the period of tremendous production acceleration in the war years, were such that suggestions for utilization of handicapped persons for certain jobs found a much more ready response. The term "selective placement" began to be used, and its true significance was to be found in the increasing number of previously disabled individuals who were able to take their place in industry and make a real contribution to national defense. Many specialized assembly jobs and even production-line assignments provided dramatic demonstrations of the value of the previously untapped reserve of manpower represented by the thousands of handicapped individuals in the population.

Development of additional rehabilitation facilities was a natural corollary to the increasing public interest in and understanding of the possibilities of complete rehabilitation for even the most severe of physical and mental disabilities. Twenty-one new rehabilitation centers were established in the decade between 1940 and 1950. At the same time, a number of general hospitals began to develop concentrated therapy programs and medical staff orientation toward rehabilitation, in connection with both in-patient and out-patient care. Sheltered workshops and vocational training schools began to visualize and practice a rehabilitation philosophy.

Physical medicine, as a treatment method and as a specialized part of medical practice, had its roots in the use of heat, massage, exercise, and mechanical devices in earlier years by medical and nonmedical practitioners. The development of physical and occupational therapy, as disciplines which were to prove most effective in the physical restoration process and as working tools for the physician's use, standardized the practices and the aims of medical rehabilitation. The success of the restoration methods and programs in Europe, in the armed forces during the war, led to increasing interest in the establishment of a definite specialty within medicine. The Baruch Committee on Physical Medicine, established in 1943, and the dedicated efforts of doctors such as the Mayos, Krusen, Rusk, Deaver, and others laid the groundwork for the establishment of the Council on Physical Medicine of the American Medical Association in 1944 and the eventual creation of a specialty Board of Physical Medicine in 1947. The words "and Rehabilitation" were added to the name of this Board and to this practicing specialty two years later. Comprehensive rehabilitation had indeed become a "third phase of medical care,"[1] the others being preventive and curative.

In addition to the specific developments outlined above, it should not be overlooked that the nation was maturing rapidly in its general social consciousness. The Roosevelt Era, with its New Deal, Social Security, Unemployment Compensation, Fair Employment Practices Act, and other types of socioeconomic legislation, served as a practical demonstration of our increasing concern for the minority; the sufferer from discrimination and prejudice; the victim of financial, physical or mental distress. Human freedoms and individual rights had become more than political catchwords; they were becoming the hallmark of the twentieth century—the social and economic responsibility of each one of us.

In the person of Franklin Delano Roosevelt, the United States and the free world had a dynamic example of rehabilitation in a man who had overcome tremendous physical handicap to the point of being able to assume the duties and responsibilities of the most exacting job

[1] Rusk, Howard A., and Taylor, Eugene, *New Hope for the Handicapped*, Harper & Brothers, New York, 1949, pp. 78–90.

in the world. Largely through his inspiration, the March of Dimes was organized as a means of national fund raising to provide research, teaching, treatment, facilities, and equipment for the benefit of polio sufferers. A whole host of similar drives for specific diseases or disabilities followed in the succeeding years. Regrettable as this trend may have been from an academic and organizational standpoint, it has provided the funds, has dramatized the problem, and has focused public attention on the need. Rehabilitation has been a working goal for much of the effort and money enlisted in these specialized campaigns.

The ten years following the close of World War II were marked by steady progress in the development of rehabilitation programs and facilities but also by growing realization that the scope of rehabilitation was increasing far more rapidly than available funds, personnel, or facilities. For this reason, 1954 was to prove a key year in rehabilitation. On January 18, of that year, for the first time in our history, a president was to devote an entire special message to the Congress to the subject of the health needs of the nation, with a major portion of the message being directly concerned with rehabilitation. President Eisenhower asked the Congress to consider the needs carefully and to draft legislation which would help to meet those needs. More than the request for Congressional action, however, the special message meant that the whole job of rehabilitation, in all its many aspects, had now become a matter for national concern and action. The spirit of the message is indicated by the following excerpts:

One such goal is that the means for achieving good health should be accessible to all. A person's location, occupation, age, race, creed, or financial status should not bar him from enjoying this access.

Second, the results of our vast scientific research, which is constantly advancing our knowledge of better health protection and better care in illness, should be broadly applied for the benefit of every citizen. There must be the fullest cooperation among the individual citizen, his personal physician, the research scientists, the schools of professional education, and our private and public institutions and services—local, State, and Federal. . . .

Considerations of both humanity and national self-interest demand that steps be taken now to improve this situation. Today, for example, we are spending three times as much in public assistance to care for non-productive disabled people as it would cost to make them self-sufficient and taxpaying members of their communities. Rehabilitated persons as a group pay back in Federal income taxes many times the cost of their rehabilitation.

There are no statistics to portray the full depth and meaning in human terms of the rehabilitation program, but clearly it is a program that builds a stronger America. . . .

Physical rehabilitation services for our disabled people can best be given in hospitals or other facilities especially equipped for the purpose. Many thousands of people remain disabled today because of the lack of such facilities and services.[2]

Spurred by the President's concern, hearings were held by committees of the Senate and House with the result that final legislation to strengthen and expand the nation's resources for rehabilitation of the disabled was drafted in the form of Public Law 565 of the 83rd Congress. The new law was passed unanimously by both houses on July 7 and 8, 1954 and was signed by the President on August 3, 1954.

In the first place, it re-emphasizes to all the world the great value which we in America place upon the dignity and worth of each individual human being. Second, it is a humanitarian investment of great importance, yet it saves substantial sums of money for both Federal and State governments.[3]

The story of accomplishment for 1954 does not end here. The Medical Facilities Survey and Construction Act (Public Law 482) was passed by the 83rd Congress and signed by the President on July 12 of that year. This law amended the earlier Hill–Burton Hospital Construction Act in such a way that federal funds were to be made available to assist the states in determining their need for new or improved rehabilitation facilities and in developing construction programs for such facilities. Amendments made to the Social Security Act in 1954 provided for the preservation of benefit rights under old-age and survivor's insurance for workers and their dependents during periods of extended total disability—the so-called "disability freeze." This provision, together with the extension of Social Security to new millions of previously uncovered persons, meant many additional opportunities to discover and assist disabled workers.

It was an inspired executive and congressional effort to help the handicapped prepare themselves for new lives—indeed the beginning of a new era for disabled men and women.

In addition to the legislative changes and improvements at this time, these years witnessed the beginning of real emphasis on the need of practical rehabilitation in workmen's compensation cases. The American College of Surgeons adopted a set of operating principles which stated that "rehabilitation of the injured worker and his return to gainful employment is one of the basic concepts of workmen's compensation."[4] In this pronouncement, the College was re-emphasizing

[2] Health Message to Congress, White House Press Release, Washington, January 18, 1954.

[3] President's remarks at signing ceremony of Senate Bill 2759, N. Y. Times, Aug. 4, 1954.

[4] "Principles for Rehabilitation of Injured Worker Established," reprint from Bull. Am. Coll. Surgeons, (July–August, 1952).

and reinforcing an idea which had also been the subject of concern and public statement by labor representatives such as Jerome Pollack, administrators like Under-Secretary of Labor Arthur Larson, and research scholars such as the Somers.

During the years since 1954, most of the developments in the field of rehabilitation have represented a slow consolidation of the gains made up to that time. The impact of the rehabilitation idea upon medicine, colleges and universities, industry, public administration, politics, social welfare, and the average citizen has been erratic but noticeable. The 1956 amendments to the Social Security Law which provide for payment of benefits to disabled persons over age 50, and the coincident requirement for rehabilitation of such persons where possible, presents tremendous possibility for discovery and referral of cases to rehabilitation services. Continued increases in the Congressional appropriations for rehabilitation activity by federal and state programs means corresponding enlargement and extension of services to the handicapped. Research, training, increased community recognition and financing, and appreciable gains in numbers of facilities and disabled persons served reflect the surge of public interest in the subject.

Although 1954 marked a significant turning point in the progress of rehabilitation in this country, it cannot be assumed that all the needs have been met or even that sound planning is under way in all areas to eventually meet those needs. If such were the case, there would be no purpose to this book. The truth of the matter lies in the fact that recognition of the need in many quarters has become crystallized—that we have begun to accept the responsibility, but the real challenge lies ahead for all groups and individuals concerned. Can we meet the challenge of our present and future needs in rehabilitation? Succeeding chapters will discuss specific areas of rehabilitation in the light of this question. Only time can provide the actual answer.

CHAPTER 3

The Size
of the Problem

ESTIMATES ON A NATIONAL SCALE OF THE total number of disabled persons, of those handicapped by particular disabilities or of the chronically ill, have been many and varied. Some estimates have been little short of sheer guesses; others have been based on selective official reportings or on samplings from contacted individuals. Even estimating, much less determining, the percentage or the total number of disabled in the country is extremely difficult, without huge expenditures of time, money, and effort. Since we have no central health or social agency to whom all disabling conditions or illnesses are reported, it is possible only to use partial figures (many of which contain duplication or other statistical error) and to project these toward a tentative national total.

Although the U. S. Public Health Service and some other research groups had conducted limited illness surveys in earlier years, the first real attempt to review the problem on a national scale was the study made by the Committee on the Costs of Medical Care during the years 1928–1931. One hundred and thirty representative communities in 17 states and the District of Columbia and families of all income levels were covered in a house-to-house canvass. Final tabulations related to some 39,185 individuals in 8758 families. Whereas much of the study data was devoted to the receipt of and cost of medical care, the survey showed that, in the population studied, about 3 persons in each 1000 were reported as disabled throughout the study year. This figure did not include those in institutions. Disability was defined as being a physical or mental condition that prevented an individual

14

from carrying on his usual duties, such as working, going to school, or keeping house.[1] If this figure was valid and was applied to the national population of the nearest census year (1930), it would produce a figure of 368,325 disabled persons (outside of institutions) in a total U. S. population of 122,775,000. In the light of later studies, this figure seems ridiculously low for any true evaluation of the incidence of disabling conditions.

In 1935–1936 the U. S. Public Health Service conducted the National Health Survey to determine, among many other health statistics, the number of persons disabled by illness or suffering from chronic disease or impairment, whether disabling or not. A house-to-house canvass in 83 representative cities produced a study total of 2,502,391 individuals in 703,092 households. Tabulation of the so-called "invalid" group (described as persons who, by reason of disease, accident, of physical or mental impairment, were unable to work, go to school, keep house, or carry on their usual activities for a full year preceding the survey visit) revealed 11.7 out of each 1000 in the surveyed population were in this category. If this figure were applied to the national population for the nearest census year (1940), it would produce a figure of slightly more than 1,580,000 disabled persons (outside of institutions) in a total U. S. population of 131,669,000.[2]

The Bureau of the Census, in its Current Population Survey of February 1949 and September 1950, obtained data on the prevalence and duration of disability. These monthly surveys are ordinarily designed to provide, from samplings of 25,000 households, current data on employment. In these two monthly studies, however, questions on disability were added to the survey schedule, as part of a joint project of the Social Security Administration, Public Health Service, and the Office of Vocational Rehabilitation. Disabled persons were considered as those who, on the day of the contact, were unable to do their regular work or carry on other duties because of disease or injury (it included those who had a long-term physical or mental impairment which prevented or limited their working and excluded those in institutions). The survey was limited to persons between the ages of 14 and 64. The most significant figures were those relating to the group who had been disabled for more than one year at time of interview. It was estimated from the sampling that 1.70% of the civilian, noninstitutional, popu-

[1] U. S. Dept. of Health, Education and Welfare, "Study of the Homebound Programs for Physically Handicapped Homebound Individuals," Feb. 2, 1955 Report to the Congress, pp. 5 and 6.

[2] Division of Public Health Methods, National Institute of Health, U. S. Public Health Service—*Bibliography Series No. 5, Sickness and Medical Care Series,* Bulletin Nos. 1, 6, and 9, "The National Health Survey 1935–36," Washington 1938.

lation for the indicated age group had a disabling condition or illness which had incapacitated them for more than a year. Applied to the national population for the nearest census year (1950), it would produce a figure of somewhat more than 2,561,000 disabled persons (outside of institutions) in a total U. S. population of 150,697,000.[3] At the present time, a much more comprehensive survey is planned by the Bureau of the Census on the extent of handicapping conditions in the U. S. population.

The Commission on Chronic Illness, as a result of its concern for health services needed by disabled persons and particularly as a result of its Conference on Care of the Long-Term Patient held in March, 1954, has ably translated some of the earlier study figures to the present-day and the future populations of the United States. Of particular interest in considering the over-all problem for rehabilitation in the United States was their adjustment of the findings of the National Health Survey to the 1950 population. Their resulting estimate was to the effect that approximately 28 million persons (one out of every six) has some disabling or nondisabling physical or mental impairment. It is further estimated that 3.5% (35 out of each 1000) of the national population were disabled more than three months—this would produce a total of 5,298,000 on the basis of the 1950 census figures[4] and, with projections for estimated population[5] in 1960 and 1970, would mean totals of 6,383,000 and 7,413,000, respectively.

From these national samplings and surveys, with estimates from projections to the national population for given years, it can be readily appreciated that there are many methods of approaching the whole problem; that much depends upon definition, upon inclusion or exclusion of certain categories of disability, and upon character and methodology of the surveys. Regardless of these variables, however, it can be said that we probably have a total of people in this country at the present time suffering from some type of identifiable physical or mental disability which is in the neighborhood of 30 million. We can state further that perhaps five to six million of these have "major" disabilities which prevent them from working or carrying on their normal activities for part or all of the time. It can be anticipated that during

[3] Woolsey, Theodore D., "Estimates of Disabling Illness Prevalence in the U. S.," *Public Health Monograph No. 4.*, Washington, 1952.

[4] Commission on Chronic Illness, "Care of the Long-Term Patient," Vol. II of *Chronic Illness in U. S.*, Harvard Univ. Press, Cambridge, 1956, pp. 1 and 2 and Appendix A.

[5] U. S. Dept. of Commerce, Bureau of the Census, *Statistical Abstract of the United States 1956*, Washington, 1956, p. 6.

the next ten to fifteen years, the number of these people is going to increase by about 20%.

In addition to the national surveys of general disability and illness, there have been many estimates by different groups of more specific kinds of disability. The National Safety Council provides figures on accidental injuries which reveal that about two million persons are injured at work each year, over one million in motor vehicle accidents, over four million at home, and another two million in so-called public accidents—a total of over nine million injured in some fashion each year.[6] Both public and private agencies dealing with special diseases or disability problems, such as those for the blind, deaf, cardiac, tubercular, arthritic, and mentally and emotionally handicapped, have estimated the extent of disability related to their own immediate interest. Selective Service figures during and since the last war have given some indication of medical bases for rejection of young men. The Bureau of Labor Statistics has estimated that there are perhaps five to six million persons of working age who have disabilities serious enough to present difficulty in finding suitable jobs.[7]

Subdivision of disability by cause indicates that 88% of all disabling conditions is due to disease, particularly chronic disease, 10% is due to accidents, and the other 2% results from congenital handicap.[8]

It is interesting to note that there is often a tendency to correlate the need for rehabilitation services with the possibility of vocational rehabilitation; i.e., the possibility of placing the disabled person on a job or in his own business venture. Frequent reference is made, for instance, to figures presented by the Office of Vocational Rehabilitation that there are some two million people who have disabilities which require rehabilitation services to make them employable.[9] We are told that some 250,000 additional persons are added to this number each year.[9] Although these figures may be perfectly valid, they represent only a part of the problem of rehabilitation. If we are to accept rehabilitation as the broad and comprehensive philosophy and practice

[6] National Safety Council, *Accident Facts, 1957 Edition,* Chicago, 1957, p. 3.

[7] U. S. Dept. of Labor Bulletin No. 923, *The Performance of Physically Impaired Workers in Manufacturing Industries,* Washington, 1948.

[8] Hearings before Subcommittee on Health of the Committee on Labor and Public Welfare, U. S. Senate, 83rd Congress. "President's Health Recommendations and Related Measures, Part 2," Statement of Nelson A. Rockefeller, March 30, 1954, Washington, p. 315.

[9] U. S. Dept. of Health, Education and Welfare, Office of Vocational Rehabilitation, Division of Research and Statistics, *Number of Disabled Persons in Need of Vocational Rehabilitation,* Rehabilitation Service Series No. 274, Washington, 1954, p. 1.

described earlier, then vocational rehabilitation becomes only part of the job, important as that part may be. If we accept as the goal of comprehensive rehabilitation such things as the removal of the institutionalized patient to effective home living, the development in very severely handicapped or mentally deficient adult or child of self-care and social acceptability, then we are necessarily concerned with many thousands of individuals who may never be the object of vocational rehabilitation.

Although the broad-scale figures and estimates are of interest in dramatizing the national problem and the need for legislation, funds, facilities, and personnel, the real appreciation of present and future services and need must necessarily be related to disability as it exists within each community. Later chapters will be devoted to the question of community need and responsibility. However, the present discussion of the size of the problem warrants consideration of the community as the focal point of measurement and evaluation. Several very significant surveys have been made which point the way toward informative community estimation of disability and chronic illness.

The Hunterdon County (New Jersey) Health Survey, sponsored by the Commission on Chronic Illness and the Hunterdon Medical Center (with financial assistance from the Commonwealth Fund), started in 1952 and was intended to study the prevalence of chronic illness and needs for care in a rural area with population of 43,000. House-to-house interviews with 4000 families (including 13,000 people) revealed, according to preliminary information, that a little less than 1% of persons studied had been prevented, by some disabling condition, from going out of doors for a full year prior to date of interview.[10] A parallel survey on urban population was also undertaken in 1952 by the Commission on Chronic Illness, with assistance from the Department of Health, Education, and Welfare, within the city of Baltimore. Interviews in 3657 households (including 11,574 people) between Sept. 1953 and Sept. 1954 indicated that 2% of all persons surveyed had been disabled 3 months or more during the year preceding the survey.[11] These two investigations utilized mailed questionnaires and house-to-house interviews, screening tests on undiagnosed disorders, check of medical records, and diagnostic examinations and evaluations

[10] U. S. Dept. of Health, Education, and Welfare, "Study of the Homebound Programs for Physically Handicapped Homebound Individuals," Feb. 2, 1955, Report to the Congress, p. 9.

[11] Roberts, D. W., and Glasser, M., "Chronic Illness in an Urban Area—A Progress Report," *Chronic Illness Newsletter*, Vol. 6, No. 9 (November, 1955). Commission on Chronic Illness, Baltimore.

by physician, nurse, social worker, and vocational counselor of the need and value of rehabilitation services for persons found to be disabled. Later detailed evaluations and conclusions on these two research projects will be published by the Commission on Chronic Illness.

The Rehabilitation Survey and Demonstration Project in Kansas City, undertaken by Community Studies, Inc., a local, nonprofit research group, in cooperation with the U. S. Public Health Service and Office of Vocational Rehabilitation, is designed to provide data on prevalence of disability in an urban area, size of rehabilitation potential, costs and benefits of a comprehensive rehabilitation program. A limited study group will be matched against a control group to measure the effectiveness of rehabilitation provided by community facilities. This study was started in December 1954 and the complete findings will not be available until 1959. Interviews will be conducted in 8300 households (including 27,000 persons, or 5% of the population of Greater Kansas City). Persons with disabilities in these households will be examined by an evaluation team to determine feasibility of rehabilitation.

A preliminary report was prepared for the Office of Vocational Rehabilitation at about the halfway point in the survey. Of the 17,000 persons covered at that time, 46.3% had chronic conditions that had existed three months or longer. It is reported that 5.2% of the population is handicapped. Of these persons, 65.7% are feasible for rehabilitation. Forty per cent could be rehabilitated for remunerative employment in the following categories: competitive, 20%; sheltered, 15%; homebound, 1%. Of those feasible for rehabilitation, 6% are over 65 years of age, 39% are under 18 years of age, and 4% are housewives.[12]

The 1956 El Paso County Health Survey, El Paso, Colorado, had the objective of obtaining statistical information on the chronically ill and aged. Visits were made to 13,560 households which represented nearly 40,000 persons or 46% of the county's population. Based on this sample, it is estimated that 3.6% of the county's population are handicapped.[13]

There have been a number of other types of community surveys, such as the New Haven Chronic Disease Study in 1947, the Rhode

[12] Bryant, W. D., "Highlights of the Greater Kansas City Rehabilitation Survey and Demonstration," Community Studies, Inc., Kansas City, Missouri, September, 1956.

[13] Report, 1956 El Paso County Health Survey, Colorado Springs, Chamber of Commerce, Colorado Springs, Colorado.

Island Old Age Survey in 1953, the Cleveland Sheltered Employment Study in 1950, the San Jose current morbidity study in 1952, and the New York City studies in 1952 and 1954 on homebound handicapped children and employable homebound adults. There have also been limited studies of community groups in specific diseases, usually carried on by research, teaching, or health agency people particularly interested in the selected disease or disabling condition. Although a number of the more important surveys are still incomplete, it is beginning to look as though somewhere between 2 and 5% of urban populations and a somewhat smaller percentage of rural populations may reasonably be expected to be fairly seriously disabled. The percentages increase markedly with age, as one would expect. Determination of the actual numbers needing rehabilitation services is still inconclusive, although it may run as high as two-thirds if the preliminary Kansas City study figures are a true indication. All the studies show that a significant number of handicapped persons do not know about or are not taking advantage of existing rehabilitation services.

Limited in scope as these community surveys may be, they are probably a truer index of disability in a given area and of the need for rehabilitation services. Although communities can use the results of national or regional studies and apply the statistical estimates to their own population, the possibility for error is considerable and more exact and useful data can usually be obtained by studying and measuring the community's own problem.

CHAPTER 4

The Tools
of Rehabilitation

ALTHOUGH REHABILITATION IS A PHILOSOPHY which permeates many aspects of our cultural life, both for groups and individuals, it is primarily the performance of a task; namely, the organization of the means to overcome the effects of disability. Like all assignments, it requires tools and, in general, these may be broken down into four categories: (1) programs, (2) services, (3) personnel, and (4) facilities.

Programs may be described, for purposes of this book, as broad plans of procedure initiated and carried out by groups of individuals not directly concerned with the details of rendering a service in some specific area of rehabilitation but rather with the planning and organization incident to rehabilitation generally, either on a comprehensive or specialized basis. Rehabilitation programs differ in scope, organization, purpose, and practical operation.

The scope of a program may be national, state, or local. Many programs operate at all three levels and thus tie together their activities in the promotional, informational, and service areas. An example of a national program would be the National Society for Crippled Children and Adults; of a state program, the State Crippled Children's Services; of a local program (which could be on a regional, county, or single-community basis), the Rehabilitation Council of the United Community Services of Greater Boston. Certain programs will be exclusively devoted to rehabilitation as a reason for their very existence; others will deal with rehabilitation through only one part of their organization or as only a portion of their over-all activity. The

National Rehabilitation Association would be typical of the former, and the American Heart Association would exemplify an organization devoting only a part of its time and effort to the subject of rehabilitation.

Organization of a program may be either public, such as the Office of Vocational Rehabilitation, or private, such as the National Foundation for Infantile Paralysis. By the same token, organization may be along professional lines, such as the American Congress of Physical Medicine, disciplinary, as in the American Physical Therapy Association, technical, as in the Orthopedic Appliance and Limb Manufacturers of America, or general, as in the case of civic groups like the "Just One Break" committees, the fraternal associations of the Shriners and Lions, or the charitable activities of women's clubs, Junior League, and the like.

The purpose of a program may be related to a single type of disability, as in the case of the National Tuberculosis Association and its subsidiary chapters and divisions; it may deal with a more general category or group of handicaps, as would be true of the National Association for Mental Health and the Commission on Chronic Illness; or it may concern itself with a comprehensive approach to the whole field of disablement, as in the Goodwill Industries. The purpose often is concerned with a particular part of the rehabilitation process. For instance, the American Speech and Hearing Association is interested primarily in therapy and training directed at the correction of vocal and auditory handicaps as an important segment of rehabilitation activity. The Conference of Rehabilitation Centers, Inc., attacks the problem of better organization and administration of centers.

The practical operation of programs in rehabilitation may be along several lines of endeavor (examples of each are given):

Establishment of services	State and county Societies for Crippled Children and Adults.
Information and publicity	President's and Governors' Committees on Employment of the Physically Handicapped.
Coordination of activities	U. S. Public Health Service or the National Industries for the Blind.
Professional or disciplinary exchange of ideas	American College of Surgeons or American Association of Medical Social Workers.
Fund-raising	National Society for Crippled Children and Adults (Easter Seal drive). Community funds or "red feather" services.
Research or education	Baruch Committee on Physical Medicine and Rehabilitation, Commission on Chronic Illness.

Superficially it might seem desirable to attempt a listing of all the individual programs and organizations which are interested or active in the general or specific areas of rehabilitation at the present time. Such a list would cover pages, would surely be subject to grave omissions in the complexity of this whole field, and would rapidly become out-dated. It is suggested, however, that any community planning group or any continuing council or committee set about the task of amassing such data in relation to all the agencies, institutions, and organizations in the community which are carrying on programs of rehabilitation, either general or specialized.

It should be readily appreciated that the distinctions made in this chapter as to scope, organization, purpose, and operation of rehabilitation programs are not intended to be arbitrary or exclusive in nature. Most programs include a combination of the components or classifications outlined. Admittedly, there is as yet no national program or organization in rehabilitation which cuts across all professional and disciplinary lines, which is inclusive of all phases of rehabilitation activity, or which understands and supports every facet of rehabilitation from education to definitive service. In the public domain, the Office of Vocational Rehabilitation since the 1954 amendments has greatly extended its interests and activities in all areas, but it still has its primary emphasis on the vocational aspects and is somewhat limited by the legal and practical definitions of eligibility. Among private organizations, the National Rehabilitation Association has the best opportunity to represent the broad spectrum of rehabilitation concern but has not yet been able to spread its wings fully, and it is still entangled in its roots within the federal–state vocational rehabilitation program. Much of its concern has been with national legislation. If this association could find the way to translate its activities in the rehabilitation field into an all-inclusive organization, similar to the American Medical Association, with over-all policy directed at solidifying and improving rehabilitation in all its aspects, it could become the true leader in the field. Such an organization would permit the main body of the association to draw into membership all professions and disciplines, support research and education, follow legislation, and provide information or publicity for all kinds of rehabilitation activity. Sections of the association could be formed for each professional, disciplinary, or technical group in the field and those sections could meet, discuss, and publish reports on their own particular interests.

The second category in the tools of rehabilitation is composed of the services, which are specific in nature and organized for the direct benefit of the disabled person. Webster defines a service as "any result of useful labor which does not produce a tangible commodity" or as "conduct contributing to the advantage of another or others." In rehabilitation parlance, a service is the application of a combination of talents and methods, usually professional or technical in character, which produce a result; in this case, the alleviation of the consequences of disability. The services normally included in rehabilitation can be listed as follows:

Institutional care (hospital, nursing home, rehabilitation center, etc.)

Medical treatment (including diagnosis, examination, laboratory studies, X-ray, therapy prescription, evaluation of disability, reconstructive surgery)

Nursing

Physical therapy

Occupational therapy

Corrective therapy

Diversional therapy (recreational, music, group activity, etc.)

Speech and hearing therapy

Counseling (personal, psychological, psychiatric, vocational)

Testing (psychological, aptitude, vocational, guidance)

Special education (applicable mostly to children)

Work evaluation

Sheltered employment

Homebound care

Manual arts therapy or training

Self-care training (so-called activities of daily living)

Prosthetic service (selection, fitting and training in use of artificial limb, brace or other device)

Mobility training (such as gait training for amputee, ambulation with crutches for paraplegic, polio, cerebral palsied, cane walking for blind)

Vocational training

Vocational placement

These services in rehabilitation are not necessarily all rendered in separate places or by separate individuals. A rehabilitation center, for instance, may incorporate in its program a large number of the services listed above. On the other hand, a specialized school offering vocational training may restrict its function entirely to that particular aspect of the rehabilitation process. In the same vein, any one of these services may be rendered by one or several kinds of individuals and, again, one individual may be in a position to render more than one kind of service.

A listing of the personnel who participate directly in provision of service is necessarily attempted with some qualms because of the scope of activity which, by various definitions and interpretations, might be termed as properly included in rehabilitation. However, there are certain classifications which would normally be accepted by most knowledgeable people in the field as having a role of more than passing significance in the rehabilitation process. Those would be as follows:

Physicians (not confined to any specialty—all doctors, from the general practitioner through the range of more than twenty specialties in medicine, may and do participate and contribute to the eventual rehabilitation result)

Nurses (hospital, visiting, public health or rehabilitation)

Physical therapists

Occupational therapists

Corrective therapists

Speech and hearing therapists

Social workers

Medical social workers

Psychiatric social workers

Clinical psychologists

Counseling psychologists

Guidance counselors or teachers

Vocational counselors

Manual or industrial arts teachers (especially those in vocational schools)

Special education teachers (teachers of exceptional children)

Prosthetists

Directors and administrators of rehabilitation centers, sheltered workshops, special schools for handicapped, and similar facilities

Directors or coordinators of agency programs which may include one or more kinds of rehabilitation service

Lay executives of rehabilitation programs in public agencies, insurance companies, private foundations and the like

This tally of personnel obviously does not attempt to include the many interested people who may participate indirectly in the initiation and carrying through to completion of a rehabilitation program for one or more disabled persons. All the lay volunteers, the fund-raisers, the health and welfare workers, the labor and industry people, the civic, service and fraternal organization members, the parent groups, and the religious and other charitable movements carry out a contributive function in the whole rehabilitation procedure. Without their help and understanding, the efforts of the professionals and technicians could not succeed.

A facility is defined in accepted dictionaries as "a thing that promotes the ease of any action, operation or course of conduct." It has the connotation in medical and rehabilitation circles of the institution or the actual building in which certain definitive services for the patient are rendered. In other words, the specific locations for medical, psychological, and vocational rehabilitation of the disabled. Such facilities would be of the following types:

Hospitals (particularly rehabilitation departments or wards)

Rehabilitation institutes or centers

Sheltered workshops

Vocational training schools

Special institutions or schools for particular disabilities

It should be borne in mind that these are the places which provide a specialized part of rehabilitation. This does not imply that the whole of the rehabilitation process is conducted within these specified locations. Obviously there are many hours of professional, technical, administrative, and even lay assistance through guidance, counseling, coordinating, and other procedures which take place in agency quarters, industrial firms, doctors' offices, and in private homes that contribute equally effectively to the final result. But rehabilitation, as it has now evolved in thinking and practice, requires for most cases involving a disability of any real consequence a specific place for the scientific application of the restorative and adaptive techniques inherent in the process. Learning to recognize and properly use such facilities is basic to effective rehabilitation.

Nothing has been said in this chapter about equipment, which conceivably could have been a fifth component among the tools of rehabilitation. Any effort to catalogue equipment ordinarily used in the complex process of rehabilitation would take pages and would require many kinds of breakdown and explanation. Even the human hand, as it performs the functions of massage and manipulation, might properly be considered part of the equipment for rehabilitation. Devices for therapeutic use develop, are modified, and lose popularity with the changing concepts and techniques of the professions and disciplines involved. Those requiring information as to the basic equipment used in physical therapy, occupational therapy, prevocational training, and the like can obtain definitive data from government manuals, professional guides and lists published by the major rehabilitation organizations. The best source of guidance in this area is first-hand observation in a comprehensive rehabilitation center, sheltered workshop, vocational training school, and other similar facilities.

Thomas Carlyle wrote the cogent phrase, "the tools to him that can handle them." In that sense, the planning group which takes the time to explore the limited number of practical programs, services, personnel, and facilities for rehabilitation developed and utilized both in its own area and elsewhere and which adapts and improves ideas and practices of others to its own advantage will travel far on the road to successful rehabilitation in the community.

CHAPTER 5

The Role
of the Physician

FOR CENTURIES, THE GOALS OF MEDICAL PRACtice have been the saving of human life and the alleviation or curing of the effects of illness and injury. Until fairly recently, medicine was largely oriented to the individual problem of disease or injury; to the specific procedures and modalities of curative treatment. Medical teaching was directed toward the anatomical concept of health, toward the use of surgery and drugs as the principal tools in the fight against the ravages of illness and injury. The individual physician was basically interested in his patient getting well, but he seldom recognized or accepted the broader social and economic responsibilities involved in the improvement of his patient's lot in life. The person disabled by congenital condition, chronic or acute disease, injury, or the infirmities of age was accepted as having suffered the natural consequence of his difficulties, with no real promise of remedial measures leading toward better adjustment to his handicap. Prime concentration was upon the curative or acute treatment phase of medical care.

Oddly enough, the old-fashioned "family doctor" was probably more concerned with some phases of what we now call psychological counseling and vocational counseling; he was interested and involved in the restoration of his patient not only to good health but also to normal living. In small communities and with limited numbers of patients, he found time for a real interest in his patient's problems and could often help in their solution by direct contact with others in the community. The advance in specialization, the growing urban populations, the increase in the use of hospitals as a focal point of definitive medical care, and higher standards of living brought changes in the physician's attitudes and opportunities. He found himself more and more restricted to treatment—it required more and more of his time to keep abreast of new research, new methods of care, and greatly increased patient loads in hospital and office.

With the advances in the complexity of our industrial civilization, however, new hazards to life and limb were presenting a new kind of challenge to medicine. Traumatic injuries were on the increase; new production processes and chemical components created great potential for damage to employee health. Gradually, as a scientific method of meeting the demand for safer working conditions, there began to evolve a branch of medical practice which was to concern itself with industrial medicine. The sum total of those things which could injure the person or affect the health of the working man or woman became the responsibility of those who entered this new specialty. Largely concerned at first with the results of work injuries and occupational diseases, the doctor began to interest himself more and more in the pattern of general health for the working population, in the provision of all possible safeguards against accident or sickness.

About this same time, there began to be an increasing concern on the part of federal, state, and local governments for the health of people generally. Appropriations were made from public funds to establish departments of health and public health services which would function not so much in the area of definitive case treatment but more in the field of research, teaching, public information, and education. This work was aimed initially at the communicable diseases but later began to broaden its interest to include the planning and establishment of better health services and agencies at the community level, the education of local physician and the general public to health needs and facilities.

With these two broad developments, medicine had entered a second phase, the so-called preventive phase, in which the physician accepted responsibility for not only treating specific conditions in each individual patient but also trying to prevent illness and injury and improve general health in all his patients and, indeed, in the community as a whole. Advances in research methods, particularly in the infectious diseases; health control measures, especially the immunization by vaccines; development of "wonder drugs" such as penicillin and a host of others, meant that the life-saving and disease prevention functions of medicine had now reached mass effectiveness.

It is such advances, together with steadily improving standards of living involving better education, housing, nutrition, that have led to the creation of a new problem and the necessity for medicine's entry into a "third phase."[1] This problem involves the thousands of our people who are alive today because of medical progress. Many have survived the critical periods of severe illness, the traumatic effects of serious injury, the physical malformations of birth, or the complications of advancing age only to be shackled by a disability which limits their usefulness and their sense of fulfillment. Faced with a growing number of disabled persons and a larger percentage of aging population, medicine is called upon to accept a larger responsibility for the social and economic welfare of the patient. The third phase of medical care is rehabilitation, and the physician needs to understand it, accept it, use it, and improve it.

Some physicians will insist that they have always practiced rehabilitation, and if we accept the loose definition of rehabilitation as the process of getting well, then it must be conceded as we have seen earlier that some of the reassurance, the reconstructive surgery, even the use of exercise and heat, has been a part of medical curative procedures. Nonetheless, rehabilitation in its modern definition has come to mean much more in the way of basic philosophy and comprehensive, specialized techniques. In this new sense, relatively few physicians as yet fully understand or effectively utilize the present rehabilitation programs and facilities.

A large segment of the medical profession has obviously regarded rehabilitation as having little significance or concern for the average doctor. Dr. A. R. Shands, Jr., has characterized this as "the apathetic attitude of 80% or more of the medical profession toward rehabilitation."[2] Unfortunately, doctors have often regarded rehabilitation as something which is really outside the province of their profession—something which is primarily of concern to social workers, various types of therapists, vocational and psychological counselors, and lay workers in voluntary or public agencies. The recognition and use of rehabilitation by the paramedical disciplines and the social agencies, even its general acknowledgement by the public as a new and more hopeful service for people, has acted to place the doctor even more on the defensive. He may deplore the development of rehabilitation programs without good medical direction, but he has not often moved

[1] Rusk, Howard A., and Taylor, Eugene, *New Hope for the Handicapped,* Harper & Brothers, New York, 1949, pp. 78–90.

[2] Shands, A. R., "The Attitude of the Physician Toward Rehabilitation," included in "Changing Attitudes Towards the Disabled," Proceedings of 6th World Congress of International Society for Welfare of Cripples, The Hague, September, 1954, p. 26.

forward to provide such direction and integration of effort as is badly
needed. Both undergraduate and graduate medical training have provided little if anything in the field of rehabilitation, except for those
who were to specialize in physical medicine.

Although the orthopedic surgeons, particularly those involved in
programs for crippled children, have long had an interest in the prevention and early treatment of deformity by exercise and bracing
devices as well as by surgery, the real impetus toward effective rehabilitation was provided by those pioneers in what has come to be called
"physical medicine." The Council on Physical Medicine and Rehabilitation of the American Medical Association defined physical medicine as "the employment of the physical and other effective properties
of light, heat, cold, water, electricity, massage, manipulation, exercise,
and mechanical devices for physical and occupational therapy in the
diagnosis or treatment of disease."[3] In the early twenties, the development of various devices and procedures for physical therapy and the
influx of insufficiently trained treatment personnel led to the establishment in 1925 of a Council of Physical Therapy by the American
Medical Association to protect physicians and public alike from useless
or harmful devices or methods and from exploitation by incompetents
who professed to skills in the use of the new physical agents. The later
addition of occupational and other types of therapy to the treatment
picture led to the change in name of the Council to the Council on
Physical Medicine in 1945.

During World War II, the close relationship between the rapidly
growing field of rehabilitation and the specialty of physical medicine
became increasingly evident. The military services and the government hospitals had already coordinated their programs of physical
medicine, physical reconditioning and rehabilitation. In 1949 the
A.M.A. council became the Council on Physical Medicine and Rehabilitation. In that same year, residencies and fellowships in the new
specialty began to be offered and teaching along these lines was in full
force and effect. The American Board of Physical Medicine was
formed in 1947 and two years later its title included the word Rehabilitation. This move marked the recognition and acceptance of this new
specialty as having a definite place in medical practice.

In reality, however, physical medicine is only one of the many parts
of the rehabilitation process. Although the early proponents of physical medicine such as Coulter, Krusen, Rusk, Deaver, and others were
truly path-finders in the maze of multidisciplinary confusion over

[3] Council on Physical Medicine and Rehabilitation, A. M. A. *Handbook of
Physical Medicine and Rehabilitation,* The Blakiston Co., New York, 1950, p. *vii.*

rehabilitation, its aims and methods, actually rehabilitation is much more than merely physical medicine. The practice of rehabilitation for any doctor rests on the conviction that his responsibility continues beyond the stage of acute illness or the convalescence from surgery; that it must continue until the patient has been trained to live and work to the maximum effectiveness permitted by his residual disability. Rehabilitation can never be the responsibility of only one small specialized group of physicians; it is necessarily an integral part of any complete medical service. Many of the procedures in the rehabilitation process can and should be done by, or at least under the direction of, the attending physician, be he specialist or general practitioner.

Practical programs of rehabilitation have demonstrated clearly that there are few cases, however severe the disability, which cannot be rehabilitated to the level of self-care and social acceptance, if not to actual work. It has also become increasingly evident that the assistance of a comprehensive and concentrated program in a rehabilitation center or some similar specialized facility is often vital to the accomplishment of maximum success. The doctor needs to clearly understand what such facilities can provide toward his patient's recovery and to utilize them as a medical tool, just as he uses the hospital, the laboratory, the special diagnostic or treatment equipment in his office. Rehabilitation cannot make significant progress on a sound, scientific basis without the direction and guidance of medicine; in that sense it becomes the job and the responsibility of every physician.

Much has been said, and will be said later in this book, on the "team approach" to rehabilitation. Regardless of whom is selected as the "coordinator" or "director" or "administrator" of any rehabilitation program, there can be no doubt that the definitive medical guidance, the sound prescription for treatment and therapy procedures, can come only from the doctor.

Medical groups such as the American College of Surgeons, the American Medical Association; individual physicians such as Krusen, Rusk, Aitken, Kessler, and others; administrative agencies such as the Veterans' Administration, the Office of Vocational Rehabilitation; private agencies such as the National Society for Crippled Children and Adults; professional associations like the Conference of Rehabilitation Centers, have done yeoman work in recent years in defining and headlining the need of responsibility on the part of the individual physician in the rehabilitation process. Medical schools are gradually starting to provide definitive instruction and field work in rehabilitation; the promise for the future is great.

Increasing recognition of the social, emotional, and economic factors which play a part, and often a complicating role, in illness and disability has led to a concept of "treating the whole man," instead of merely the illness or injury. This concept has been a part of accepted psychiatric treatment for many years. In the realm of physical, as well as emotional or mental, illness, the goal of complete functional as well as physical restoration of the patient is a valid one. A simple removal or alleviation of symptoms is of no value unless it is a part of a more comprehensive program directed at restoration of the patient to a full life.

In time, all practicing physicians will come to think of rehabilitation as a vital component of the treatment of people; they will initiate and supervise such a program of specialized care; they will be leaders in promoting rehabilitation programs in their respective communities; they will serve on advisory or consultant boards of rehabilitation centers; they will encourage the teaching and research needed to constantly improve practical rehabilitation techniques. The doctor has not been shirking his responsibility, he has been trying to learn and absorb a body of fast-changing and evergrowing knowledge amid an age of great scientific and medical progress. His devotion to the best interests of his patient guarantees the only possible result—the gradual recognition, acceptance, and fulfillment of his responsibilities in the provision of effective rehabilitation services to all those in need of them.

CHAPTER 6

The Nurse
and the Therapist

THE WORK OF THE NURSE AND THE THERAPIST on the "medical rehabilitation team" constitutes a vital adjunct to the services of the physician. In the past year, there has been increasing use of the word "paramedical personnel" to describe the disciplines other than the doctor which play a part in the rehabilitation process. The original Greek word "para" meant "beside" and as a modern English prefix it has retained this meaning, with a particular connotation in medical terminology of "associated in a subsidiary or accessory capacity." This chapter will deal specifically with the role of the nurse and the therapist as paramedical personnel most effective during the medical phase of rehabilitation while a later chapter on counseling will cover some of the other disciplines contributing to the psychological, social, and economic phases.

Rehabilitation as an integral part of nursing care has gradually assumed both a general and a special significance. Nurses have always been concerned with the psychological reactions of the patient to disease and injury; they have combated discouragement and defeat with reassurance, sympathy, and understanding. In that sense, any nurse dealing with an ill or injured patient finds an opportunity to apply some of the inherent philosophy and practices of rehabilitation. However, there has come to be recognized a special area of nursing in the organized bed-patient care associated with departments of physical medicine and rehabilitation, with specialized chronic disease or single-disability hospital programs, and with rehabilitation institutes or in-patient centers.

In her ordinary role as a staff nurse in a general hospital, rehabilitation is a working tool to be used in the recovery process of most of her patients. Although some of the very early functions of the nurse in the areas of therapy, social work, and counseling have now been made the special province of trained therapist, social worker, or counselor, it must be recognized that the nurse is often the very first contact for the patient when he enters the hospital or when he begins to emerge from anesthesia following surgery. The old adage about every man being in love with his nurse has an element of truth in the fact that she represents most clearly to him the person who ministers to his needs in a time of physical and emotional crisis. To the extent that she understands his fears, doubts, and worries can she help the patient to accept, to adjust, and to look forward with confidence.

The nurse who works in the specialized environment of the medical facilities which are particularly designed for rehabilitation of either chronic or short-term patients learns to apply the techniques of rehabilitation in a well-defined pattern and as part of a medical team dedicated to comprehensive restoration and adjustment to disability. Alice Morrissey, in her stimulating work on rehabilitation nursing, sets forth the principal contributions of the nurse in rehabilitation care as being in the areas of rehabilitation nursing service management, clinical teaching, and basic bedside nursing.[1] In the controlled environment of a hospital rehabilitation service, the nurse must recognize and utilize the hygiene, nutrition, exercise, elimination, relaxation, recreation, and occupational preparation which contribute markedly toward maximum possibility of successful rehabilitation.

The true value of knowledgeable nursing care can be readily distinguished in the medical progress of the more severe disabilities. Physical deformity can be prevented by early and correct exercise, bladder and bowel incontinence can be overcome or controlled, pressure sores can be avoided, amputation stumps can be properly prepared for wearing of the prosthesis (artificial limb). Without proper understanding of the basic therapeutic principles which underlie effective physical restoration of the major disabling conditions and injuries, the attempt to provide adequate nursing care for such cases is doomed to tragic failure. Nothing is more frustrating than the recognition that severe contractures, large bedsores, and the like could have been entirely prevented by competent nursing care and the further recognition that the crippling complications may now be too great to ever completely overcome. Such needless developments should serve as an eternal "night-

[1] Morrissey, Alice B., *Rehabilitation Nursing*, G. P. Putnam's Sons, New York, 1951, p. 62.

mare" for physician and nurse; the warning that they owe their patient the duty of learning about and practicing the recognized methods of rehabilitative after-care.

The nurse may play other roles in relation to rehabilitation. Those who are in nursing education have the significant task of finding the ways and means to interest more high school girls in nursing and to develop a consciousness of rehabilitation and all its implications within the nursing student. The field of industrial nursing offers an opportunity and a challenge for the development of good human relations, for the practice of selective job placement, and for the organization of a medical department which is oriented to rehabilitation ideas and practices. Public health nursing, in particular, demonstrates the need for knowledge of and use of community rehabilitation services, as well as the practical counseling, follow-up nursing routines, and social consciousness which are the bases of good home-care programs.

Some organizations, such as the Liberty Mutual Insurance Company, have started the use of "rehabilitation nurses" as coordinators of the whole rehabilitation process, particularly in traumatic injury cases. This involves the use of counseling methods which are more fully described in a later chapter. However, it does illustrate the increasing importance which has been attached to the nurse as part of the medical team in the rehabilitation process.

Therapy is an ancient art; in its broad sense it refers to the whole process of healing, curing, or prescribing remedies. In its more restricted definition, as connected with a particular type of treatment, it has come to imply a set of methods and applied principles, together with the use of specialized equipment, which are designed to restore function and assist in the process of social and economic adjustment to disability. Thus we hear of physical therapy as including the use of light, heat, massage, exercise, water, and electrical stimulation; occupational therapy as including the use of tools, crafts, and other equipment. Around these and similar specialized therapies there have grown a whole new set of disciplines, schools of instruction, boards of accreditation, professional associations, and defined areas of applied methods in the general plan for rehabilitation. Practitioners of these several therapies are commonly referred to as therapists, and they comprise a major segment of the paramedical personnel active in the rehabilitation field.

The well-defined therapy groups are as follows:

1. *Physical therapists* supervise and carry out a program designed to accomplish the maximum of physical restoration. It consists of active

and passive exercise, often against resistance, to develop strength, muscle re-education, increased range of motion. Various exercise devices such as pulleys, weights, wheels, steps, and walking rails are used to bring about the desired results. Heat from lamps, paraffin baths and the like, water and heat in whirlpool baths or tanks, electrical stimulation or sound waves, massage of injured parts are all designed to increase circulation, relieve pain, relax muscles, and make the patient feel better. Instruction in daily activities or home exercise routines, as well as certain testing and measuring for diagnostic or prognostic purposes, is also part of the physical therapist's job. Physical therapists may work in general or specialized hospital programs, in rehabilitation centers, in doctors' offices, or in the patient's home. There are presently 35 schools of physical therapy approved by the Council on Medical Education of the American Medical Association. Courses for certification or degree range in length from 49 weeks to 4 years.[2]

2. *Occupational therapists* supervise and carry out a program aimed at restoring function and enabling the patient to work or to pursue creative interests. Manual and industrial skills are developed as a means of promoting better motion, strength, and coordination, but also as a means of helping the patient to go back to work. Creative arts and crafts, recreational activities, self-help devices and programs, and testing for ability to hold a job, are all a part of this specific therapy. In addition to the physical restoration techniques, the therapist is interested in the mental and psychological adjustment of the patient. Wood-working shops, bench lathes, and other machines, hand and power tools, hand looms, and other craft devices help the patient to regain his working ability and tolerance or to prepare for additional vocational training. The occupational therapist may also be called upon to develop and teach the handicapped individual how to live self-sufficiently in his home environment. In some programs, the occupational therapy is almost entirely functional and practical, in others it may be more diversionary, as in the case of the chronically ill, the mentally disturbed, or the elderly. Because of the nature of their equipment, the occupational therapist works more often in the hospital, rehabilitation center or sheltered workshop with a fairly comprehensive program, although there has been some attempt to adapt certain of the procedures to the patient who is homebound. There are presently 30 schools of occupational therapy approved by the Council

2 *Mobilization and Health Manpower*, II, A Report of the Subcommittee on Paramedical Personnel in Rehabilitation and Care of the Chronically Ill, Office of Defense Mobilization, Washington, January, 1956, p. 13.

on Medical Education and Hospitals of the American Medical Association. Courses for certification or degree range in length from 16 months to 5 years.[3]

3. *Speech and hearing therapists* supervise and carry out a program which is designed to correct or to compensate for defects in speech or hearing. Professional terminology in this area of rehabilitation activity is a little confusing, but it is more or less an accepted fact that the speech pathologist and the audiologist are the possessors of a doctorate in philosophy or education, whereas the speech and hearing teachers and therapists constitute the bulk of the paramedical personnel in this work. This type of therapy is directed at speech or hearing disorders which may be either organic or functional in nature and which may be either congenital or the sequelae of disease or injury. Skill is required in the testing and evaluation of hearing loss through the use of modern acoustical equipment. Speech reading, correction, and conservation of speech contribute to the conquest of disorders which halt or interrupt the patient's communication with the world around him. Therapists in this field function effectively in hospitals, rehabilitation centers, special schools, and in the public school system. Some 115 schools and colleges now provide training in the area of the speech handicapped, 68 for hard of hearing, 22 for the deaf, all leading to basic certification or to degrees.[4] The American Speech and Hearing Association has established standards in the field.

4. *Corrective therapists* supervise and carry out a program which consists of medically prescribed physical activity, primarily exercise and self-care. A series of conditioning exercises, ambulation, and socialization activities are given to the bed, wheel-chair, or ambulant patient. Highly individualized routines may be devised for each patient or the work may be done in groups. Gymnasium-type facilities and equipment, swimming pools, and adapted gear for bed exercise form the working tools for the corrective therapist. The great majority of the corrective therapy personnel are working in Veterans' Administration Hospitals. Four colleges and universities and the Veterans' Administration combine to offer a four-year college course in physical education which must include, either at undergraduate or graduate level, a minimum of 250 hours of clinical experience.[5] The certification board of the Association for Physical and Mental Rehabilitation has established standards for the group.

5. *Recreational therapists* are delegated the assignment of conduct-

[3] *Ibid.*, p. 19.
[4] *Ibid.*, p. 48.
[5] *Ibid.*, p. 57.

ing recreational programs for patients in hospitals or institutions. A combination of social activities, less active sports and games, movies, and dances are designed to assist in the psychological and social adjustment of the physically or mentally handicapped. The work is limited mostly to Veterans' Administration hospitals, mental hospitals, and special institutions for children or the aged. At least four colleges offer a major in this kind of training and others have selected courses in the field. There is a National Association of Recreation Therapists but no formal registry or accrediting body.[6]

There are other less well-defined and nonaccredited groups such as those dealing with group therapy, music therapy, and the like. There are also the teachers of exceptional (handicapped) children who really fall in the area of special education rather than specific therapy. All of the groups listed play a definite role in the rehabilitation process, just as do the various kinds of counselors reviewed in a later chapter. They all form a more or less active part of the rehabilitation team which has the responsibility for achieving the greatest possible recovery from disabling injury or illness.

[6] *Ibid.*, p. 56.

CHAPTER 7

Medical Rehabilitation
in the Hospital

OUR WORD "HOSPITAL" IS DERIVED FROM THE Latin *hospitalis* which meant "relating to a guest" and the French "hospes," or "guests." The original and historical use of the word was in connection with "a place for shelter or entertainment of travelers, strangers, etc."[1] Later its connotation changed to imply a place of refuge or maintenance for travelers who were ill and still later to suggest a charitable institution for the needy, the aged, or the infirm. In the era of the "plagues," hospitals became known as "pest houses" and were remote from the rest of the community both in location and in social concept. The great majority of sick and injured people were still cared for in their own homes by the private physician and by the members of their families.

During the eighteenth and nineteenth centuries there was a gradual transition in the role played by the hospital; it became a place for surgical and medical care to some extent but it still had the aura of being mostly for terminal illness. The state of knowledge regarding infection and the lack of antiseptic procedures made it difficult for physician or patient to visualize the hospital as anything but a place from which there was little hope of returning alive.

In the twentieth century, with its phenomenal advances in scientific knowledge, the hospital developed rapidly into a full-fledged medical facility which could provide all types of treatment in a controlled environment. New surgical skills, expensive and complicated equipment,

[1] *Webster's New International Dictionary*, 2nd ed., G. & C. Merriam Co., New York, 1934.

highly trained nursing care, and regulation of diet and drug therapy all contributed to the patient's medical welfare and enhanced his chances of successful recovery.

As we move into an age of scientific prevention of disease and rehabilitation from disability, the character and contribution of the hospital must change again. Greater interest and progress in treating the effects of trauma, congenital conditions, and chronic and degenerative diseases, rather than the earlier concentration upon the control of infection and the alleviation of acute illness, means that rehabilitation must become a prime concern for the hospital. Increased populations, greater ability of patients to pay for care and the consequent demand for beds has initiated the awareness by the hospital of rehabilitation as a means of earlier discharge and greater availability of bed space. The patients' demand for restoration to usefulness in the community has awakened the interest of the medical staffs in the provision of services directed at medical rehabilitation in the fullest sense.

There has been a marked difference of opinion on the provision of rehabilitation services within the institutional confines of a hospital. Some have maintained that, since rehabilitation services are a part of the over-all treatment of a patient, it must necessarily follow that the hospital is the proper place to provide such specialized care. Others have indicated that the special nature of a rehabilitation program, particularly if it is to be a comprehensive one, requires that other types of facilities, completely outside the hospital proper, are a surer guarantee of success. As in most such questions, the practical answer probably lies somewhere between the two extremes.

Certainly if rehabilitation is to be considered in a broad sense as something which must be planned for or actually begun as soon as the patient has fallen victim to illness or injury, then it must of necessity be a prime concern of the hospital and its medical staff from the day of admission.

Hospitals have often been criticized in the past for their concentration upon getting the patient well enough to go home, with little concern for rehabilitation procedures which might be needed before that time or for adequate follow-up after actual discharge. In the case of the chronically ill, the hospitals have complained that badly needed beds are occupied for long periods by these cases with resultant lack of accommodations for the acutely ill.

It is true that, in recent years, with staff shortages and the speeding up of treatment, many general hospitals have been slow to understand or adopt the philosophy and methods of rehabilitation. The general practitioners and specialists on the treatment staff of general hospitals have often been slow to accept rehabilitation as an integral part of medical care. Too often it has been considered as action to be taken by others following the completion of definitive medical treatment. The Chronic Illness Commission states that "In too many hospitals, disregard of rehabilitation possibilities is the rule."[2]

Yet some of the medical procedures that are now considered basic to good rehabilitation had their beginnings within hospitals. Reconstructive surgery, exercise, and massage, use of heat, water, and other therapy procedures, and bracing of limbs and back had their origins in the special hospitals for crippled children at the turn of the century. The new specialty of physical medicine found its greatest acceptance in the military hospitals and the Veterans' Administration hospitals during and after World War II.

There have been many demonstrations that rehabilitation to the point of self-care at home and even to employment is a practical possibility for many of the chronically ill and the severely disabled to be found in general hospitals. In a series of 476 cases of severe disability studied by Rusk and McCoy, approximately 98% were found to be feasible for development and improvement of residual abilities.[3] Even in the relatively short-term cases involving the more common injuries and illnesses, there can often be a material reduction in hospitalization stay, loss of time from work, and permanent loss of function, together with a better psychological adjustment to residual disability.

In this sense, then, there are few cases in the hospital which do not offer some possibilities for rehabilitation and for eventual discharge to the home. Such a program in the hospital, however, cannot be a casual one or one which is predicated upon some public or private agency sending personnel into the hospital to get the job done. Medical rehabilitation within the hospital, as in the other components of a complete rehabilitation program, is a team effort, involving the combined services of the hospital. The degree and the character of the effort may differ with the hospital and the convictions of its staff, but it should be well integrated within the hospital as well as with the community health and social services outside.

Many hospitals have centered their programs for planned convalescent care along rehabilitation lines around a department or a service of physical medicine and rehabilitation. In some instances, such a

[2] Commission on Chronic Illness, *Care of the Long-Term Patient*, Vol. II of *Chronic Illness in U. S.*, Harvard Univ. Press, Cambridge, 1956, p. 193.

[3] McCoy, G. F., and Rusk, H. A., *An Evaluation of Rehabilitation*, Rehabilitation Monograph I, The Institute of Physical Medicine and Rehabilitation, N.Y.U. Bellevue Medical Center, 1953, p. 16.

service is headed by a specialist in physical medicine and rehabilitation, although there are outstanding examples of these services being directed by physicians in other specialties. He may act as coordinator of the whole program in the hospital or he may function in a more limited way through supervision of the immediate therapy programs provided to the patient in a particular section of the hospital. Some institutions have adopted the idea of a "rehabilitation council" or group of staff physicians of several specialties who combine their efforts toward effective rehabilitation. This kind of team approach has enhanced the opportunity for cooperation.

Regardless of the precise method, it is imperative that there be essential agreement on the philosophy and the plan of operation, if the medical rehabilitation program in the hospital is to be truly effective. Complete cooperation and support of the surgical and medical staffs of the hospital is needed if there is to be any hope of success. In addition, the social work section, the therapy units, nursing staff, and even the volunteer workers and maintenance staff must understand and participate in the over-all process of rehabilitation.

In its most effective form, the rehabilitation program in the general hospital will make significant contributions in the following areas:

1. Insure more prompt recovery and a shorter hospital stay for the patient with the acute medical or surgical condition.

2. Insure maximum functional use of affected body parts.

3. Prepare the severely disabled patient for self-sufficient living at home.

4. Assist the long-term patient in arriving at a stage of independence from constant attention, making possible a sort of "residential" or "dormitory" care in the hospital or in a nursing home.

5. Lay the groundwork for much more effective vocational or other special rehabilitation therapy and training after discharge.

In the specialized hospitals such as those for the tubercular, the cancer patient, or the victim of chronic disease of any kind, there is even greater need for adoption of the principles and practices of rehabilitation. There has been a regrettable tendency in recent years to think of institutional care as the crux of long-term patient care. State and federal money, as well as private funds, have been poured into "chronic illness" hospitals, institutions for the aging, and the like. The Commission on Chronic Illness has indicated clearly that large numbers of patients in the institutions for long-term care could probably be cared for as well or better, and more economically, at home. The Commission stated as follows:

With full appreciation of the necessity for adequate institutional facilities, and realizing that some areas do not have such accomodations and should provide them, the Commission nevertheless feels that henceforth communities generally should place the greater emphasis on planning for care in and around the home.[4]

If proper nursing service, therapy service, or other kinds of technical care were available, many of such patients could leave the hospital and live effectively at home. There has been an abdication from individual responsibility and community acceptance of the real need. Continued construction of custodial facilities, considering the aging of our population and the prevalence of long-term illness, will eventually constitute a great burden on the taxpayer. Much of this burden and the allocation of medical and therapy or nursing personnel for care of these patients could be avoided if rehabilitation could become the focal point in institutional care. If amounts comparable to those spent on long-term institutional care could be expended on improved and enlarged rehabilitation programs and facilities, the results would be astonishing to the community and to the individuals involved.

There are undoubtedly areas in the rehabilitation process which the hospital cannot effectively handle and which should not properly concern it. There have been grandiose plans for eventual incorporation into the hospital rehabilitation departments of all the components of a comprehensive rehabilitation program. These would include workshops for occupational evaluation and even preliminary vocational training. The argument is advanced that, since the hospital is the focal point in patient care and that since the physician turns to the hospital for such definitive care, the hospital must provide the whole gamut of rehabilitation services if rehabilitation is to become a significant part of the treatment of all kinds of cases. Such a viewpoint disregards two important elements in the basic consideration of rehabilitation; namely, the psychological stimulus of a "graduation" from the hospital atmosphere as a definite sign of progress to full recovery, and the fact that large numbers of handicapped are already outside the hospital or have never been in one. Many hospitals might more effectively and economically coordinate their services with other community services outside the hospital to afford the patient a fully integrated and complete program of rehabilitation.

The true role of medical rehabilitation in the hospital lies in the whole-hearted adoption of a philosophy toward patient care which is oriented from the day of admission toward rehabilitation; the organization of medical staff consultation and participation in the process

4 Commission on Chronic Illness, *op. cit.*, p. 424.

of rehabilitative therapy; the development of some type of rehabilitation service which can assume responsibility for coordinating and directing the whole program; the gearing of nursing, therapy, and social work programs in the direction of rehabilitation as a goal; the provision for therapy equipment and space with all prescriptions for therapy, counseling, and the like being under continuous, competent medical supervision. Most of all, the hospital needs to link its efforts for the patient with the other community rehabilitation programs and services, to the end that maximum restoration of function and adjustment to handicap becomes not merely a possibility but a probability.

CHAPTER 8

The Rehabilitation Center

A PHENOMENON IN THE RAPID DEVELOPMENT of rehabilitation interest and activity over the past two decades has been the growth of that specialized facility known as a rehabilitation center. The idea of concentrating a variety of specialized services within the professional and therapeutic framework of a single unit or program goes back to the latter part of the nineteenth century. The crippled children's clinics, the orthopedic hospitals, and, finally, the program of the Cleveland Rehabilitation Center, which dates back to 1889, were early milestones in the search for a better way to serve the needs of the disabled. However, the real impetus to the organization of centers was provided by the comprehensive services developed in military hospitals during World War II. The lessons learned from the rehabilitation of battle casualties were gradually translated to the civilian population and to community health services.

Although its development has been erratic and somewhat amorphous, the rehabilitation center has emerged as a definite entity, distinct from other facilities which may be involved in the recovery of an individual from disease and injury or in his adjustment to mental or physical handicap. Although it may have certain of the characteristics and even employ some of the methods of the hospital, workshop, school, or social service agency, it is none of these. Basically, its approach and method is more functional than clinical; it is more concerned with adjustment than cure.

Terminology has been confusing and conflicting in the growth of the center idea. Some of the early facilities and even some of the

45

present-day services utilize such names as "rehabilitation institutes," "curative workshops," and "rehabilitation hospitals or clinics." The title assumes no real importance, except in connection with the attempt of each facility to publicize its program. Fundamentally, the direction and purpose of all is much the same although the physical setting and the degree of comprehensiveness may differ.

The national organization of administrative personnel in rehabilitation centers, Conference of Rehabilitation Centers, Inc., in its constitution and by-laws, has defined a center as follows:

> A rehabilitation center is defined as a facility which is operated for the primary purpose of assisting in the rehabilitation of handicapped and disabled persons through an integrated program of medical, psychological, social, and vocational evaluation and services under competent professional supervision.[1]

The definition contained in the Surgeon-General's regulations establishing standards of adequacy for conduct of program under the amended Hill–Burton Act, since it affects the allotment of federal–state monies to the proposed construction or renovation of rehabilitation facilities (the term "center" is not specified in the wording) in communities, is of interest. Section 631 (n) of the Public Health Service Act reads:

> The term "rehabilitation facility" means a facility which is operated for the primary purpose of assisting in the rehabilitation of disabled persons through an integrated program of medical, psychological, social, and vocational evaluation and services under competent professional supervision and in the course of which the major portion of such evaluation and service is furnished within the facility; and either (A) the facility is operated in connection with a hospital, or (B) all medical and related health services are prescribed by, or are under the general direction of, persons licensed to practice medicine and surgery in the State.[2]

It may be helpful to consider the specific services which may be rendered by a rehabilitation center, within the four general categories contained in the definitions. The medical services may involve diagnosis, evaluation, treatment prescription, and general supervision of patient and staff activity; all performed by the medical staff either on a full-time basis or in a consulting or advisory capacity. Also considered a part of the medical services of a center are the physical, occupational, recreational, group, corrective, music, speech and hearing

[1] "Conference of Rehabilitation Centers Constitution and By-Laws" (as amended Nov. 15, 1955), Workshop Findings, Fourth Annual Workshop, St. Louis, 1955, p. 10.

[2] Title VI, Public Health Service Act, Section 631 (n).

therapies, as well as nursing care, prosthetic fitting and training. The psychological services include such areas as psychological counseling, psychological evaluation, psychiatric analysis, aptitude testing. The social services would comprise the medical social work on cases, personal counseling, outside or in-center social and recreational functions and activities, and liaison with other community health and welfare services. Within the vocational category are found such services as vocational or employment counseling, training and placement; prevocational testing, job evaluation, and transitional workshop employment.

Not all of these services are to be found in every center. However, it may reasonably be expected that the better the center program, the more such services it would offer. The key word in the present-day concept of the proper role for the rehabilitation center is *comprehensive.* There should be some aspects of all the designated services in any center which considers itself as offering a complete rehabilitation program. All parts of all services need not necessarily be within the four walls of the center building—some may be supplied through consultation, some through coordination with other public or private institutions and agencies.

There have been numerous attempts to divide rehabilitation centers into types. One such method, utilized in the first publication of data compiled by the Conference of Rehabilitation Centers in 1952, attempted to establish categories such as teaching and research centers, centers located in and operated by hospitals and medical schools, community centers with in-patient facilities, community out-patient centers, insurance centers and vocational rehabilitation centers.[3] Others have talked of "treatment centers" in the sense of in-patient hospital facilities for rehabilitation and have contrasted these with "comprehensive rehabilitation centers" and the "vocational workshop." These supposed distinctions are artificial to some extent in that they attempt to differentiate the centers on the basis of location, type of patient, sponsoring or administrating body, and specific phase or goal.

If we assume rehabilitation to be a fluid, not a static, process and if we further assume the rehabilitation center to be the focal point for integration and coordination of the rehabilitation process, then there seems to be little point in such differentiation. Regardless of particular areas of attention and interest within each center and regardless of location or sponsoring group, the common denominator for all reha-

[3] Redkey, H., *Rehabilitation Centers in the United States,* National Society for Crippled Children and Adults and Office of Vocational Rehabilitation, U. S. Dept. of Health, Education and Welfare, Chicago. 1953, p. 1.

bilitation centers would appear to lie in the meaning of the word "rehabilitation"—in its goal of achievement which must be decisive, positive,
and inclusive. There is a substantial difference between a center and
a hospital, even the physical medicine and rehabilitation wards or
departments of the hospital. There is an equally great difference
between the center and a true sheltered workshop or vocational training school. The differences are measurable in terms of over-all approach, in acceptance of responsibility not for just one phase or the
work of just one profession or discipline, but for the final objective as
it concerns total patient adjustment. The center undertakes to not
merely render medical treatment, nor to provide sheltered employment, nor simply to test, train, counsel, and evaluate. It may perform
any or all of these functions to a greater or less degree, but primarily
it is devoted to rendering a *combination* of such services with the aim
of restoring the disabled person physically, socially, and economically
to the greatest possible degree.

There has been much discussion and, indeed, argument as to the
proper locale for the development of a rehabilitation center. There
are those who maintain that rehabilitation belongs in the hospital setting; that it is the logical sequence of the definitive treatment and the
in-patient care which is rendered by the hospital and its staff. There
are equally strong assertions by others that the true rehabilitation
center should be an establishment and a program which is divorced
from the hospital; that the psychological impact on the patient of pro-
gression from hospital care and the opportunity to develop services
other than medical is greater when the center is separate from the hospital. Actually, this is again an artificial distinction. The significance
of a rehabilitation center lies not in its physical location but in its
program and its services. Equally good and equally comprehensive
centers ought to be possible of development, theoretically at least,
either in the hospital environment or outside it.

However, it must be admitted that, so far at least, the hospital rehabilitation programs have tended to weigh heavily on the medical and
physical therapy side, whereas the independent, community centers
have trended more in the direction of functional therapy and vocational preparation. It would be rash indeed to attempt a clear prediction of the course that the future development of centers will follow.
There are some who fear that already established, independent community centers, or even those now in the process of organization by
community groups, will be threatened by a continued trend toward the
development of extensive rehabilitation services and departments in
both the general and specialized hospitals. Talk is rife of competition

for cases, for staff personnel, for medical direction and interest, and for financial support. Although it is easy to recognize the basis for a certain amount of understandable concern in these areas on the part of established programs and facilities, there are valid reasons for believing that the concern is probably premature and perhaps even unrealistic.

If the need for rehabilitation services, both at present and in the future, proves to be as great as it would now appear, there should be a definite place for both the hospital and the independent center rehabilitation programs. The hospital may reasonably be expected to trend heavily toward the in-patient type of rehabilitation care and toward physical restoration; the independent community centers may become more deeply involved in pre-vocational testing, work preparation, psychological adjustment to community life. The independent centers will perhaps be more involved in relationships with social and economic resources for the eventual total rehabilitation of the individual patient. Their concern for and appeal to the handicapped individual, who has not been in a hospital recently but who needs a comprehensive program to help him overcome the effects of an existing disability, is probably greater than that of the general hospital. They can also be a potent force in the area of habilitation, particularly of children or the aged, where there is no need for a large measure of physical restoration but rather a planned program for successful living with the existing and static handicap.

There is no feasible way to outline a prototype of a rehabilitation center, either as to staffing, services rendered, construction of facility, type of patient, or even budget. The development of centers has been too diverse and individualized to permit any such prescribed delineation. Furthermore, there is general agreement among rehabilitation center administrators that there is much to be gained by building many different kinds of facilities. This is in order that opportunity will be provided for testing and analysis of results and for eventual determination of what kinds of programs are best for particular community needs and disability case requirements.

Figure 1 on page 50 is intended merely to outline certain basic service components, some or all of which would be included in most kinds of rehabilitation centers. Figures 2, 3, and 4 on pages 51–59 are floor plans of three different types of centers, one being the metropolitan hospital or institute type, involving both in-patient and out-patient care; the second being the more typical comprehensive community center in a sizable city; and the third being the combination center and sheltered workshop in a smaller community. On

BASIC SERVICE COMPONENTS OF CENTER

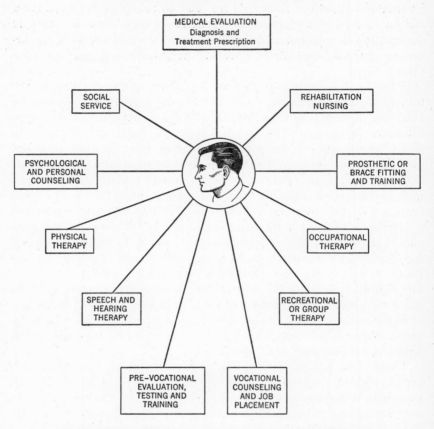

MEDICAL EVALUATION
Diagnosis and
Treatment Prescription

SOCIAL
SERVICE

REHABILITATION
NURSING

PSYCHOLOGICAL
AND PERSONAL
COUNSELING

PROSTHETIC OR
BRACE FITTING
AND TRAINING

PHYSICAL
THERAPY

OCCUPATIONAL
THERAPY

SPEECH AND
HEARING
THERAPY

RECREATIONAL
OR GROUP
THERAPY

PRE-VOCATIONAL
EVALUATION,
TESTING AND
TRAINING

VOCATIONAL
COUNSELING
AND JOB
PLACEMENT

Centers might contain modifications or extensions of this basic service plan and might provide all services by staff within center or provide some by outside consultative referral.

FIGURE 1

pages 60 and 61 is an analysis of basic budget requirements to be taken into consideration in organizing, and effectively operating thereafter, one kind of community rehabilitation center with services provided for various kinds of disability. Figure 5 on page 62 indicates sources of case referral and financial support. None of these plans or charts should be considered as in any way conclusive as to needs but rather as a rough guide to preliminary thinking and action; as some kind of base on which each group or each community can decide as to its own particular needs and variations. Other sources for such planning material are suggested in the bibliography.

FLOOR PLANS FOR THE
REHABILITATION INSTITUTE
OF
METROPOLITAN DETROIT

1 TECHNICAL DIRECTOR
2 SECRETARY
3 INSTRUCTOR
4 STORAGE
5 LECTURE ROOM
6 PREPARATION & STORAGE
7 LIBRARY
8 PHYSICAL THERAPY
   CLASS ROOM
9 WATER METER ROOM
10 TELEPHONE EQUIPMENT
11 MEDICAL RECORDS
   LIBRARY
12 OCCUPATIONAL THERAPY
   CLASS ROOM
13 PROSTHETIST
14 PROSTHETIC & BRACE
   SHOP
15 POOL ABOVE
16 DRESSING ROOM
17 DARK ROOM
18 VISUAL EDUCATION
19 RECEIVING AND
   HOUSEKEEPER
20 JANITOR'S CLOSET
21 ORDERLIES
22 DOCTORS
23 DOCTORS' LOUNGE
24 WOMEN ATTENDANTS
25 JANITORS
26 OFFICE
27 PROJECTION ROOM
28 ELECTRICAL EQUIPMENT
29 MECHANICAL EQUIPMENT

BASEMENT PLAN

N

SCALE   FEET   METERS

Teaching, Training and Research Areas, Brace and Prosthetic Shop

FIGURE 2

1 EXAM
2 UTILITY
3 NURSES STATION
4 ADMITTING OFFICE
5 SECRETARY
6 PHYSIATRISTS
7 VESTIBULE
8 CASHIER
9 RECEPTION
10 COAT ROOM
11 STAFF LOUNGE
12 CENTRAL APPOINTMENTS
13 CHIEF THERAPIST
14 INSTRUMENT ROOM
15 MYOGRAPH ROOM
16 ELECTRICAL THERAPY
17 ELECTRIC DIAGNOSTIC
18 STORAGE
19 MOIST AIR
20 SOCIAL SERVICE

FIRST FLOOR PLAN

N   SCALE   FEET   METERS

Physical Therapy Area, Out-Patient Clinic Area, Reception and Admitting Area

FIGURE 2 (Continued)

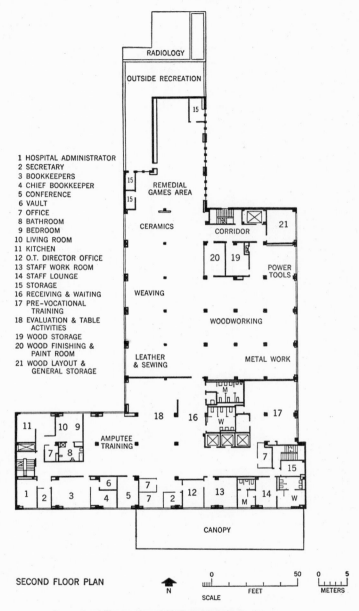

1 HOSPITAL ADMINISTRATOR
2 SECRETARY
3 BOOKKEEPERS
4 CHIEF BOOKKEEPER
5 CONFERENCE
6 VAULT
7 OFFICE
8 BATHROOM
9 BEDROOM
10 LIVING ROOM
11 KITCHEN
12 O.T. DIRECTOR OFFICE
13 STAFF WORK ROOM
14 STAFF LOUNGE
15 STORAGE
16 RECEIVING & WAITING
17 PRE-VOCATIONAL
   TRAINING
18 EVALUATION & TABLE
   ACTIVITIES
19 WOOD STORAGE
20 WOOD FINISHING &
   PAINT ROOM
21 WOOD LAYOUT &
   GENERAL STORAGE

SECOND FLOOR PLAN

Occupational Therapy Area, Activities of Daily Living Area,
Pre-Vocational Training Area, Business Offices

FIGURE 2 (*Continued*)

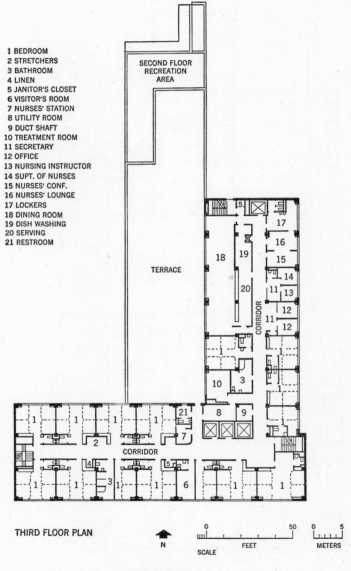

1 BEDROOM
2 STRETCHERS
3 BATHROOM
4 LINEN
5 JANITOR'S CLOSET
6 VISITOR'S ROOM
7 NURSES' STATION
8 UTILITY ROOM
9 DUCT SHAFT
10 TREATMENT ROOM
11 SECRETARY
12 OFFICE
13 NURSING INSTRUCTOR
14 SUPT. OF NURSES
15 NURSES' CONF.
16 NURSES' LOUNGE
17 LOCKERS
18 DINING ROOM
19 DISH WASHING
20 SERVING
21 RESTROOM

SECOND FLOOR
RECREATION
AREA

TERRACE

THIRD FLOOR PLAN

N

SCALE

0   50
FEET

0   5
METERS

Adult In-Patient Unit

FIGURE 2 (*Continued*)

54

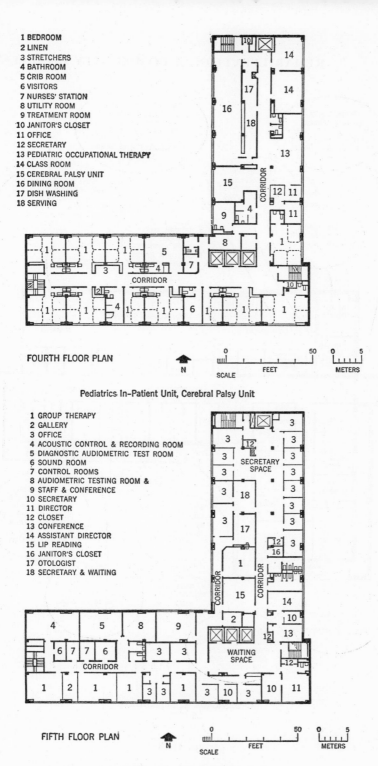

1 BEDROOM
2 LINEN
3 STRETCHERS
4 BATHROOM
5 CRIB ROOM
6 VISITORS
7 NURSES' STATION
8 UTILITY ROOM
9 TREATMENT ROOM
10 JANITOR'S CLOSET
11 OFFICE
12 SECRETARY
13 PEDIATRIC OCCUPATIONAL THERAPY
14 CLASS ROOM
15 CEREBRAL PALSY UNIT
16 DINING ROOM
17 DISH WASHING
18 SERVING

FOURTH FLOOR PLAN

N   SCALE   FEET   METERS

Pediatrics In-Patient Unit, Cerebral Palsy Unit

1 GROUP THERAPY
2 GALLERY
3 OFFICE
4 ACOUSTIC CONTROL & RECORDING ROOM
5 DIAGNOSTIC AUDIOMETRIC TEST ROOM
6 SOUND ROOM
7 CONTROL ROOMS
8 AUDIOMETRIC TESTING ROOM &
9 STAFF & CONFERENCE
10 SECRETARY
11 DIRECTOR
12 CLOSET
13 CONFERENCE
14 ASSISTANT DIRECTOR
15 LIP READING
16 JANITOR'S CLOSET
17 OTOLOGIST
18 SECRETARY & WAITING

FIFTH FLOOR PLAN

N   SCALE   FEET   METERS

Speech and Hearing Area, Administrative and Staff Offices

FIGURE 2 (Continued)

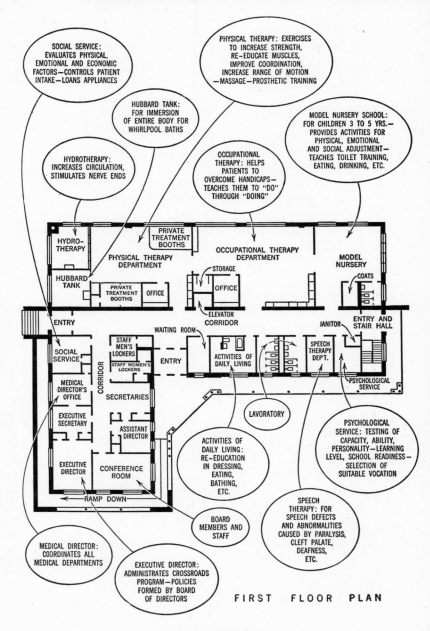

FIRST FLOOR PLAN

CROSSROADS REHABILITATION
CENTER
Indianapolis, Indiana

FIGURE 3

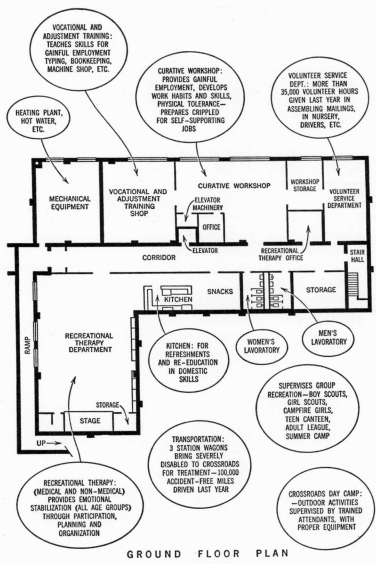

GROUND FLOOR PLAN

FIGURE 3 (*Continued*)

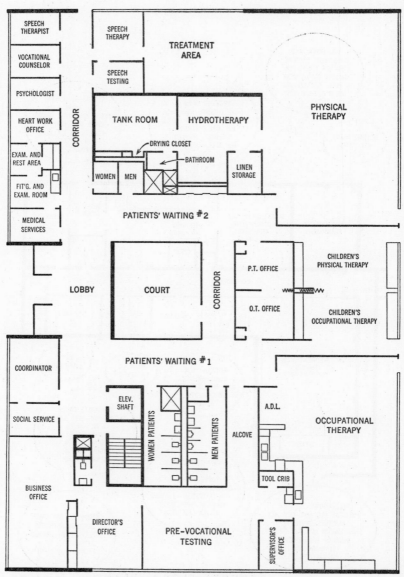

FIRST FLOOR PLAN
REHABILITATION CENTER FOR THE PHYSICALLY HANDICAPPED, INC.,
STAMFORD, CONNECTICUT

FIGURE 4

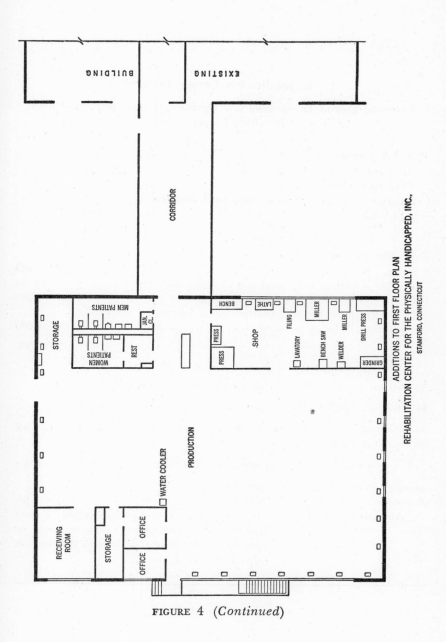

FIGURE 4 (*Continued*)

Rehabilitation Center Budget

Estimated Cost of Establishing and Operating Community Out-Patient
Center Handling Fifty Patients a Day

Initial Acquisition Expense

Land and building	$140,000
Therapy equipment	20,000
Administrative and general equipment and furnishings	40,000
	$200,000

Operating Expenses

Salaries (see next page)	$129,000
Funded amortization of land and building cost (20 years)	10,000
Depreciation of equipment and building	5,000
General expense (utility costs, transportation, public relations, printing, supplies, laundry, etc.)	50,000
	$194,000

50 patients × 5 day week = 250 per week × 52 weeks in year = 13,000

$194,000 divided by 13,000 = $14.92 per patient daily treatment cost

Assuming 12 cases per day as charity cases and 37 cases per day as paying all inclusive rate of $14.92:

37 × 5 = 185 per week × 52 weeks per year = 9,620 × $15.00 = $144,300

Annual operating expense − $194,000
Annual income from cases − $144,300
Annual deficit $49,700 (Must be defrayed by annual "subsidy", from contributions, Community Chest, national or local funds, drives or foundations, fraternal or other benefit societies)

Rehabilitation Center Personnel and Salaries

Administrator	$ 10,000
General secretary	4,500
Bookkeeper	3,500
Clerk	2,500
Stenographer	3,000
Medical director	10,000
Medical secretary	4,500
Consultant services: (hourly basis)	
Orthopedist (2 hours a week)	3,500
Physiatrist (10 hours a week)	6,000
Internist (6 hours a week)	4,500
Consultant services: (fee basis)	
Roentgenologist	3,000
Neurosurgeon	2,500
Psychiatrist	2,500
Other specialties	2,000
Physical therapist (chief)	5,000
Physical therapists (assistants) 3 at $4,500	13,500
Speech and hearing therapist	5,000
Occupational therapist (chief)	5,000
Occupational therapists (assistants) 3 at $4,500	13,500
Rehabilitation nurse	5,000
Medical social worker	5,000
Certified prosthetist or Orthotist (consultant on fee basis)	2,000
Vocational or rehabilitation counselor or employment manager (Handles the prevocational and vocational programs and acts as liaison person with divisions of vocational rehabilitation)	6,000
Secretary	4,000
Porter	3,000
Annual total	$129,000

SOURCES OF FINANCIAL SUPPORT (other than case referrals)
Public Fund Drive
Individual Donations or Gifts
Foundation Grants
Community Chest or United Fund
Civic Group Projects
National Health Agencies
Grants–in–aid, Public or Private
Industrial Firms
Labor Unions

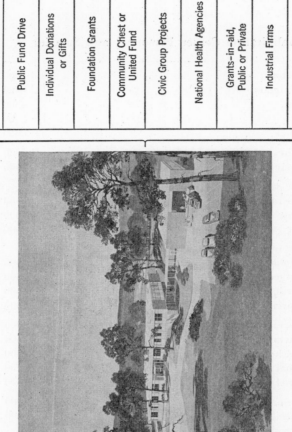

SOURCES OF INCOME FROM CASE REFERRALS
Private Health Agencies
Individual Patients
Insurance Companies
Union Welfare Funds
Self–insured Business Firms
State Divisions of Vocational Rehabilitation
State Crippled Children's Services
Departments of Public Welfare
Private or Public Agencies for Particular Disabilities (blind, mentally ill, etc.)

CENTER FINANCIAL SUPPORT STRUCTURE

FIGURE 5

Certain general considerations in the planning and establishment of a rehabilitation center may be of value. Some of these same principles may be helpful in the measurement of the effectiveness of existing rehabilitation center programs. The first, and perhaps most vital, of these considerations is the importance of direct and detailed *medical supervision*. A number of the early centers, and even some of a later vintage, attempted to operate without any or with insufficient medical direction. Some relied upon the attending physician to prescribe a therapy program on some sort of written form at the time his patient was referred to the center. This approach was unscientific and often unfair to the patient, the therapists, and even to the referring physician. It was a little like a doctor referring a patient to the administrative, nursing, and orderly staffs of a hospital with written or oral instructions that the patient needed an appendectomy, without any professional referral to a qualified surgeon to prescribe, direct, and perform such surgery. Fortunately the trend is now strongly in the direction of clearly recognizing the need for definitive medical direction and supervision of the rehabilitation program within the center. The professional associations interested in rehabilitation have supported this trend and the qualifying regulations implementing the 1954 amendments to the Hospital Construction (Hill–Burton) Act make certain stipulations in regard to the direction of medical and related health services within a center, if such a facility is to qualify for grant consideration under the Act.[4]

The qualifications of the medical staff, insofar as any particular specialty in medicine is concerned, are less important than that there be a real dedication to total rehabilitation for the disabled as well as an ability to command the respect and confidence of the local medical profession. Good medical direction of a center program implies not only the aura of professional approach but, more specifically, the actual examination of each patient, review of diagnosis, consideration of past medical history, and the completion of needed laboratory tests, X-rays, etc. This study is necessary in order to determine whether the patient is ready to undertake a rehabilitation program in a center and whether such a program can reasonably be expected to materially assist in his physical or mental recovery, in his adjustment to the remaining handicap, and in his restoration to social and work activity. A prescription for concentrated therapy is designed and this becomes the pattern for the work of the therapists with the patient. Periodic evaluations as to progress benefit both patient and staff. In a well-organized center, the physician becomes the guiding force in the work of the

[4] Title VI, Public Health Service Act, Section 631 (n).

rehabilitation team. The value of definitive medical direction and supervision can best be realized in the full-time or part-time director or consultant, with whatever associate medical staff is required, rather than through the efforts of a purely advisory medical board.

The second of these general considerations involves the much over-worked, but nonetheless important, concept of *staff teamwork* within the center and in relation to the use of other community resources outside the center. Since the center quite naturally becomes a focal point in the rehabilitation process and since the center professional and technical staff involves a number of different disciplines, the basic requirement for team approach, common understanding, and broad evaluation of patient need seems obvious. However, there is some chance for the staff to err in the direction of one extreme or another; toward jealous assumption of prerogatives by one particular discipline or toward the undiscerning insistence upon all members of the reha-bilitation team exerting their efforts upon each and every patient, regardless of whether he may have any real need for some of the services. Either pitfall can be avoided by common sense evaluation and perceptive direction by the doctor, administrator, and counselor or coordinator. Teamwork is the very essence of good rehabilitation, both from a broad-scale approach to principle and practice and from the practical operation of a rehabilitation center. Constant staff edu-cation, group discussion of both patients and methods, definitive lead-ership on the part of medical and lay administrative personnel can become the balance wheel upon which the level of center accomplish-ment turns.

Third point of emphasis relates to *a functional approach* to therapy and to the individual patient program. The term "functional" is used not only in the sense of restoration of anatomical function, although that is often a major part of the work of a rehabilitation center, but rather in the concept of economic and social function. The aim of most rehabilitation is to restore ability of the individual to function properly and constructively in the community, even if the goal is only a limited ability on the part of the patient to care for his own needs at home. The rehabilitation center has little place for the purely diversional type of therapy. In this respect it may differ markedly from the chronic disease hospital, the mental hospital, or the custodial care wards of public or private medical institutions. Particularly in its occupational therapy program, the center provides marked em-phasis upon work or self-care as the desired end result of such therapy. The center is a place for progress toward some greater accomplishment on the part of the patient; it is not a place for stagnation, shelter, or recreation.

A fourth necessary principle of operation in the rehabilitation center is the *individualized program* for each patient. There can be no such thing as a standard method for the handling of all amputee cases or an accepted therapy prescription for all those disabled by poliomyelitis. Each patient reacts differently to his disability, to his treatment, and to those who are trying to help him. If rehabilitation is to be truly successful, every step in the process must be carefully planned to take into account the patient's attitudes, his tolerance, and his eventual goal. There are few short cuts or pat answers in any program which is so deeply involved with human relations. Every human being is affected in a variety of ways by disease or injury and by their aftermath of disability. Constant re-evaluation, careful counseling, and continual reassurance become a significant part of the attempt of the center staff to obtain a successful result in the light of individual potential.

The fifth element involves a willingness to accept a wide variety of cases which in turn demands *a flexible program* in terms of both equipment and case handling. There is an unfortunate tendency to think of rehabilitation centers as being primarily for the severe, complicated, dramatic disability. The value of a center program for the less severely handicapped is overlooked. The contribution of a therapy program and the other components of a center can be just as significant in the fracture case or the back condition as in a spinal cord injury or the case of an older person who has had a "stroke." The greater number of the less severely handicapped means that there is correspondingly greater opportunity for a sizable number of referrals of such cases. Not only the humanitarian principles involved are important but the problem of financial support of most centers demands that they adapt their program to handle the more routine disability cases. By the same token, the center needs to understand its role in the "habilitation" of children with congenital conditions or handicaps arising from early childhood disease. The scarcely understood challenges of the aging and their degenerative diseases or conditions demand a policy of center administration which foresees and adapts to meet the future needs in this area. Not all centers will be multiple-disability centers, but the center movement as a whole must avoid rigidity, fixed patterns, and limited imagination if it is to continue to be the working core of rehabilitation thinking and practice.

The last, and a very basic, need in center management is *coordination and follow-up* to insure maximum success in case handling. Centers cannot exist as isolated facilities in the over-all rehabilitation process. A working relationship with all the other medical, health, social service, and vocational training or placement resources in the community is vital to the success of any center program. Enlistment of the understanding help and advice of all such groups is the best insurance of satisfactory case results. Through advisory boards, councils, boards of directors, or sponsors, the center can effectively obtain the support of community-minded individuals and organizations. Likewise, the follow-up necessary to complete the patient rehabilitation which the center has begun requires thought and effort on the part of the center staff. The center which knows nothing of what becomes of its cases after they leave the doors of the center has little on which to measure its effectiveness and attempt to improve its program. Statistics of accomplishment are important in the public relations sphere and may well make the difference between adequate and inadequate case referral, between sound and deficit financing, and between whole-hearted community support and community indifference. Meaningful statistics are impossible without proper case follow-up. If the role of the rehabilitation center is to expand and prove increasingly significant, the coordination and follow-up needs to be administratively sound and professionally significant.

The rehabilitation center has become the keystone in the bridge between hospital treatment and employment or home self-care. It serves the patient in a positive and functional way during a period when his doubts about his economic and social recovery are at their height. It offers supervised activity and planned motivation instead of enforced inactivity and corroding discouragement. Its program of physical restoration and occupational guidance can make all the difference between the man who resigns himself to a life of inability and one who grasps the promise of a rewarding future. Those who plan, administer, and operate these havens of hope bear a great responsibility; the need to visualize the complex nature of the rehabilitation process, to treasure its principles, to learn, adapt, and progress with the moving frontiers of human knowledge and human endeavor.

CHAPTER 9

Counseling

bilitation program for any disabled individual is good counseling. Although, in a broad sense, all participants in the rehabilitation effort provide some measure of counsel, the art or profession of counseling has become the special province of people trained in this particular field.   Rehabilitation is a complex process, as we have already seen from the description of some of its major components, and this fact will be increasingly evident from the later discussion of community organization and effort.   The many services, facilities, disciplines, and individuals seeking to answer some part of the rehabilitation need in the community badly need interpretation to the handicapped person. Responsibility for such interpretation and for the coordination of the whole rehabilitation process must be assumed by someone if the end result is to be at all successful.   The trained counselor is in the best position to perform this vital function.

Hamilton, in his definitive work on this subject, refers to "rehabilitation as a field of practice, a distinct skill in human relations."[1]   He further states that the relationship between the counselor and the disabled person is "the germ which makes the process of rehabilitation bear fruit."[2]   Opinions vary as to what discipline or profession has the best training for this responsible job of counseling and as to who, in the multiplicity of community services, is in the best position to carry out the assignment.   In an attempt to arrive at some conclusions in

[1] Hamilton, K. W., *Counseling the Handicapped in the Rehabilitation Process,* Ronald Press, New York, 1950, p. 206.
[2] *Ibid.,* p. 207.

that regard, it would be well to take a look at what kinds of people are currently engaged in performing some or all of this counseling task. Counseling in the area of social adjustment has been performed for many years by the trained social worker, particularly the medical social worker. In hospitals, both general and specialized, as well as in rehabilitation centers and in community health services of other kinds, the social worker has provided guidance in personal or family problems, acceptance of disability, utilization of community services, and realistic approach to self-care and employment. Caroline Elledge, in her book on social casework in the rehabilitation program, makes the following significant comment on the role of the medical social worker:

> The hospital or other agency providing medical care is often in a strategic position to recognize personal problems in the life of an individual who is seeking a specialized service designed to minimize his physical handicap. Physical restoration is often the first step toward total rehabilitation. A man or woman who has difficulty in accepting medical treatment may have personal problems which stem from family responsibilities or fears which are related directly to the implications, for him, of the physical impairment. He may express his need for help in working out these problems in a variety of ways—he may seem fearful, emotionally upset, irritable, critical, or apathetic. He may discuss his personal difficulties with members of the medical and nursing staff and others who assist in his care. A medical social worker who is a member of the staff of the medical care agency can, in cooperation with other members of the medical team, help the patient to work through some of these problems. This frequently influences the effectiveness of the medical treatment and strengthens the patient's personal resources so that he can take the next steps toward independence more easily.
>
> The medical social worker, whether offering direct social case-work service or consultation, may also be helpful to other members of the rehabilitation team through contributing to their understanding of the individual. Individuals can be helped to make the most of their capacities if all those who are helping them, figure out how to modify possible long-range plans, in the light of personal handicaps as well as physical and intellectual limitations and capacities.[3]

The field of psychiatric social work has developed in recent years into a definitive area of activity with trained graduates in this field being engaged in psychiatric hospitals, departments, or clinics, and also in certain community health or welfare agencies. The growing recognition of the problem of mental health and the possibilities for rehabilitation of the mentally or emotionally handicapped person has greatly stimulated interest in the specialized counseling necessary for such a person.

[3] Elledge, Caroline, *The Rehabilitation of the Patient—Social Casework in Medicine*, J. B. Lippincott Co., Phila., 1948, pp. 100–101.

At the present time there are 25 universities and colleges offering approved courses in medical social work and 35 offering approved courses in psychiatric social work.[4] About eight to nine hundred graduates annually in these fields of training are not nearly sufficient to meet the need.[5] Two years of graduate training, leading to the master's degree, plus two years of supervised field training, are considered essential for successful practice in this field.

Psychological counseling has been a much discussed but loosely defined phase of activity in rehabilitation. To a degree, all the professional and lay persons participating in rehabilitation programs are concerned with certain principles of individual psychology. The entire reaction of a person to his mental or physical handicap, and the whole process of rehabilitation as related to that handicap, are based upon psychological adjustment. In a formal sense, however, there has not been as much use of the trained psychologist in rehabilitation as one might reasonably expect. Data collected by the American Psychological Association on specialized work within the field of psychology for the year 1954 shows only 2.5% of those in the field are engaged in programs for the physically handicapped and another 2.9% working in the area of mental deficiency.[6]

There has been some confusion between the terms "clinical psychologist" and "counseling psychologist." The report of the Subcommittee on Paramedical Personnel in Rehabilitation and Care of the Chronically Ill to its parent body, the Health Resources Advisory Committee of the Office of Defense Mobilization, published in January 1956, contains a practical and meaningful comment:

> The clinical psychologist is one who works in a hospital, clinic or similar medical setting. He assists in the diagnosis and treatment of individuals with mental and emotional problems or illness. His purpose is to help the maladjusted learn new and better habits of behavior. The difference between the clinical and counseling psychologist is quite subtle. The counseling psychologist may be considered a specialist in average, everyday problems. His purpose is to help people understand themselves so that they can deal sensibly with their own problems and decisions and take advantage of their abilities, emphasizing the forestalling of mental illness.

About one-half of the practicing psychologists hold a doctor's degree and practically all the rest have a master's degree in this special field. Eighty-three universities and colleges offer graduate training in

4 Office of Defense Mobilization, "Mobilization and Health Manpower," A Report of the Subcommittee on Paramedical Personnel in Rehabilitation and Care of the Chronically Ill, Washington, Jan. 1956, p. 29.

5 Ibid., p. 28.

6 Ibid., p. 33.

clinical psychology with 45 offering similar education in counseling psychology.[7]

Those few rehabilitation programs or facilities which have utilized the services of a psychologist to perform counseling on a regular basis have been impressed with the results. The role of the psychologist on the rehabilitation team lies in the area of objective assessment of intellectual and emotional ability and disability; a measurement of the potential of the disabled patient. In the more serious cases, involving deep-seated neuroses or psychoses, where referral for psychiatric or neurological consultation is indicated, the psychologist may act as liaison in interpreting psychiatric findings for the rest of the rehabilitation staff and helping them to carry through treatment recommendations.

One organization[8] conducting a program of rehabilitation for those involved in accidental injuries and particularly industrial injuries has utilized the services of registered nurses with an academic degree as a focal point in counseling of the individual patient. These girls provide a specialized counseling service for the seriously injured worker in workmen's compensation cases. As soon as liability has been determined by claims investigation on cases involving serious injury, referral is made to the rehabilitation nurse. Usually, while the employee is still in the hospital, she makes her initial contact with him, his family, and his attending physician. Her aim is to elicit the trust and cooperation of all the parties in a carefully planned and coordinated program of rehabilitation designed to effect maximum physical restoration in the shortest period of time. The program may involve eventual referral of the employee to one of the company's rehabilitation centers in Boston or Chicago, may also make use of local rehabilitation facilities, or entail additional specialized surgery, hospital care, or vocational retraining by public and private agencies. The final phases of the program involve contact with the employer to encourage re-employment of the handicapped employee at the same or a different job; it may also involve the utilization of special training facilities to prepare the employee for a different occupation or for establishment of his own business.

The accomplishment of these aims requires the solution of many personal and family problems which may act as a barrier to full recovery of self-confidence and the physical and mental readiness to resume work. The work of the nurses has done much to overcome the psychological mishandling of serious injury cases which often resulted in a

[7] Ibid., pp. 36 and 37.

[8] Schiffer, D. M., "Liberty Mutual's Rehabilitation Program," Am. J. Nursing, 53, pp. 834–837 (July 1953).

complete unwillingness to cooperate in any return-to-work program. Because of her professional status and her complete divorcement from the liability phases of the case, the nurse is able to win the confidence of the employee and get his cooperation for a selective medical program. Her background of training and education enables her to understand the medical problems involved and to talk and work with doctors and hospital staffs on a professional level. Her experience with the problems of the sick and the injured enable her to handle sympathetically the worries and reactions of the seriously disabled. Most of all, she personally represents the vital interest of the employer and carrier in the employee and his welfare. The rehabilitation nurse serves as the integrating force, the coordinator, indeed the catalyst of the whole program of medical care and rehabilitation. She can build the "umbrella" or the "package" under which and within which the entire process of recovery from accidental injury can be developed.

One of the most significant developments in the realm of counseling is the increasing importance of the vocational counselor or vocational rehabilitation counselor. Although the field of vocational guidance and teaching had existed in the school systems and in certain specialized institutions for many years, the area of vocational counseling in relation to the handicapped, as a particular field of endeavor, had its inception with the Vocational Rehabilitation Act of 1920 and the consequent development of the federal–state programs for vocational training and placement. The individual counselor in the state agency was the key to the successful operation of these programs. It was he who evaluated the need of each disabled "client" and utilized the community services necessary to place the handicapped person in a job, if it were humanly possible to do so.

There was little professional stature or formalized training connected with vocational rehabilitation counseling until the passage of Public Law 565 in 1954 and the subsequent teaching and training grants to universities and colleges. These grants were made for the purpose of encouraging the development of graduate teaching and the awarding of degrees in the specific field of vocational rehabilitation counseling. Now some 35 universities and colleges offer graduate instruction in this highly specialized field and more schools are organizing such courses each year.

The advances in academic training promise to enlarge and develop the role of the vocational rehabilitation counselor to some extent, but basically it has been his responsibility to assist the disabled individual in securing employment consistent with his physical or mental capacities and with his preparation by training or "on-the-job" instruction and experience. Most of the vocational counseling, specifically labeled as such, has been done in the government agencies such as the divisions of vocational rehabilitation, state employment services, and Veterans' Administration offices. A few such counselors have functioned in the setting of a special school, rehabilitation center, sheltered workshop, or community job-placement program, but these have been the exception. In general, the private agencies have been content to leave this area of vocational training and job placement to the federal and state programs which have had long experience in the special knowledge and skills required.

At the 1956 annual conference of the National Rehabilitation Association, papers presented on the subject of the vocational rehabilitation counselor, his background and duties, were both timely and definitive. Excerpts from one of the discussions are helpful in understanding this particular member of the rehabilitation team.

Counselors, in the vocational rehabilitation effort, have been drawn from many walks of life; but the great majority come from those areas which have to do with human reactions and human relationships: education, social work, psychology. Few indeed are those in whose background experience the human relation components were concerned only obliquely.

Vocational rehabilitation counseling has its roots in all of these disciplines. As it evolves, however, it becomes an entity in itself. The vocational rehabilitation counselor represents an individual who is drawing his professional strengths from many sources of energy.

. . . He learns to recognize the basic principles involved in medicine and psychiatry, psychology, sociology, social work, law, education, and other fields. He takes these basic principles and contrives a more catholic approach. To be more specific, he is able to draw from these fields whatever information is available and interpret this information in terms of vocational objectives.

. . . It is in the field of occupational information for the handicapped that the rehabilitation counselor becomes expert. His knowledge of job resource facilities for the handicapped in a given territory is large and complete. He is on several committees for employment of the handicapped. He is in daily phone communication with many personnel men, knows them by their first name, drinks coffee with them, and attends their meetings. He is constantly on the alert for new placement opportunities. He is well versed in the job demands of many, many jobs available to his clients. He is familiar with major job classifications and sources of occupational information. The rehabilitation counselor is well versed in educational opportunities, prerequisites, and educational costs.[9]

[9] Johnston, L. T., "The Counselor as He Really Is," one paper in series of four on symposium on "What Is A Rehabilitation Counselor," *J. Rehabilitation*, XXIII, No. 3, pp. 9 and 10 (May–June 1957) .

Regardless of the type of counseling and any manifest concern with one particular aspect of the rehabilitation process, there are certain elements common to all counseling endeavors and procedures. Counseling implies an organized attack upon certain of the residuals of disability or handicap; by its very nature it involves an evaluation of assets and liabilities, a recognition of problems and the action necessary to resolve them. Instead of a primary concern with one particular therapeutic or technical phase of the restoration process, the counselor is more apt to be concerned with the broader development and integration of the whole rehabilitation plan. In this sense he becomes the interpreter of services, facilities, and goals for the disabled individual.

Despite the obvious interest of the counselor in a broader approach to rehabilitation and despite the equally obvious need for greater coordination and integration of services (which will be explored more fully in a later chapter), there is a misconception regarding some kind of over-all counselor as the final answer to successful rehabilitation. It is doubtful if any such panacea is actually practical of accomplishment or desirable in essence. Hamilton speaks of a " 'quarterback'—a rehabilitation counselor–competent to assume the responsibility"[10] for planning and coordinating the entire rehabilitation program. The federal–state program, under the Office of Vocational Rehabilitation, both through the changing legislative concept and directives and the practical assumption of new responsibilities beyond the strictly vocational aspects, has trended in the direction of visualizing its vocational rehabilitation counselors as the coordinators of the whole rehabilitation process. Training and other definitive data prepared for both in-service instruction and outside education refer to "rehabilitation counselors" rather than the older terminology of the "vocational rehabilitation counselor." There is much talk in these publications of "rehabilitation counselor" as a kind of professional relationship extending from the first recognition of disability to the final job placement or attainment of maximum physical or mental capacity.[11]

Recognizing rehabilitation as one of the most democratic of processes in our present-day social thinking and practice, and appreciating the basic values of the team concept in a practical rehabilitation program, it is difficult to concede the emergence of a "super-counselor" who would run the whole show. Like many suggested authoritative solutions, it would appear to be an easy answer to the recognized conflicts

10 Hamilton, K. W., *op. cit.*, p. 205.

11 Hall, J. H., and Warren, S. L., *Rehabilitation Counselor Preparation*, National Rehabilitation Association and National Vocational Guidance Association, Washington, 1956, pp. 13–20.

in disciplines, services, and objectives which sometimes distort and confuse the attempts to help the handicapped person. However, the joint evaluation, the healthy exchange of ideas, the resolution of differences of opinion in the interest of the patient, and the gradual organization of an individualized plan for rehabilitation in each case are vital to the spirit and the practice of successful rehabilitation. The contributions of counseling, both personal and objective, must come from several sources during the rehabilitation process and yet can be effectively woven into a pattern of practical accomplishment by teamwork at the local level.

CHAPTER 10

Work Evaluation

WHETHER WE ARE TALKING ABOUT HABILITA-
tion for the disabled individual who has never worked or rehabilitation for the person who has become disabled and must be returned,
if possible, to work ability, the general question of work evaluation
assumes great importance. Galen, in the second century A.D., stated
that "Employment is nature's best physician and essential to happi-
ness." No modern scientist or professional worker could express the
goal of much of our rehabilitation effort more simply. But this goal
is not reached by merely providing a certain measure of physical restoration or mental recovery with the fond expectation that this will
automatically insure successful employment. The development of a
well-rounded and practical program of work evaluation is a precedent
to meaningful employment, whether in competitive industry, in the
sheltered workshop, or in the home.

The basic components of work evaluation consist of occupational
therapy, vocational or occupational counseling, intelligence and aptitude testing, prevocational evaluation or work classification, and trial
or transitional employment. There is also the important element of
job placement as the climax to work evaluation procedures, together
with scheduled follow-up after placement; but these are discussed in a
later chapter. All of these components may be provided in the rehabilitation process through the services of different trained people, working in different disciplines, and they may also be provided in separate
and diverse facilities, but essentially they form a pattern of purpose
and progress which is patient-centered and vocationally oriented.

The occupational therapist, by virtue of both title and professional responsibility, has long been concerned with the eventual occupational possibilities of the patient. The activities in the occupational therapy departments of hospital rehabilitation programs or rehabilitation centers attempt to improve physical function and mental adjustment but also have the aim of preliminary evaluation of actual work potential.

In the observation of the patient's reaction to several kinds of work activities and situations, as well as his actual physical performance, the therapist has an opportunity to contribute valuable information to the physician, administrator, counselor, and others who will play a part in the orientation of the patient's program toward practical occupational results. Some rehabilitation facilities have devised a work-evaluation progress report which will assist the therapist in organizing and recording the work behavior pattern.

The immediate interest of the vocational rehabilitation counselor has always been the occupational or work evaluation of the disabled person. As was pointed out in the chapter on counseling, the majority of such activity has existed in the state divisions of vocational rehabilitation. In the syllabus for training of vocational rehabilitation counselors prepared and used by the Office of Vocational Rehabilitation the following definition is found:

A Definition of Vocational Evaluation—Vocational evaluation means to gather, to interpret, to analyze, and to synthesize all the vocationally significant data regarding the individual and to relate them to occupational requirements and opportunities.[1]

This kind of work evaluation by the trained counselor will usually take the form of interviews with the disabled person to review work history, job skills and interests, basic attitudes toward work generally, etc. Medical or psychiatric opinions on the disabling conditions, testing results, social service reports, vocational evaluation in rehabilitation facilities, and reports from former employers will all assist the counselor in his attempt to understand the patient's potential and to properly advise him on specific work possibilities. The counselor will continue to function throughout the sometimes lengthy process of rehabilitation. He will work closely with all the other persons and organizations concerned with the patient's progress.

There has existed in the past the false impression that vocational counseling was a specialized resource only to be used as a last resort

[1] Rehabilitation Service Series No. 332, *Orientation Training for Vocational Rehabilitation Counselors*, U. S. Dept. of Health, Education and Welfare, Office of Vocational Rehabilitation, Washington, Oct. 1955, p. 72.

after all else had failed. If the attending physician, the private health or rehabilitation agency, the former employer, and the patient himself had all been unable to develop any kind of successful work program, then the case would be referred to the vocational rehabilitation agency and counselor. This meant that months, and more often years, had passed since the onset of disability; patterns and attitudes had become fixed, the best employment chances had dwindled. It was little wonder that the records of accomplishment were not of the best; no one recognized this better than the vocational counselor himself.

During recent years, there has been increasing recognition of the fact that the vocational aspects of rehabilitation must receive attention even in the very early phases of a case. While the medical and therapeutic considerations of a case are still of paramount importance during the early stages of recovery from disabling disease or injury, it is not too soon for the vocational history, interests, and employment possibilities to receive appropriate consideration. One of the first psychological barriers which may be raised in the patient's mind, and which may make all the difference in his acceptance of disability and his desire to fully rehabilitate himself, is the possibility of work and self-sufficiency in an economic sense. Vocational counseling can be most effective if it starts with the onset of disability and continues to final work discovery and realization.

Discovery of the true work potential, particularly in the disabled person who has never previously held a job or the one who cannot return to former employment because of the limiting nature of his disability, is often attainable through psychological and vocational testing. The standard tests for interest and aptitude, together with measurement of basic intelligence, are usually given by staff personnel in the departments of education or psychology in the colleges and universities. Through the use of such trained personnel in the areas of psychological testing and vocational education and guidance, fairly accurate measurements may be made of manual dexterity, work interests, adaptability to work situations and routines, supervisory potential, comparison with work norms for particular types of work, and the like. None of these batteries of tests are conclusive by themselves. They require interpretation by skilled people and adaptation to the rest of the individual patient pattern as the counselor has come to know it. The tests can be valuable in forming opinions as to work potential in such a way as to prevent the waste of time and money on fruitless training or education. They can be dangerous if utilized academically to channel further vocational planning into only one arbitrarily selected niche which may be in direct conflict with the actual interests and views of the disabled person. Some state vocational personnel and certain of the larger rehabilitation programs have included vocational testing in their own agency programs but most rely upon the educational institutions for this part of the evaluation process.

Prevocational evaluation has become a recent catch-phrase in rehabilitation circles and this practical method of measuring vocational effectiveness has permeated the planning of both public and private programs. A statement issued by the Division of Hospital and Medical Facilities of the Public Health Service and the Office of Vocational Rehabilitation on the development of rehabilitation facilities under the Hill-Burton program outlines prevocational "experience" as follows:

> Pre-vocational experiences may be defined as those experiences offered in the facility which simulate conditions in employment, but do not include definitive vocational training. They are of value to the patient in determining the relationship of his capacities and disabilities to a given occupation and are designed to build up his confidence in his ability to overcome the vocational handicap inherent in his disability.[2]

Use of supervised work activity to provide a practical test for the evaluation and development of work skills and attitudes is not entirely new, although its recent applications are somewhat more scientific and concentrated. Elton described this concept in connection with the activities of the American Rehabilitation Committee in 1924. The Institute for the Crippled and Disabled in 1936 established prevocational evaluation and guidance test classes, which attempted to measure the capacities of disabled patients and which were patterned on techniques utilized previously by a few industrial concerns and trade schools for the prediction of vocational possibilities of able-bodied workers or students.[3]

Following World War II, the Veterans' Administration developed work adjustment training and in its hospitals carried on manual arts therapy with former teachers of industrial arts providing a prevocational type of evaluation for the disabled veteran. Some private institutions, particularly those serving the specialized or long-term disabilities, have adapted their programs to allow for a measure of pre-vocational work in industrial shops. Sheltered workshops and comprehensive rehabilitation centers have carried on this kind of

---

[2] "Rehabilitation Facilities under the Hill-Burton Program," a statement prepared by Division of Hospital and Medical Facilities of the Public Health Service and the Office of Vocational Rehabilitation, Washington, 1954, p. 5.

[3] Institute for the Crippled and Disabled, *Rehabilitation Trends—Midcentury to 1956*, New York, 1956, pp. 8 and 60.

evaluation, not always on a formal basis but as part of the attempt of the rehabilitation team to properly orient the handicapped person along vocational lines.

Like the testing procedures described previously, the pre-vocational evaluation in a unit designed to do this specific task has the advantage of giving practical direction to those who are trying to decide where the best work possibilities may lie for a given patient. Instead of relying entirely on guesswork, even though it may be based on considerable experience and on testing of aptitudes and interests, the prevocational evaluation program offers a chance to see by actual trial the reactions of the disabled to particular work assignments. As a latter phase of the rehabilitation process, it can well be the demonstrable proof of what the rehabilitation effort has really accomplished.

The excellent publication by the Office of Vocational Rehabilitation entitled "The Pre-Vocational Unit in a Rehabilitation Center" summarizes very succinctly the nature and purpose of such a unit:

> The pre-vocational unit is a vocational evaluation laboratory. For a specified period of time, the patient has a trial in the performance of a wide variety of work experiences. The period of time the patient is assigned to the unit should be for a period of not less than three weeks. To achieve the best vocational evaluation of the patient, his condition should warrant his spending a full day in the program. This will vary with the individual, and the program must be planned on an individual basis, taking into consideration the medical aspects of the patient's condition, his mental outlook, emotional adjustment and his concurrent programs. For the majority of cases an initial period of anything less than a day is considered impracticable.
>
> The work experiences in which he will engage should be provided in actual work situations or in environments which simulate work situations. Obviously, sampling in all occupations which offer possible employment opportunities for physically handicapped persons cannot be offered in the pre-vocational unit. The basic skills and job operations evaluated in the unit nevertheless should be fundamental to occupational areas such as clerical, skilled, semiskilled, subprofessional, agricultural and service occupations. The evaluation made must be based on standards which have direct relationship to employment requirements.
>
> Specific activities within these areas should take into consideration placement opportunities in the community and in the area served by the facility. This will be particularly true in reference to light industrial and agricultural activities. In some instances, community resources can be utilized to implement the facilities of the center and to provide more realistic work situations. Whenever possible, opportunities of this kind should be developed.[4]

[4] White, B., and Redkey, H., U. S. Dept. of Health, Education and Welfare, Office of Vocational Rehabilitation, *The Pre-Vocational Unit in a Rehabilitation Center,* Washington, 1956, p. 2.

The immediate objective of the prevocational unit or procedure is to determine the patient's interests, aptitudes, and abilities in a controlled and supervised setting, by exposing him to actual work situations and challenges. The types of work activity range from the clerical and service jobs through the skilled and semi-skilled industrial occupations to laboring work. Production quality and quantity and his reaction to the working environment can be carefully charted. Relationships with fellow-workers and with supervisors become a tangible and measurable factor. Observations can be made of his whole attitude toward each kind of assigned work. Work habits can be understood and improved to a degree necessary to insure chance of successful outside employment.

Most important of all contributions of the prevocational evaluation unit is the wonderful opportunity to determine and develop confidence and tolerance in definite work situations. This is an area which has been almost a "blank spot" in the transitional period between the definitive program in a rehabilitation center and the actual job selection and placement. It is all very well to line up a job possibility for a patient with post-concussion syndrome, back injury, heart condition, or epilepsy (to cite only a few examples), but, if he fears that every motion, every effort is going to again disable him or even cause his death, then his work attempts are doomed to defeat. The resultant discouragement to patient and employer alike serves only to weaken the whole chain of rehabilitation effort. The prevocational testing and evaluation program offers an opportunity for the patient himself, as well as those concerned with his rehabilitation, to see that he can work without danger to himself or others, to observe that he can earn a living and make his own way. The value of this practical lesson in psychology can hardly be over-estimated.

The approach to development of a prevocational program or unit requires flexibility in thinking and practice. As Usdane states:

> The individual nature of each severely handicapped person, however, negates the development of rigid criteria. Instead, judgment and appraisal of work samples might be considered in five classifications: superior, above average, average, below average, and inferior. Final decisions should be made through the pooling of all information concerning the individual from the rehabilitation team.[5]

The so-called "work classification units" have become another

5 Usdane, W. M., "Pre-vocational Evaluation Criteria for the Severely Handicapped," *Archives of Physical Medicine and Rehabilitation*, 38, No. 5, American Congress of Physical Medicine and Rehabilitation, Chicago (May, 1957), p. 314.

means of evaluating the work capacity of disabled individuals. These units have served an important function in the area of heart disease particularly. A basic team of physician, social worker, and vocational counselor, utilizing general hospital rehabilitation departments, rehabilitation centers, or workshops, attempt to measure the work capacity of persons with heart conditions. In 1952, an agreement between the American Heart Association, U. S. Public Health Service, U. S. Employment Service, and the Office of Vocational Rehabilitation made it possible for local affiliates of the American Heart Association to organize work classification units in their respective communities. The practical efforts thus made to really determine how the heart patient could perform in a controlled work setting, to properly orient him to his physical capacities in the work situation, permitted a much more constructive approach on the part of both patient and professional workers to definitive work possibilities. A somewhat similar team and work-testing idea has been utilized in the field of the mentally or emotionally handicapped. These programs have revolved around the state institutions for this type of disability and have opened new doors of opportunity for productive rather than charitable jobs.

The newer ideas and techniques of vocational evaluation can be invaluable in helping to avoid serious mistakes and defeating discouragement in the difficult process of actual job placement. Whitehouse has used a provocative phrase in calling this time of practical evaluation in center or workshop a "living period" and in stressing that "the key is the opportunity it gives to the client to compound small triumphs of achievement and reality testing into a background of increasing substance."[6] The "habilitee," or disabled person who has never worked, probably requires this kind of exposure and orientation to work situations more desperately, but even many working people who have suffered severe disability from disease or injury can materially benefit from such a program. Few who have not experienced it themselves can have any true conception of the fears, doubts, and discouragements of physical or mental disability. The paradox of wanting and needing to work but, at the same time, fearing to do so can be the roadblock for many who need vocational rehabilitation. The opportunity to clinically test and observe, to demonstrate and reassure, afforded by a practical work-evaluation procedure, can immeasurably improve the chances of successfully placing the handicapped person in a worthwhile occupation.

[6] Whitehouse, F. A., "Habilitation—Concept and Process," reprint from *J. Rehabilitation*, p. 6 (March–April 1953).

CHAPTER 11

Sheltered Workshops
and Retraining
Facilities

SHELTERED WORKSHOPS CONSTITUTE THE EAR-
liest type of facility serving the specialized vocational needs of the
disabled. In 1840 the Perkins Institution for the Blind, in Water-
town, Massachusetts, established a workshop to serve the visually
handicapped. It is estimated that there are more than 600 sheltered
workshops in the United States at the present time. Some of them
serve only a single type of handicap, but more of them are designed
to handle a wide range of disabilities.

The National Association of Sheltered Workshops and Homebound
Programs, Inc., accepts the following definition, adopted in 1950:

> A sheltered workshop is a voluntary organization or institution conducted
> not for profit but for the purpose of carrying out a recognized program of
> rehabilitation for physically, mentally, and socially handicapped individuals
> by providing such individuals with remunerative employment and one or
> more other rehabilitating activities of an educational psychosocial, thera-
> peutic, or spiritual nature.[1]

It is interesting that the current definition emphasizes the rehabilitative function of the workshops because their early history was more
closely associated with almost the antithesis of what is now recog-

[1] Chouinard, E. L., and Garrett, J. F., *Workshops for the Disabled—a Vocational
Rehabilitation Resource,* U. S. Department of Health, Education and Welfare, Office
of Vocational Rehabilitation, Rehabilitation Services Series 371, Washington, 1956,
p. 15.

nized as one of the major goals of rehabilitation, namely, restoration to ordinary types of employment in the industrial and business field. The establishment of sheltered workshops was predicated on the theory that certain kinds of disability constituted an insuperable barrier to regular employment and that persons suffering such disabilities should be provided with a "sheltered" environment as their only possible vocational opportunity.

To quote from the introduction to the Handbook on Sheltered Workshops and Homebound Programs published in 1952:

> In the past one hundred years we have made some progress in our thinking as it relates to sheltered employment. Even though we accept the fact that some handicapped people will never move out of the sheltered shop, yet it is no longer accepted that the sheltered shop is the only means of employment for handicapped people, but is a link in the whole chain of the rehabilitation process.[2]

The National Association, as well as other groups, has attempted a differentiation between the so-called "industrial workshop for sheltered employment" as a place for those who cannot be absorbed in the labor market; the "industrial rehabilitation workshop" as a place for preparation toward fully competitive employment; and the "institutional rehabilitation shop" as a place for emotional and behavioral cases, mostly delinquent youths, to be prepared for restoration to community life and employment. Although such attempted distinctions may be technically valid in the administrative designation and operation of workshops, it is apparent that the rapidly moving rehabilitation trends and forces are molding the workshop and its role into a different, yet more constructive, pattern. As our ideas about rehabilitation possibilities become more perceptive and our practice of rehabilitation methods more definitive, the workshop will more completely emerge from its cocoon of protective employment for the vocationally handicapped and develop into an effective research and hardening medium for outside job placement.

The sheltered workshop, to the present at least, has been a combination of manual and machine operations, loosely organized in a factory-like atmosphere but having certain of the medical and social responsibilities of a health service. The operations are of three main types; manufacture of new merchandise, remodeling of discarded or salvaged material, industrial subcontracts for specified production parts or services. In former years, the pay scales in these workshops

---

2 National Committee on Sheltered Workshops and Homebound Programs, *Sheltered Workshops and Homebound Programs—a Handbook on Their Establishment and Standards of Operation*, First Edition, N. Y., 1952, pp. 1–2.

were far below standard rates and the so-called "employment" for the disabled individual smacked more of charity than self-respecting and productive work opportunity. More recently, modernized work schedules and production methods, interest and support by industrial firms, labor regulations, and union interest have brought about wage rates which compare more favorably with comparable jobs in industry. This trend has served to greatly increase the patient's work dignity and has narrowed the gap between "sheltered employment" and regular job opportunity.

The changing trends in vocational rehabilitation since World War II and the development of comprehensive rehabilitation practices in more communities meant a corresponding change in the adaptation of the workshop to broader aims as a part of the rehabilitation team. There was increasing recognition that "a workshop helps to bridge the gap between medical care and employment through its facilities for training, work exploration, and psycho-social adjustment."[3]

The amendments to the Vocational Rehabilitation Act in 1954 made it possible for workshops to receive grants for expanding or remodeling their facilities to permit more effective rehabilitation service. The law defines "workshop" as "a place where any manufacture or handiwork is carried on and which is operated for the primary purpose of providing remunerative employment to severely handicapped individuals (1) as an interim step in the rehabilitation process for those who cannot be readily absorbed in the competitive labor market; or (2) during such time as employment opportunities for them in the competitive labor market do not exist."[4] The Senate Committee on Labor and Public Welfare, in its deliberations on the changes to be made in the law, stated in its report that

> It appears from the experience of many workshops which have operated successfully for several years that such facilities can and do serve a basic function in the rehabilitation program. This is particularly true when the workshop serves as an interim step in the rehabilitation process, leading to full employment in a competitive job. It is clearly intended in this legislation that any workshop provided for thereunder be conceived and operated principally as a creative force for restoring the handicapped person to the point where he is capable of "outside" employment in every case where this is possible.[5]

Although there are always going to be certain cases of so-called

[3] Chouinard, E. L., and Garrett, J. F., op. cit., p. 7.
[4] Ibid., pp. 3–4.
[5] U. S. Senate Calendar No. 1639, Report No. 1626, 83rd Congress, 2nd Session, "Vocational Rehabilitation of the Disabled," Senate Committee on Labor and Public Welfare, Washington, June 22, 1954, p. 12.

"terminal" employment and an additional number who, because of complicated disabilities or complete lack of adjustment, can never be moved out of the sheltered workshop or home work setting, there is increasing recognition of the true function of the workshop as "an industrial laboratory in which handicapped people can be trained better to industrial conditions."[6] This means that there are new challenges for the community in its planning for effective services in this area of rehabilitation activity. For instance, where is the best place to establish a workshop? Should it be in a hospital, factory, school, rehabilitation center, or an independent and separate unit? As in the case of the rehabilitation center location, there is no easy or dogmatic answer. If the workshop kind of activity is to become truly an important part of the rehabilitation process and, therefore, requires close integration with the other components of the program, it would seem logical that such a workshop should properly not be some separate unit in another part of the community but an integral part of the rehabilitation center or institute. Such an arrangement would permit coordination of program and the common physical plant, staff, and equipment could be more effectively utilized to obtain the best possible end result for the patient. Workshops have suffered from a lack of adequate or qualified medical supervision—many times they have been more of a business than a treatment facility. Integration into the rehabilitation center or institute program would permit much more continuous and conclusive medical management of not only the physical and mental restoration phases but also the social, vocational, and economic factors in the rehabilitation process.

Even the term "sheltered" in conjunction with the workshop idea is becoming somewhat inappropriate. Words such as "work adjustment center," "retraining shops," "vocational institute," and "curative workshop" imply the more determinedly rehabilitative aspects of the workshop. Regardless of terminology or precise definitions, it seems probable that the sheltered workshop, as it has functioned in the past, will become a less significant community resource. There may still remain some workshops which continue to function as places of truly sheltered employment and there may be others which serve a similar purpose in institutions for chronic disease or for mental incurables. The majority of others will gradually progress toward incorporating their programs into full-fledged and comprehensive rehabilitation services where they will form one part of the over-all service rather than separate and distinct facilities.

The two principal organizations dealing with the administration of

[6] Chouinard, E. L., and Garrett, J. F., op. cit., p. 11.

rehabilitation facilities, the Conference of Rehabilitation Centers, Inc., and the National Association of Sheltered Workshops and Homebound Programs, Inc., might do well to consider joint planning, joint meetings, and possible eventual merger in the interest of more effective long-range development of comprehensive facilities. Both groups already have members who belong to the two organizations and the opportunity for coordinated thinking and action would undoubtedly lead to better administration of comprehensive rehabilitation services. Each type of facility, as it has developed to the present time, contains important aspects of the other—each would avoid possible duplication or rivalry by combining forces in a common community effort.

There is grave doubt as to whether a workshop concerned primarily with total rehabilitation can at the same time be a successful business venture. There is a temptation to hold patients who are productive and to reduce costs by procedure which may not be soundly therapeutic for the patient; but the ultimate goal in a workshop program is remunerative employment and any workshop operation must exist principally as a service in rehabilitation for the community and only secondarily as a financially successful business. This means, of course, that additional funds must be sought from foundations, community groups, public agencies, and the like, but this is the typical picture of community health services of many kinds.

Some grandiose plans for workshop operations have attempted to include great varieties of work, in the mistaken belief that a kind of vocational trade school for the handicapped is the real need. In terms of personnel, equipment, space, and well-defined program, such a development would be wasteful and often a duplication of services already available or possible in community educational systems. The Altro Work Shops, as well as other successful programs, have demonstrated clearly that no workshop can effectively provide all types of work, and that the particular selected occupations in a workshop are much less important than that the work be productive and clearly related to outside industrial procedures, that it be sedentary or leisurely in character, and that there be a variety of work from routine to complex, from individual to group, requiring adaptation to different motions or pace.

The need for workshop activity in the community rehabilitation picture seems destined to expand. The Altro Work Shops and a few others have already embarked upon practical programs for the mentally ill. There is much to be done in understanding and successfully handling the child disabled from birth or early life who must be taught the very rudiments of work behavior, incentive, and attitude, as well as considered for a particular occupation. The increasing numbers of our aging population with their concomitant disabilities from degenerative disease processes offer a real challenge for selective replacement in our work force. If industry is to properly place these people in jobs where their infirmities or disabilities offer no barrier to effective productivity, it will need the help of trained personnel in the evaluation of work capacity, tolerance, attitude, and motivation. What better source for such evaluation than the vocational or workshop unit in a comprehensive rehabilitation facility?

Retraining facilities, in the sense used in this book and as contrasted with the prevocational training units or workshop operations, are those programs for actually teaching a trade or skill which can be used as a means of getting a job in industry or running a small business. Usually, such teaching programs are found in public or private schools which have adapted a portion of their vocational teaching program to the needs of the handicapped or who work exclusively with this type of student. Unlike the hospital, rehabilitation center, or the workshop, they usually have no real medical direction or treatment purpose. Their intent is to teach a particular trade or a variety of trades which offer good job potential. The disabled person is usually referred to such a facility by a rehabilitation or vocational counselor after careful exploration of aptitudes, interests, and basic physical or mental capabilities. Length of training may vary from several weeks to a full college course of four years.

Most of the vocational or trade high schools in the larger communities, or serving a region, can and do provide opportunities for the disabled child who is not so severely handicapped that he or she cannot carry out even a modified class and work routine. For the handicapped adult there is much less opportunity in the public education system. Night classes are usually not definitive in the trade or vocational areas. The adult usually has to seek some kind of facility which has had experience in or is geared to the particular vocational needs of the disabled.

There are certain schools, both public and private, which have made a specialty of serving the disabled student, particularly those who are severely handicapped. Outstanding examples for adults are the Joseph Bulova School of Watchmaking on Long Island and the Williamsport Institute in Williamsport, Pa.

CHAPTER 12

Services for
the Homebound

disease or injury stand as a living reproach in the light of our modern concepts of rehabilitation. Any precise estimate of the number of such individuals is difficult to obtain. The studies previously cited as a basis for estimating those in need of rehabilitation services contained fragmentary data on the persons who were confined to their homes. The report to the Congress dated Feb. 2, 1955, by the Secretary of Health, Education, and Welfare on a study of programs for homebound physically handicapped individuals contains the figure of one million persons as an estimate of those of any age who have been confined to their homes for at least one year.[1] This does not include any figure for those confined to home by mental or emotional handicap. The figures prepared by the Division of Public Health Methods of the U. S. Public Health Service and cited in the volume published by the Commission on Chronic Illness estimate the total number of persons (both physical and mentally handicapped), as of 1950, who have been disabled for over three months, as 5.3 million. Of that number, somewhat more than four million are living at home.[2] Perhaps the true figure lies somewhere between these two extremes. In any event, the number confined to the home in any given period is at least two to

[1] U. S. Dept. of Health, Education and Welfare, "Study of Programs for Homebound Physically Handicapped Individuals," a Report to the Congress, Feb. 2, 1955, p. 4.

[2] Commission on Chronic Illness, *Care of the Long-Term Patient*—Vol. II of *Chronic Illness in the U. S.*, Commonwealth Fund, Harvard University Press, Cambridge, 1956, pp. 5 and 7.

three times the total of those in general hospitals and long-term institutions. Granting that there are many in the hospitals and institutions who can benefit materially from rehabilitation services, it would appear that there is an even larger number confined to the home who could benefit from similar services.

Realizing that the home was the scene of medical care long before there were any hospitals, it is not surprising to find that home-care programs as an extension of hospital services were organized very early in the United States. The Philadelphia Dispensary was opened in 1786 and similar institutions in New York and Boston during the next ten years. The principle laid down in the regulations of one of these dispensaries was to the effect that "the sick . . . may be attended and relieved in their own houses . . . at a less expense than in an hospital, (and) those who have seen better days may be comforted without being humiliated."[3] At a later date, the public health nursing organizations, visiting nurse associations, and community health or welfare departments instituted home medical care programs. Many of these services were extremely limited and most were oriented to the needs of the indigent patient.

Modern organization of home-care programs began in 1940 with the University Hospital in Syracuse, to be closely followed by the Montefiore Hospital in New York City in 1947 and the New York City Hospital system in 1948. These programs involved a continuous and coordinated follow-up on the patient discharged to his home through a comprehensive series of health services. The Commission on Chronic Illness estimated that there were some 50 modern home-care programs in operation as of the time of its report published in 1956.[4]

The need for constructive planning and organization of home-care programs is rooted in the increase of chronic illness, particularly among our aging population, the sky-rocketing cost of hospital and other institutional care, efficacy of modern drug therapy, improved housing, and the recognition of the adverse effects of prolonged hospitalization on the patient. Effective methods of follow-up care in the home help to motivate both doctor and patient to accept the earliest possible transition from hospital to home.

The home-care programs require a carefully prepared plan of services to be rendered in the home and the coordination of those services under a central administration which can and does practice the team approach. The administrative body need not necessarily be the hospital, although it frequently may be; other community health or

---

[3] 160th Anniversary Brochure of the Boston Dispensary, Boston, 1956.
[4] Commission on Chronic Illness, *op. cit.*, p. 67.

service agencies can organize and operate the program, if proper medical direction and coordination with hospital treatment is obtained. The battery of services must be flexible and responsive to the over-all needs of the patient, but the principal components would seem to be the following:

1. Medical treatment—provided by physician in private practice, from clinic or from out-patient department of hospital.

2. Nursing care—provided by visiting registered nurse or qualified practical nurse on full-time or part-time basis.

3. Homemaker or housekeeper service—personal and household tasks performed by experienced and mature person, not ordinarily a professional person but not merely a domestic either.

4. Psycho-social services—involving use of psychiatrist, clinical psychologist, counselor, and social case-worker to function in areas of personal adjustment, motivation, financial and family planning, community acceptance.

5. Restorative services—provided by physical therapist, occupational therapist, and the like.

6. Recreational and educational services—utilizing special teachers, public and private school systems, libraries, audio-visual aids, arts and crafts.

7. Vocational training and employment—provided by vocational rehabilitation counselor, vocational guidance teacher, correspondence courses, sheltered workshop or other rehabilitation program staff, public or private home industry, and homecraft supervisors.

The ramifications and the diversity of home-care programs are such that no attempt to thoroughly discuss them can be made in this brief consideration. The principal relationship which they bear to the theme of this book lies in the possibilities inherent in them for increased rehabilitation services to a larger segment of the community. It is generally agreed that one important goal of rehabilitation is self-care, the raising of the patient to a plateau of independent living as far as his daily activities are concerned. Attainment of this objective ordinarily means that the patient can then live effectively at home. Development of a sound and comprehensive home-care program, incorporating the principles of continued rehabilitative therapy and counseling, can reduce sharply the need of continued institutional care and lead toward maximum rehabilitation in other areas which could not be handled in the hospital setting.

However, it must be realized that, as comprehensive rehabilitation services are developed and improved in hospitals, rehabilitation centers, and other comparable facilities, the successful application of these services to an ever-increasing number of patients will gradually but steadily minimize the need for follow-up rehabilitation services in the home. The primary attack upon disability will be mounted at the earliest opportunity rather than as a rear-guard action. Only the irreducible minimum of the severest disabilities will become the homebound of tomorrow.

Of greater import to present-day rehabilitation services and those planned for the immediate future are the handicapped persons now homebound who should not be. Discovery of these cases and their referral for proper evaluation and possible treatment by comprehensive or specialized rehabilitation facilities and personnel is the greatest challenge of our day. Yeoman work has been done by many organizations to reduce the numbers of these prisoners of their own disability. The crippled children's programs on a federal—state level, private groups such as National Foundation for Infantile Paralysis, United Cerebral Palsy Association, National Society for Crippled Children and Adults, together with civic and fraternal organizations, have given generously of time and money to improve the lot of the homebound. Much of their endeavor has been in the realm of the disabled child, however, and comparable programs for the handicapped adult have lagged far behind.

Far too little is known about the real numbers and problems of the homebound adult, and few studies have been conducted to prove the efficacy of concentrated rehabilitation services in removing the factors which limit him to a home existence. One project, organized cooperatively by the New York State Departments of Health, Social Welfare, and Education, was started in April, 1955, and provided for admitting a series of cases, receiving public assistance as permanently and totally disabled, to the New York State Rehabilitation Hospital in West Haverstraw. By Dec. 31, 1956, a total of 200 welfare patients had been admitted and 130 discharged. An analysis of the first 100 cases showed that 73% were considered materially improved; 43% had been bedridden, and 78% unable to walk at time of admission; at time of discharge, only 9% were confined to bed and 33% unable to walk. Those considered capable of living independently in their own homes constituted only 19% of the total at the time of admission, but this number had risen to 43% at time of discharge.[5]

In another study at the Veterans Administration hospital at Manhattan Beach, Brooklyn, a rehabilitation program involving 126 patients with such conditions as arthritis, multiple sclerosis, paralysis,

[5] Rusk, H. A., Weekly column, N. Y. Times, Sunday, Feb. 24, 1957.

Buerger's disease, Parkinson's disease, and heart disease resulted in discharge to home of 74 of the group. At the beginning of the program, 83 veterans were "completely hopeless and helpless" but 49 of these were rehabilitated to a point of complete independence and the remainder were all capable of caring for the majority of their own needs.[6] Admittedly these are small samplings, but it is nonetheless supportive of the thinking of most knowledgeable people in the field that selective application to the homebound of rehabilitation services in hospitals, centers, and other facilities should remove many of the barriers to greater mobility, independent living, and social or economic improvement.

So far, programs directed at the homebound have been limited to the larger communities and little has been accomplished in the towns and rural areas. Many well-intentioned programs have failed because of lack of funds, personnel, facilities, or coordinated effort. These failures have been discouraging to planning groups but renewed impetus has been given to thinking and action in this area by governmental recognition of the need and the concentration of public and private interest on chronic disease and the aging.

The vocational possibilities for the homebound have occupied the attention of rehabilitation people as well as those in public assistance programs, social service, and similar fields. Home-employment programs have been operated as extensions of sheltered workshops or under the aegis of state divisions of vocational rehabilitation, as well as by public and private agencies concerned with one particular handicap, such as blindness. The accepted definition of an industrial homework program is that used by the National Association of Sheltered Workshops and Homebound Programs:

> A service to be rendered by an accredited agency—designed and developed with the intention of adhering to health and labor laws—to offer regular work training and remunerative work opportunities to those eligible disabled persons who cannot for physical, psychological, or geographic reasons leave their homes to travel to and from a place of business.[7]

There are four main categories of home employment: (1) the contract or subcontract types of work, in which the homebound person produces a stipulated number of parts or articles at a set price and with

[6] U. S. Senate Committee on Labor and Public Welfare, 83rd Congress 2nd Session, Report of Hearings before Subcommittee on Health as to President's Health Recommendations and Related Matters, April 5, 1954, p. 412.

[7] National Committee on Sheltered Workshops and Homebound Programs, *Sheltered Workshops and Homebound Programs—a Handbook on Their Establishment and Standards of Operation*, First Edition, N. Y., 1952, p. 6.

specifications and materials supplied by the commercial manufacturer; (2) home manufacture (sometimes confusingly called "homecraft"), in which the materials may be supplied and sales distribution arranged by a public or a nonprofit agency; (3) handicraft, in which the homebound person fashions by hand, as the result of long experience or careful training, craft articles for sale directly or through outlets; (4) small business enterprise in which an independent, profit-making activity is carried on in the home and where there is no continuing affiliation with an organized agency program. The first two types are more often established in urban areas, especially those with a number of light manufacturing firms or activities. The third type is almost entirely confined to rural areas, and the last type would be possible in any area.

Few tasks set for the vocational rehabilitation counselor, or any interested agency representative, pose as difficult a problem as the decision of homebound employment. Not the least of the difficulties are the frequently unrealistic ideas of the handicapped person himself on what kind of endeavor would hold the best chance of success for him. This is particularly true of the home manufacture, handicraft, and small business enterprise. Lack of ability to meet standards of fine workmanship, failure to realize what makes a salable article, inability to provide or reach a promising market, lack of imagination in making necessary changes to fit style changes or customer demands, all constitute barriers which may well doom these ventures to failure. In addition, there are personal qualities and circumstances of the home environment which may militate against successful home work. If the homebound person is receiving public assistance, workmen's compensation, social security, or other benefits, some assurances may be needed to allay fears that such benefits would be jeopardized by any earnings, particularly during early phases when income is lower than benefits. Labor law restrictions, local industrial or zoning regulations, or union attitudes may offer complications which must be clearly understood and overcome. Often it may be necessary to obtain certification of the sponsoring agency or project as a sheltered workshop in order to comply with labor laws and make it possible to pay subminimum hourly rates. Great imagination, practical experience, keen insight into the possibilities of each patient, and benefit of work testing and possible training by supervisors skilled in the trade are basic requirements for success in the counseling of the homebound toward beneficial and profitable employment.

Just as in the case of the sheltered workshop operations, homebound employment has been hampered by the difficulties of providing a living wage. Early abuses in the utilization of home workers as "cheap labor" has created a stigma which still affects both commercial employer and home worker alike. Admittedly it is sometimes hard to insure the acceptance and following of ordinary standards for working conditions, hours, and wages in a home-employment program, but such standards must be zealously guarded and maintained if this kind of endeavor is to receive community acceptance and support.

Despite the high financial cost and despite the practical difficulties inherent in any homebound program, the challenge of taking positive action toward this group of the handicapped looms large in any constructive community rehabilitation planning. From a medical, psychological, social, and economic viewpoint, the rewards of a coordinated effort to provide supportive services and work experience for the homebound lie in the very real possibility that many of these people may eventually become candidates for full community participation, including employment in competitive industry.

CHAPTER 13

Vocational Placement

PRODUCTIVE EMPLOYMENT IS THE GOAL OF much of our rehabilitation effort in the United States. Although it is perfectly true that there are in our population several million chronically disabled persons who, by reason of age, extent of disability, or personal desire represent no real potential for remunerative employment, it is equally true that work is often the measure of social as well as economic status. In the words of Dr. Rusk, "society today pays for only two things: what we have in our heads and the skill in our hands." For the child growing into adulthood, for the man or woman under 65, rehabilitation short of employment opportunity is like the proverbial cart without the horse or, in modern parlance, the engine without the sparkplug to make it go.

Yet, even with the clear recognition of work opportunity as an important focus for rehabilitation services and even with an industrial economy second to none, realization of and technical know-how for the proper placement of handicapped persons is a rank newcomer on the American social and economic scene. The virus of ancient prejudices concerning the superiority of the able-bodied and the relegation of the crippled to beggary had deeply infected the personnel practices of the burgeoning corporate structure in our country. In the years after the industrial revolution, big and little business had callously cast aside the victims of disease and injury. Labor, both native and immigrant, was plentiful; there was no time for social welfare schemes. Production-wise, it was a keep-up or get-out philosophy.

World War I brought some consciousness of the problem of making proper use of handicapped persons in the labor force; there were sporadic efforts at placement and a degree of governmental action, particularly in connection with the veteran disabled. The Smith–Sears Act of 1918 marked the beginning of the long sequence of federal and state legislation in the vocational rehabilitation field.

The year 1920 and the passage of the Vocational Rehabilitation Act sparked the development of federal and state agencies specifically interested in the welfare of the disabled, and particularly his vocational welfare. However, appropriations were meager, staffs were limited, and concentration was on training rather than placement. In the economic depression of the thirties, there were scores of men for every job and little incentive for utilizing the handicapped in the population. The phrase, "last to be hired, first to be fired" became no idle jest for those with physical or mental impairment.

The depression years, defeating and frustrating as they may have been in regard to opportunities for placement of the disabled, nonetheless spawned the social consciousness toward the welfare of the individual which was gradually to make significant inroads on the hard shell of industrial placement practices. For these were the years of the "New Deal," the "forgotten man," Social Security, unemployment compensation, and "the welfare state." The right of the individual to work had become as important as his right to vote.

The greatest stimulant to vocational rehabilitation philosophy and practice was afforded by World War II and its critical shortages of manpower. Almost a rash of interest and action sprang up on all sides. Government agencies such as the Employment Service, Social Security Board, War Manpower Commission, Civil Service Commission, U. S. Public Health Service, and Veterans' Administration, together with the enlarged Office of Vocational Rehabilitation, began to bring all the knowledge and experience of their skilled people to bear on the several aspects of successful placement of the handicapped. At the same time, key industrial organizations such as Westinghouse Electric, General Motors, Caterpillar Tractor, International Harvester, and Arma Corporation began to evolve regular plans which not only helped to bring the handicapped individual into the war production lines but also paved the way for absorption of the returning and disabled war veteran. Private organizations and associations such as the National Society for Crippled Children and Adults, National Rehabilitation Association, Goodwill Industries, National Tuberculosis Association, Welfare and Retirement Fund of the United Mine Workers of America, International Association for the Welfare of Cripples, and Liberty Mutual Insurance Co. and many veteran, fraternal, and civic groups contributed their practical ideas on the techniques of rehabilitating and placing the veteran or civilian disabled.

A large part of the task was public education on the true work needs and possibilities of the handicapped. One of the principal instrumentalities for the focusing of attention upon the particular challenge of successful employment was to grow out of the executive action taken in August, 1945, by President Truman, following passage of a resolution by the Seventy-Ninth Congress, in designating the first week in October of each year as National Employ the Physically Handicapped Week. The described purpose of this week was "to enlist public support for and interest in the employment of otherwise qualified but physically handicapped workers."[1] In August, 1947 the President suggested that the Secretary of Labor establish a permanent committee, to be known as the President's Committee on Employment of the Physically Handicapped, for the purpose of providing a continuing program of public information and education about the employment of handicapped persons. This was followed by successive creation of Governors' committees in each state to supplement the national program with local action. The relationships with industrial groups, the national and local meetings, the expositions and demonstrations of work by disabled persons, the publications and films, and the awards to outstanding individuals and corporations, all sponsored and organized by the President's and the Governors' committees, have proved a tremendous stimulus to the better understanding of proper job placement of handicapped individuals.

The augmenting of the federal–state programs of vocational rehabilitation by the 1954 amendments to the Vocational Rehabilitation Act, leading directly to the improvement of facilities and services, the training of additional personnel, and the increasing of counselor staffs meant that more time and attention could be given to placement procedures in the rehabilitation process. Measurement of vocational rehabilitation results are now predicated upon restoration to productive jobs and not on training or counseling contacts.

Despite the growing sympathy and tolerance toward the placement of the handicapped, there is still considerable lack of knowledge, confusion, and misunderstanding about the entire subject. Seven main points seem essential to good placement:

1. Early consideration
2. Competent medical management
3. Careful evaluation
4. Practical plan
5. Coordinated effort
6. Informed selling
7. Perceptive follow-up

[1] House Joint Resolution 23, now Public Law 176 of the 79th Congress, signed by President, Aug. 11, 1945.

Early consideration of placement seems so consistent with present-day rehabilitation thinking that it would appear to need no particular emphasis. Oddly enough, however, there has been a consistent tendency to think of vocational opportunities and placement potential as the final act of the rehabilitation drama, with no need for the vocational counselor or other placement people to make their stage appearances until just before the curtain comes down for the last time. The Report of the President's Commission on the Health Needs of the Nation, submitted in December, 1952, emphasized an average time lag for workmen's compensation cases of seven years between date of injury and referral to state vocational rehabilitation agencies.[2] This discouraging time interval was an indictment, not so much of the agencies involved as it was of all the parties to the handling of these cases, from physician to employer. It simply never occurred to many people that successful vocational rehabilitation must start soon after injury or disabling illness and not months or years later when the disability had become fixed, the attitudes inflexible, and the work potential greatly diminished. The picture is gradually improving on referral lag. In the program of the Liberty Mutual Insurance Co., involving its centers for traumatic injuries in both Chicago and Boston, the average length of time from date of injury to date of admission to the center is just six months. In many hospitals, combining in-patient medical and surgical care with a concentrated rehabilitation program, the time interval will be still less.

It is an amazing truism that most business corporations have little or no mechanics for planned follow-up on injured or ill employees. Even in this age of concentrated attention to good employer—employee relations, it is seldom indeed that an employer will send any official representative to reassure an injured or ill employee as to his job status. Yet there are few greater worries to a disabled worker than the gnawing doubt as to whether he can ever work again and, particularly, work at his old job or for his former employer. Early discussion of possibilities and plans, however tentative and incomplete, while the employee is still flat on his back in the hospital can do much to allay fears, prevent discouragement and resentment, and develop cooperation and optimism for later definite planning. Such discussion can be handled by employer, insurance carrier, physician, counselor, social worker, or other representatives from public or private agencies; the important thing is that it be done and done early. Just someone taking an inter-

[2] *Building America's Health, America's Health Status, Needs and Resources,* Vol. II, a Report to the President by the President's Commission on the Health Needs of the Nation, Washington, 1953, p. 32.

est in their difficulties will encourage many handicapped people to seek employment on their own initiative. This is just as important as actual placement by a vocational counselor or other rehabilitation worker.

The factor of early discussion is less demanding in the long-term chronic or congenital handicap but it has some pertinence even in those cases. In childhood crippling conditions, for instance, the early planning for special schooling, for counseling with child and parent, for careful exploration of work opportunities, is vital to success. Waiting until adulthood, when it is proportionately much harder to overcome unfavorable attitudes and to effectively motivate, may well defeat the vocational attempts.

Competent medical management of the whole process of rehabilitation in its vocational aspects as well as those dealing with physical restoration and personal adjustment is basic to eventual successful placement in the right job for the particular individual. Such medical supervision means not only the prescription of the treatment program and use of proper rehabilitation facilities to achieve maximum physical and mental recovery but also the careful measurement of residual abilities, work tolerances, and limitations which must be placed on kinds of jobs for the patient involved. These opinions and conclusions are not necessarily all the product of one physician; they may be the outgrowth of many examinations, observations, and tests conducted by a number of consultants in private offices, hospitals, rehabilitation centers, workshops, or other specialized facilities during the whole recovery process. They may involve the medical departments of the former or potential employer.

Whole-hearted and perceptive participation in case-evaluation sessions on vocational possibilities with the other members of the rehabilitation team can lead to effective coordination of effort toward final job placement. Some physicians feel that the vocational aspects of rehabilitation are not their concern; by the same token, some counselors, social workers, and other paramedical personnel think they can find jobs and place workers without the help of the doctor. Vocational placement has the best chance of success if predicated upon a sound medical blueprint; the recognition of this principle is growing apace in rehabilitation circles and should insure much sounder practices in the future.

The "light work" concept on the part of doctors and other placement people is an erroneous and misleading one. The term itself is an intangible. What is "light work" in the understanding of one doctor may not be at all consistent with the interpretation placed on this term by a potential employer. We should strive for a meaningful delineation of remaining physical abilities which can then be translated in a specific way to a prospective employer. If a man has a fused spine, for instance, the doctors may contraindicate his doing any heavy lifting or prolonged stooping but they may feel he is perfectly capable of doing a full day's work at a bench assembly job, in a supervisory capacity in his old department, in a quality inspection procedure, or in other areas of activity which will not put undue strain on his back. Under such circumstances, it is our job to interpret those facts for the employer—utilizing all we know of the employee's personality, ambition, character, previous work experience, etc. to get the employer to realize that this man can do a number of specific jobs in view of his remaining capabilities. We should not be content with "light work" or generalized and vague evaluations of work ability from attending physicians, examining doctors, and staff doctors at hospitals or centers. The time should be taken to pin the doctor down on just exactly what physical abilities—translated in terms of basic job motions and activities, such as bending, stooping, lifting, standing, working on ladders, carrying heavy objects, etc.—the patient still has and can effectively utilize on an actual job. This kind of information will help immeasurably in clarifying the picture for the prospective employer. Certain physical capacity measurement plans and forms can be utilized by doctors to advantage in this regard.[3]

Careful evaluation has received detailed attention in an earlier chapter and need not be reviewed in this section. The utilization of the modern concepts of testing, prevocational evaluation, trial employment, and effective counseling procedures make for correspondingly more successful placements. Ill-founded conclusions based upon theoretical work possibilities or preconceived notions of job categories for particular types of disabilities can lead not only to wasted time and money but the considerable discouragement of the handicapped person. It is always harder to gear up interest, cooperation, and confidence for a second try if the first has been unrealistic and unsuccessful.

A practical plan is the essence of a good result in vocational placement. Even after careful evaluation by the rehabilitation team and by the vocational counselor, there is no guarantee of success inherent in this kind of academic and theoretical consideration. The "proof of the pudding" lies in the practicality of the final plan designed and carried out by the counselor or others. For instance, there can be

---

[3] See Hanman, B., *Physical Capacities and Job Placement*, Nordisk Rotogravy, Stockholm and John De Graff, Inc., New York, 1951; also *Physical Abilities to Fit the Job*, American Mutual Liability Insurance Co., Boston, 1956.

no quarrel with the fact that return to the former employer, either at the same or a different job, is the best answer if it is possible. The reason that the rehabilitation and placement of workmen's compensation cases by an insurance carrier such as Liberty Mutual has so much chance of final success, as compared to the problems of general disability faced by the community rehabilitation agencies, is due to the tremendous "lever," or argument, which can be presented to the former employer and policyholder on the merits of rehiring the disabled employee. More than 80% of Liberty Mutual rehabilitated cases returned to the same employer.

Foremen and supervisory personnel in plants and on construction work—in other than sedentary businesses—tend to think of the jobs in their departments or sections as requiring physically perfect people. Even key executives or administrative people often express this idea. Although sometimes the physical requirements of given jobs are excessively demanding, most of the time this kind of thinking is due to the fact that the time has never been taken to really evaluate jobs in the plant or business. Job analysis is an "art" in itself, but it can be applied to a greater or lesser degree by any firm. It has particular value in connection with fitting of handicapped persons into the right job. It involves careful study of the physical motions and demands of specific jobs to the end that the employer or his key personnel know exactly what the job needs are and whether a person handicapped in a particular way by injury or disease could meet the job requirements. Hanman and others have written extensively on this subject as the key to successful placement.[4]

There must be this careful study of available jobs in the light of the physical abilities of the handicapped person if the placement plan is to be practical. The actual employment of a handicapped worker is on a sound basis only if that employment is productive for both employer and employee. The supposedly charitable gesture of "a sweeping job for old Charlie," of the "made work" as night watchman, timekeeper, or elevator operator is out of date and unrealistic in the present-day approach to vocational placement. The proper job is one which is worthy of the individual employee's abilities and which merits his real interest and attention; one which makes him an asset to the plant, to his family, and to society. Personal interview with the injured worker regarding his outside interests and abilities often leads to consideration of job possibilities not otherwise suspected. Development of on-the-job apprenticeship programs sometimes provides a "learn and earn" answer to the need. If schooling or formalized train-

4 *Ibid.*

ing is needed to develop real job opportunity, it should follow a pattern of skills which are "marketable," in a vocational sense, in the locality. Not all job possibilities are to be found in "big business"; sometimes the small firms and community service jobs offer better opportunities.

Coordinated effort in relation to the placement of the handicapped is just as essential as the "team approach" so repeatedly emphasized in the other parts of the rehabilitation process. Counselor and counseled cannot do the job alone. There is no simple solution to the successful rehabilitation and placement on a job of a disabled person. It requires the time and effort and patience of a great many people. It must be based on a complete program, utilizing the assistance of the medical profession, the trained professional technician, public and private agencies, industrial management, and organized labor. No single component is enough to do the job alone. At the core of the program must lie the conviction that every disabled person is a potential for complete rehabilitation until proven otherwise and that the effort is worth while, because the salvage of the self-respect and initiative of the individual is the true reflection of a democratic economy.

Coordination is effective not only between individuals concerned with the handicapped person but also between agencies and organizations. Nothing is more disheartening than to be shuttled between one agency and the next, from one employer and job possibility to yet another; this guarantees the death of initiative and the forfeiting of a successful adjustment. It is not uncommon to hear a rehabilitation staff person, perhaps from a rehabilitation center or sheltered workshop, complain that "we did a good job of physical restoration and even work analysis but then no one followed through and got this man a job." Was this failure to pick up the threads the fault of some other agency or was it the lack of perception of the further need and the unwillingness to call in others for assistance which characterized the staff person's own organization? It is easy to point the finger of criticism in rehabilitation as in all human endeavors, but this process, which is peculiarly democratic in principle and fact, places the onus of failure on all who take part; a team effort becomes necessarily a joint responsibility.

Informed selling in placement technique refers to the requirement that the counselor or other rehabilitation worker sell to industry not a disabled person but a skill. It has been fashionable to belabor industry for being resistant to the hiring of handicapped workers. Yet the attitude of business people is nothing more than the attitude of people generally. It is easy for us who are professionally concerned with rehabilitation to lose sight of the fact that flat refusals to work beside crippled individuals, protests to management and union, alleged inability to "stand the sight of," or expressed "sickness" because of the appearance of those with handicaps can and does still occur. Public and community education to remove our inherent prejudices toward "the lame, the halt, and the blind" makes steady but slow progress. Business firms are run and worked by individuals with similar individual feelings; they are no more nor less emotionally and psychologically involved.

Let us then take a look at some of the objections and barriers frequently encountered and how they may be answered. The most commonly encountered difficulties in getting a former employer, or some other prospective employer, to consider definite jobs for a worker handicapped by major injury or disease are in the following areas:

(*a*) "He can't do his old job—why should we rehire him?" indicates disregard of employee's welfare, certain moral obligations, and little knowledge of retraining and placement practices.

(*b*) "All the jobs in our line of work require a physically perfect individual—we have no jobs for cripples." This is a concept often stated in one form or another by employers. It is usually based on complete unwillingness to consider the needs of the handicapped worker or a lack of understanding of actual job requirements.

(*c*) "We have no 'light work.'" Similar to the previous idea, this point of view is based on lack of information on actual job needs or is due to insufficient information from doctors and others on what the disabled individual can really do.

(*d*) "The union won't let us hire a disabled man for that kind of job." Union seniority rules do sometimes present a barrier, but they may often be used as an excuse or because the cooperation and even negotiation of union leaders have not been sought.

(*e*) "Our insurance rates will go up if we hire this handicapped man." This old "wheeze" is still heard and is based either on complete misunderstanding of the real facts or on the wish to use the insurance company as the "whipping boy" for the employer.

(*f*) "We might try to find him a night watchman's job or let him run an elevator." This concept of a "made" or charitable job is passing out of existence and is inconsistent with present-day thinking and practice in the vocational guidance and placement field.

(*g*) "We're afraid he might have another accident and we would be stuck for possible permanent disability." This comment may be due to lack of understanding of safe job-placement techniques or to lack of knowledge of the workmen's compensation laws involved.

(h) "He won't be able to keep up the production pace—he'll fall behind his fellow workers and require all sorts of special privileges." Indicates no real knowledge of how to fit the worker to the job or the work performance of the handicapped generally.

(i) "If he didn't measure up to the job, I might find it embarrassing and even impossible to let him go." This is a fear often expressed but not really considered carefully in the light of known attitudes and work experience of handicapped persons.

Much of the answer to these various queries or arguments lies in the area of education of the employer, the patient, and the rehabilitation worker in terms of exploration of vocational opportunities, testing, training for specific trades or jobs, and actual job finding.

The idea of utilizing union seniority rules as a means of getting around the hiring of handicapped persons is still prevalent. The answer lies in the attempted education of the employer along the lines that most of the unions today are very rehabilitation-conscious. They are on record officially many times as to the need of finding proper jobs for disabled employees and they are decidedly alert as far as cooperation with the employer is concerned. If we can explain to management that union officials, particularly if they are brought into the picture early in the case, will usually be cooperative, we may go a long way toward removing any barriers as far as the union is concerned. In a large plant in New Hampshire, a union–management contract, recently made, actually specified and set aside certain job categories for disabled employees and removed seniority barriers to those jobs. Booklets prepared recently by the AFL-CIO state the union convictions on this whole subject.[5]

Increase in workmen's compensation insurance rates as a result of hiring handicapped employees is an out-dated and untrue surmise. Insurance carriers today work with policyholders to reduce loss. The fewer the accidents, the less paid out in compensation and medical costs. Because compensation insurance rates are based on previous loss experience, the less paid out, the lower future premiums will be. Employers benefit from any reduction of loss through safety engineering and safety practices, from physical restoration of injured workers, and from the proper job placement of all workers.

With the understanding of this basic premise, it would be inconceivable for an insurance company to advocate hiring the physically

[5] American Federation of Labor and Congress of Industrial Organizations, *Cooperation—the Key to Jobs for the Handicapped,* Publication No. 42, Washington, 1957.

handicapped if more costly rates, more accidents, and correspondingly larger premiums were to be the consequence. Insurance carriers are well aware that any person, whether impaired or not, if improperly placed on a job in which the abilities do not correspond to the requirements of the job may well be a hazard to himself and to the people working in his vicinity. Conversely, if all workers are placed in accordance with their skills and physical abilities, the maximum safety and productivity is obtained.

The fear of another accident and resultant permanent disability as a consequence of the hire of a handicapped employee can be combated by explaining again the necessity of careful and constructive job placement where the chances of the feared "second accident" will be at a minimum. Moreover, the explanation that nearly all states now have a "second injury fund" provision in their workmen's compensation act should help to allay the fear of repeat injury and possible cost of long-term disability to the current employer. These provisions normally establish a system of payment for the total disability but hold the current employer liable only for the single-accident loss, with the special fund being responsible for making up the difference. The purpose of such a statute is to limit liability and to give financial advantage to those employers in workmen's compensation claims who have the conscious and active policy of employing and continuing in employment persons with physical handicaps.

The beliefs that fellow employees will react unfavorably to handicapped people, that production will suffer, that the handicapped require many special privileges, and that it will be embarrassing or impossible to let such an employee go are belied by facts and statistics. Both governmental and private studies have clearly shown that handicapped workers as a group are often more conscientious, have less absenteeism, have equally good performance records, and have better safety records. This kind of result, however, depends upon proper placement in a safe and constructive job. Fellow-employees, when properly prepared and educated, do not present the difficulty that employers sometimes expect. The handicapped applicant is not looking for special favors, he wants an opportunity to try out on the job and the right to be treated the same as any other employee. Emotionalism either for or against the handicapped worker should play no part in the effective use of his skills and abilities.

Business concerns are operated for profit; they are neither charitable institutions nor service organizations. The management and personnel people in industry are interested in the hiring of people who can do the job. They are willing to make concessions in the interest of civic spirit, good public relations, and a sense of fair opportunity to those who want to work. At the same time they must turn out a product or a service which can compete for a consumer market. To do so effectively, they have a right to expect workers who are suited to the jobs and who can produce a good day's work, by any reasonable standards.

It follows that no counselor or placement person can hope to argue, cajole, or berate any business owner, personnel manager, or supervisor into giving a disabled person a job merely because that person is disabled or because of some appeal to humanitarian principles or rehabilitation philosophy. The direct approach, which no fair-minded employer could fail to consider seriously, is on the basis of filling a job opening with a person who has the native or acquired skill and knowledge and who also happens to have a handicap which, in the considered opinion of the complete rehabilitation team, should prove no major obstacle to adequate performance on that job. By such an approach, the rehabilitated individual stands squarely on his merits, without apologies and with the confidence of his employer in the accomplishments of the rehabilitation services. If the basis for employment is skill, not charity, the human attitudes and prejudices will change and the chances of similar placements with that employer in the future will be improved accordingly.

In using industrial firms and officials as the "whipping boys" for the plight of the handicapped, the professional worker has sometimes failed to realize that perhaps he has made little attempt to assist industrial people in the understanding of rehabilitation and the role which business can and should play. Offers to let business people see at first hand the operations of rehabilitation facilities, to participate in counseling or evaluation discussions, to run information courses for supervisory personnel, or to help to remove union or management regulations and procedures which might constitute barriers to placement have been few and far between. The specialists in human relations have not always been willing to share their special know-how with the big, bad world of industrial employment.

Perceptive follow-up to vocational placement is a neglected area of professional endeavor. Rehabilitation agencies and staff know precious little about what happens to a handicapped individual after he has been placed on a job. There is a universal tendency to "write off" the person who has been placed as "rehabilitated," "completed," or "terminated." Files are marked closed; time and energy are turned to the new or the unfinished case. It is admittedly hard to find the money and the personnel for adequate follow-up on cases which have been placed, but what a gold-mine of helpful information may lie in any such effort! Where else can the proof be found that medical, therapeutic, counseling, testing, training, placement methods are right or wrong? Somehow the counselor or other placement person must find the way to make this follow-up, if he is to do a better job in the future. Perhaps through public grants or privately funded project support the means can be found to study and learn from the later developments on "closed cases." Perhaps cases can be kept active a little longer until at least preliminary follow-up observations can be made.

One large organization which has specialized in the rehabilitation of the industrial amputee has no real knowledge of whether the patient properly fitted and trained in the use of the prosthesis, following his discharge from the rehabilitation program and return to work, has continued to wear the device, finds it effective in his work, wears it at home, or has discarded, replaced, or remodeled it on the basis of practical use. The new director of one state vocational rehabilitation program indicated that he was vitally interested in the research review and analysis of the thousands of closed records in his program as he felt his counselors could gain invaluable data from the practical successes and failures. It is perfectly true that some placements which fail result in the handicapped person again coming to the attention of the rehabilitation agency but many more may go to other agencies, become discouraged, or seek entirely different solutions to their difficulty. From knowledge of all such developments, the placement agencies and staffs could learn and profit.

All available statistics emphasize that the properly placed handicapped worker is at least as safe, productive, and conscientious a worker as those without a handicap. The Civil Service Commission, the Office of Vocational Rehabilitation, as well as other public and private agencies and institutions have carried out sampling studies on this point. One of the most definitive and influential reports was that made on the performance of physically impaired workers in manufacturing industries by the Bureau of Labor Statistics for the Veterans' Administration in 1948. The study covered by the report reflected the experience of 11,000 impaired workers and 18,000 matched unimpaired workers subject to the same job incentives and exposed to the same job hazards. Areas of comparison were work production, absenteeism, injury frequency rate, quit rate, and job mobility. The summary of the findings was to the effect that

> Based upon the record, it seems reasonable to conclude that physical impairment did not produce an adverse effect on either the quantity of work produced or the quality of the work performance. No matter how

different these physically impaired persons may have been in other respects, on the job they were just another group of workers able to meet their unimpaired fellow workers on an equal competitive footing.[6]

Statistics are things of little human interest, at best. But the files of every rehabilitation agency in the country are full of heart-warming stories of courage, tenacity, and endurance which represent more clearly than any figures the triumph of man's determination over adversity. Some of the case histories strain credulity and almost defy reality in their shining evidence of individual success not because of disability but despite it. Incidentally, there is a school of thought which talks glibly of "compensations" and "spirits enhanced by traumatizing experience" which would have us believe that persons suffering handicapping injury or disease suddenly blossom forth with new capabilities and more fully realized attributes. There is no scientific basis for such an assumption and it can lead to dangerous and erroneous conclusions as to the true potential of the handicapped. Some disabled and some rehabilitation workers have been misled into thinking that miracles were at hand, instead of facing up to the realities of the disability and the actual potential for both daily living and productive work. There are as many failures and as many successes among the handicapped as among the nonhandicapped and for much the same reasons. To this extent, vocational placement practices are best oriented to individual and practical evaluations and not to impressive statistics or imagined superiority of the disabled.

For a long time and even at present, there has been a common misconception as to the effect on insurance rates of an employment policy which contemplates the hiring of the handicapped. Insurance carriers do not dictate the hiring or firing policies of a company which they insure. Workmen's compensation rates are not adversely affected by the carefully planned employment of workers who have suffered a major disability. Such rates are based upon basic work hazards of the type of business (i.e., higher for steel work, lower for office work, etc.) and additionally upon the accident experience of the particular company involved (i.e., higher premium for poor accident record, lower for better safety record). These two factors operate independently of the type of worker hired or his physical and mental condition. The crux of the problem in the effective employment of handicapped workers lies in the selective and safe placement of such workers on jobs where they will not be likely to suffer further injury or any com-

6 U. S. Dept. of Labor, Bureau of Labor Statistics, *The Performance of Physically Impaired Workers in Manufacturing Industries,* Bulletin No. 923, Washington, 1948, p. 4.

plicating worsening of their existing disability. If this is properly done, there is no essential danger of increased workmen's compensation cost by reason of their hire. By the same token, group life insurance and group accident and health insurance rates are not based primarily on the disabilities of individual workers. Seldom does a carrier of such coverages for an industrial firm concern itself with detailed analyses of health or disability records in such a way that it could or would interfere with hiring policies of an employer which favored and carried out the employment of handicapped persons.

In earlier years there was considerable talk among those interested in vocational placement about job modification as a means of fitting the handicapped person into special work situations in the business world. Job modification involves the alteration or re-design of tools, machines, or work processes to fit the special abilities and the physical limitations of the handicapped worker. As a practical matter, such modifications are a poor answer to the question of properly placing the physically limited employee. Changes in machinery and work production processes often are expensive and interrupting to the smooth flow of method design in a modern industrial plant. Expressed necessity for job modification as a precedent to hiring of a handicapped worker may prove a real barrier in his acceptance by a prospective employer. At a recent exposition of programs for the disabled in industry, one large manufacturer proudly exhibited a whole sequence of lathes and other machines which had been re-designed to fit the needs of an above-elbow amputee, who was present to show how he could operate all these machines by using only one arm and hand, with occasional help from the stump of the amputated limb. How much more effective and far less expensive would have been the provision, fitting, and training in the use of a proper prosthesis which would have permitted this man to do the same job on regular machines. Any necessary adaptation of job requirements to fit the disabled worker can cause sharp limitations in the number of job possibilities. Studies made in the forties showed that actually job modifications were necessary in only a very small percentage of instances involving the employment of impaired workers in industry.[7] The present-day approach by most placement people is to train and fit the worker to the needs of a particular kind of job which he can perform efficiently despite his disability, rather than attempting to tailor the job to the particular requirements of the handicapped worker.

One of the most positive and refreshing aspects of vocational place-

7 *Ibid.*, p. 21.

ment in the United States has been the refusal of the professional worker, the business corporations, the labor unions, and the general public to adopt compulsory methods for the hiring of handicapped workers. From time to time, those who seek a legislative answer to every question have talked in glowing terms of the pattern followed in some European countries of required quotas for every employer. Insisting that every firm hire 10% or 25% of its workers from the total available handicapped group seems like an easy solution but, in practice, might prove to be a real deterrent to increasing recognition of the practicability of hiring the handicapped on their merits and without special favor. It would be an easy matter for any employer operating under an enforced quota system to go through his plant and list all those already in his employ who had any kind of major or minor impairment, whether previously known or not, and then state that his quota had been filled, there was no room for any more. The American way of gradual education, developing cooperation, and planned successful placements will prove far more effective than any imposed quotas or percentages. It may be initially slower and fraught with frustrations, but in the long run will benefit both the handicapped and our socioeconomic scheme of things.

In a somewhat similar vein, waivers have been suggested as an easy solution to the argument, admittedly tenuous, that the handicapped constitute a hazard as far as further accidents and systemic breakdowns are concerned. It is argued that the liberalization and broadened interpretation of the workmen's compensation statutes makes it hard for an employer to take on the risk of a handicapped worker. It has already been demonstrated that the research on the subject of work performance of handicapped persons does not support this alleged increased risk. But even granting an element of truth to the allegation, and granting also that there might be an occasional complication in the group health and accident, group life or retirement insurance coverages, legal waivers or other required exceptions to employee coverages would constitute a sad commentary on all that we are learning, teaching, and practicing in rehabilitation. Waivers are essentially a deprivation, in advance, of an employee's rights to certain benefits to which he is entitled by law or by custom. They are a poor substitute for understanding and productive placement procedures.

Selective job placement as both philosophy and practice holds much promise for the future need of American business to meet the challenge not only of the presently handicapped but also of those who may need to change jobs in order to prevent disability. This is an aspect of broad rehabilitation within industry that has not been too clearly recognized or emphasized as yet. The aging of our working population and the problems presented by the increasing chronic, degenerative diseases, such as heart conditions, arthritis, and the like mean greater responsibilities on corporate industry. If business firms are not to bear the burden of cost for all that happens to a man during his working lifetime they must find the way to anticipate disability and limit its potential.

Pre-employment and periodic health examinations, definitive in-plant health programs for employees are a large part of the necessary discovery of disability potential. Industrial medicine, safety engineering, and a preventive approach to employee health and working conditions have already proved enormously successful in combating industrial disability. Much more can be done in the future. Study of jobs and workers, re-allocation of work to fit the changing abilities of the worker can raise controversy. There are problems of comparable wage rates, union seniority classifications, and job flexibility which need to be solved by management—labor joint effort, but they are not insuperable and the promise for enhanced worker efficiency is great. Rehabilitation facilities, programs, and workers can offer much in the way of practical assistance to industry in the better understanding of the causes and effects of disability, the work tolerances and personal adjustments of the handicapped. Physician, psychologists, and educators can provide better knowledge of attitudes, emotions, and actions leading to continuance of disability from injury or chronic illness. There will be no over-night Utopia of a disability-free industrial economy but rather the increasingly intelligent use of vocational placement as a preventive as well as a restorative procedure.

Vocational placement is a complex and changing field; there are many aspects about which we still know relatively little. To be effective, it must remain practical. The best laboratory and training ground is the business world and the industrial plant. Successful placements are not made in classrooms or from textbook maxims. They are forged from the experience, knowledge, imagination, and ingenuity of the counselor or others who realize keenly what kinds of jobs there are and what sort of people work at them. The best job for any handicapped person is always the one for which he is best suited, for which he has been most thoroughly trained, and in which he is most interested.

CHAPTER   14

Training
for Rehabilitation

ONE OF THE PRINCIPAL POINTS OF EMPHA-
sis in the last five years, by every public or private organization interested in or concerned with rehabilitation, has been the dire shortage
of trained rehabilitation personnel. This lack can be noted in almost
every category of personnel and its impact upon the total rehabilitation picture can be measured not only against the present need but
even more dramatically against the future expectation of programs
and services.

There is little to be gained by citing all the individual estimates
of the shortages and needs in all the particular professions and disciplines dealing with the process of rehabilitation. Many of these
figures will become obsolete in a relatively short time, in any event.
It may serve to highlight the importance of the recruitment and
training challenge, however, to give one over-all figure which will
compare the actual with the needed work force in rehabilitation.
If the figures cited in the report of the Subcommittee on Paramedical
Personnel in Rehabilitation and Care of the Chronically Ill, previously referred to, on nine major categories of rehabilitation personnel,[1] are added to the best estimate of need in the physical
medicine specialty, it is apparent that the present number engaged
in these professions and disciplines is about 450,000 and the estimated

[1] Office of Defense Mobilization, Health Resources Advisory Committee, "Mobilization and Health Manpower," a report of the Sub-Committee on Paramedical
Personnel in Rehabilitation and Care of the Chronically Ill, Washington, January,
1956.

112

need as of 1956 is about 620,000. This would mean an over-all increase, in these ten categories, of 38% of personnel available to provide needed services, although the estimated need calls for an increase in individual categories ranging from 12% to 1000%.

Obviously these speculations are not completely definitive, since we have no precise statistics on how many of the individual workers counted in these categories are actually engaged full-time in rehabilitation activity. Nor do we have any reliable estimate of how much the need is likely to increase by 1965 or 1970. All agree that many more personnel will be needed, if rehabilitation continues to expand and take hold as both philosophy and practice. It would not be unreasonable to predict that a million people may need to be involved in rehabilitation activity, on more or less of a full time basis, by the year 1965 and that this figure would not include the many vital part-time activities of other professional, technical, and lay workers who contribute significantly to the rehabilitation effort. Although there is no way to finally and statistically verify these anticipated needs, the figures cited will suffice to point up the tremendous task which faces the educators and the present core of knowledgeable persons in rehabilitation if we are to even approach the goals dictated by expected future need.

Education in rehabilitation involves the explanation of philosophy and practice to those professions or disciplines which will not work full time in the field but need to know the relationships to their own endeavors. This would be true of the persons training for work in public schools, for the practice of law, for entry into ministry or priesthood, and the like. Such education also involves the specific training for direct participation in the rehabilitation process, as in the case of the medical social worker, vocational rehabilitation counselor, physician planning to practice in physical medicine, etc. Lastly, the educational process also involves the continual interchange of ideas, of staff, of case experience, and of possibilities for joint effort between the workers now active in the rehabilitation field.

There are five key aspects in a well-rounded approach to the matter of building up the total rehabilitation force to meet the demands of expected case loads. These are (1) effective recruitment, (2) traineeships, (3) expanded educational facilities, (4) practical and meaningful curricula, and (5) job attractiveness.

Effective recruitment of students to be educated in the professional or disciplinary techniques of rehabilitation is a prerequisite to meeting the eventual personnel requirements in the field. The present numbers who become interested and who seek further training in preparation for this kind of work are insufficient to meet the demand now or in the future. Since undergraduate and graduate training is required for a large number of the available positions in rehabilitation, and certain kinds of course material and preparatory orientation will be needed for effective later concentrated study in the particular profession or discipline chosen, the pool of interested and qualified potential workers must be developed first at the high school level. This is no easy assignment, considering the wealth of educational and work opportunities which await the high school boy or girl with any real evidence of ability. The successful recruitment of these students will depend to a considerable extent on the attainment of some of the other objectives emphasized in the other four key aspects, such as the availability of traineeships or other financial assistance, the good schools and good curricula in the field of rehabilitation study, and the attractive job possibilities. However, there is a less tangible area in which the whole sphere of rehabilitation activity can be made most attractive to the intense idealism of the high school youngster. This is the realm of personal satisfaction in a job which involves doing something for people. Our materialistic economy does not offer very many work opportunities which afford this kind of experience.

In this kind of approach to young people, there lies a golden opportunity for the people already active in rehabilitation to bring to bear their special knowledge and ability in such a way as to markedly influence the plans of the high school student for his or her future education. Yeoman work has already been done in this direction by the National League for Nursing Education, American Physical Therapy Association, the National Health Council (particularly its *Health Careers Guidebook*), the National Foundation for Infantile Paralysis, the National Society for Crippled Children and Adults, the Veterans' Administration, the Public Health Service, Office of Vocational Rehabilitation, and other similar groups. However, there is a need for supplementation of these efforts on the part of national or regional organizations by local communities and interested resource people in the field. Opportunities for guided tours of rehabilitation facilities, talks, and films or case demonstrations presented by authoritative individuals or groups in the field, simple publications of local activity and effective distribution of national organization literature can all help to present a picture to the high school boy or girl of his or her own personal possibilities for service. If each of us who work directly or indirectly in the general field could set ourselves the goal of interesting one high school student a year to the point of his actually going on to college and university training in preparation for work in rehabilitation, even with the normal rate of attrition in these jobs, we would soon have little to worry about in the way of sufficient trained personnel to get the job done.

Traineeships seem vital to the task of interesting appreciable numbers of young people in advanced and specialized education leading to work in the rehabilitation field. The training required for effective rehabilitation work is admittedly expensive. Many of the positions in the field require master's or doctoral degrees, in addition to the undergraduate schooling and the bachelor's degree. Although the total undergraduate enrollment in colleges and universities has increased markedly in the last fifteen years, there are still considerable numbers of high ranking students in high school who do not attend college and it is estimated that at least 50% of this number would continue their education if funds were available.[2] All universities verify the fact that many promising undergraduates are unable to continue their graduate study without substantial assistance financially.

Both from the point of view of the demonstrated need and that of the desirability of attracting the more promising students to further their education as a means of improving the quality as well as the quantity of rehabilitation workers, it appears that increased funds should be made available for this purpose. Much has been done already by the organizations listed above as having performed valuable services in interesting young people in rehabilitation careers. Many of these same groups, as well as other smaller organizations and individual foundations, have established scholarships, fellowships, and other forms of financial aid to worthy students who wanted to further their education along rehabilitation lines, or at least in a profession or discipline which was in a position to contribute materially to the rehabilitation process.

The 1954 amendments to the Vocational Rehabilitation Act, which permitted the appropriation of monies for traineeships in vocational rehabilitation counseling, social work, medicine, nursing, physical and occupational therapy, and counseling psychology, constituted a practical impetus to the field of rehabilitation training. Grants are made either on a long-term (two-year maximum course of study) basis to those entering rehabilitation training initially or as a short-term specialized fellowship for further education of those already in the field. The grants are made as the result of evaluation by the

2 *Ibid.*, p. 81.

educational institutions authorized to grant the monies, and these are ordinarily the same institutions that are geared to teach the subjects in which the student applicant is interested in receiving his training. It is a prerequisite that the student must demonstrate "expressed interest in administration, supervision, teaching, research, or clinical practice in rehabilitation of physically or mentally handicapped persons."[3]

Expanded educational facilities are necessary if the recruitment practices and the financial assistance succeed in their aim of attracting larger numbers of students into the rehabilitation field. In the chapters dealing with the roles of the physician, the nurse, the therapist, and the counselor, certain figures were cited on the number of colleges and universities now providing training in one or more of the special areas of activity in rehabilitation. In almost no case, except perhaps for the corrective therapist, are the current graduates sufficient to meet, or even approach, the demonstrated need. Just one category, for instance, that of medical and psychiatric social work (according to the Paramedical Personnel Subcommittee) had a minimum need of 2000 graduates a year to meet the increasing demands for social services in general and mental health programs and yet could expect only 800 to 900 a year on the basis of present educational facilities and already involved students.[4] Expansion of facilities implies both broadening the teaching of colleges and universities already providing some instruction in the rehabilitation field to include more teaching in other areas, perhaps leading to other degrees relating to rehabilitation specialization, and also interesting additional undergraduate and graduate schools in providing this kind of instruction. The structure for this enlarged view of education for rehabilitation work can be built on our present higher educational system, using the existing colleges and universities. It does not contemplate the building of special schools for specific rehabilitation training.

The direct financial support of colleges and universities in their attempt to develop or expand teaching programs in the various fields of rehabilitation has been limited. Among the national voluntary and professional organizations, only the National Foundation for Infantile Paralysis has done very much in the form of direct aid to

[3] U. S. Dept. of Health, Education and Welfare, Office of Vocational Rehabilitation, "Training Grant Programs of the Office of Vocational Rehabilitation—Information Statement and Instructions for Preparing Application," Washington, March, 1956, pp. 12–14.

[4] Office of Defense Mobilization, *op. cit.,* pp. 28–29.

schools engaged in training professional people for rehabilitation work and their support program has been mostly in the areas of physical therapy, occupational therapy, medical social work, and medicine. Among the governmental agencies, the more important work has been done by the Public Health Service and the Office of Vocational Rehabilitation. The former has offered teaching grants to accredited educational institutions for expansion and improvement of teaching programs in clinical psychology and psychiatric social work.[5] The latter, as the result of the 1954 amendments to the Vocational Rehabilitation Act, provides supplementary funds to assist colleges and universities in the areas of vocational rehabilitation counseling, social work, medicine, physical and occupational therapy, and nursing.[6] In the 1958 fiscal year, the amount appropriated for both teaching and training grants by OVR was $4,440,000.[7]

In the day-to-day function of community rehabilitation programs and services, there is often an opportunity to share effectively in this planned expansion of educational facilities. Active assistance, study, and support of any local colleges or schools contemplating the development or strengthening of their teaching programs in areas which can provide trained personnel for rehabilitation is tantamount to direct improvement of the personnel picture, which in the long run will benefit all participating individuals and agencies in the community.

Practical and meaningful curricula in the rehabilitation field are not easy to design nor bring to fruition. There has been a dire lack of understanding on the part of most educators as to both the theoretical and practical aspects of rehabilitation and a certain amount of resistance to the very idea of teaching rehabilitation in the usual college or university setting. There has been a dearth of good teaching literature and often no available person with any real knowledge of the subject to formulate a sound teaching program. This does not imply that there has been any lack of skill in the usual teaching methods for the schools of medicine, physical therapy, nursing, occupational therapy, social work, and the like. It does mean, however, that many of the attempts to incorporate specific teaching of rehabilitation concept and method into the curricula of these schools, and to extend this type of teaching into newer areas of rehabilitation concern such as the schools of education, psy-

[5] *Ibid.*, p. 64.

[6] U. S. Dept. of Health, Education and Welfare, *op. cit.*, pp. 8–11.

[7] National Rehabilitation Association, *Legislative News Letter*, G-57-82, Washington, July 9, 1957, p. 1.

chology and psychiatry, law, business administration, religion, etc., have been haphazard, ill-advised, and sometimes doomed to failure.

The reasons for this state of affairs are several. One is the very complexity and scope of rehabilitation itself. As both philosophy and practice, it intrudes itself upon the arts and the social sciences as taught in our major educational institutions. Only the applied sciences of physics, chemistry, mathematics, geology, and all the preparation for the so-called "world of the engineer" escape its impact. Any branch of education which concerns itself primarily with people and their activities, reactions, and beliefs must necessarily become involved at some point with the subject matter of rehabilitation from disability. A broad and tolerant outlook is required to comprehend and adapt to this kind of approach and all that it implies for a perceptive teaching pattern.

The second reason is the lack of trained teachers in colleges and universities who have themselves had any appreciable amount of exposure to the practical workings of rehabilitation programs and services. Schools interested in starting or improving rehabilitation teaching programs would do well to devise a series of practical indoctrination or refresher courses for the professors or instructors of these courses, in cooperation with local rehabilitation agencies, to provide the broad and practical look at the many ramifications of rehabilitation which would insure a better teaching program for the student.

A third reason is the weakness of the curriculum content devised for many of the rehabilitation teaching programs in the schools. A course in vocational rehabilitation counseling, for instance, which did not include any actual time spent in industrial plants and business offices to learn the facts of job analysis and placement, would be of little lasting value to a trainee in this field who would spend much of his later career trying to get jobs for disabled people. A school of social work which tried to teach rehabilitation by concentration on medical conditions, psychological reactions, and personal case analysis but which included nothing on the effect of social laws and insurance would fall far short of adequate preparation for effective rehabilitation endeavor. There is a need for much more definitive understanding of what should be included in the assigned reading, the field work, the special lectures from source people, and the round table discussions by practical rehabilitation workers already in the field if we are jointly going to improve the teaching in this area. All local personnel in rehabilitation, from administrative to technical, need to offer their services in the adaptation of curricula in local schools to the most effective presentation of the subject matter that is vital to successful work in the field.

There are encouraging signs of progress in this direction. The National Rehabilitation Association, in cooperation with the Office of Vocational Rehabilitation, is attempting a three-year study, which is designed to elicit from rehabilitation staffs the best material for incorporation in courses for rehabilitation counselors, particularly vocational rehabilitation counselors. Certain medical and other schools of special graduate study are trying to work out more effective teaching methods, sometimes by sitting down with source people in the rehabilitation field to establish better curricula. In Massachusetts, the United Community Services of Boston, through its Rehabilitation Council, acting jointly with the state chapter of the National Rehabilitation Association, has carefully reviewed the curricula and teaching methods of a number of different schools in the area which are training people for various kinds of jobs involving some aspect of rehabilitation. Plans are being made for an institute in 1958 at which educators and source people in the rehabilitation field will participate in discussions leading to the establishment of certain "core curricula" which would be a working base for the teaching of rehabilitation philosophy and practice in almost any field of concerned activity, with guidelines for the adaptation of additional special material needed for particular professions or disciplines.

Job attractiveness must necessarily be the "pay-off" as far as the translation of education into actual career is concerned. There is little benefit to successfully recruiting talent, financing the advanced study, expanding the teaching facilities, and improving the course content if the graduate student is then lost to other and more attractive fields. Working environment, personnel practices, promotion systems, retirement and group insurance benefit plans, prestige and stature of the position all contribute to attracting and holding the trained rehabilitation worker. Admittedly the various professions and disciplines, with the possible exception of the medical profession, associated with or active in rehabilitation have not had an enviable reputation as to salary scales. Although the picture has improved in recent years, it is still evident that the rehabilitation worker is apt to be underpaid considering the importance of his contribution and the amount of special education involved in getting and holding his position. More will be said on this subject in the chapter on the cost of rehabilitation.

Training for rehabilitation is not all a matter of schools and undergraduate or graduate students. There is a less tangible area of education which relates to providing information to those who are already having some part in the rehabilitation process but who may have a decided lack of information as to its present implications and scope. Persons affected by this lack of understanding may be anyone from the physician to the volunteer lay worker in an agency. All might benefit materially from "refresher courses," "institutes," "conferences," or other types of opportunities for formalized exchange of ideas and practices which help to improve their understanding of what they are trying to do. It is regrettable to see professional workers in public or private agencies and organizations who are prevented from obtaining this kind of healthy exchange because of budget restrictions, limiting regulations, or other reasons. The field of rehabilitation has been changing and growing so fast that everyone in it needs constant re-education and exposure to the thinking of others, if one has any hope at all of staying abreast of developments.

If rehabilitation of the physically and mentally handicapped is to live up to its golden promise, the total job of education for rehabilitation becomes one not merely for the educational institutions but for all of us interested or active in rehabilitation. Recruitment, financial support for study, expanded teaching facilities, broader and more definitive curricula, and modification of jobs to make them more attractive become areas in which we can all make a contribution, either individually or by joint effort. Working affiliations between rehabilitation facilities and teaching institutions, organized cooperative plans for informal discussions among educators and rehabilitation workers, and utilization of community rehabilitation committees as a source of help toward better training procedures are ways in which participation can be both direct and effective.

The challenge for those already in the field extends not only to the student seeking to work in rehabilitation and the institutions which are endeavoring to train him, but also to fellow-workers insofar as the improvement of their knowledge and experience is concerned. Our educational task is one of sharing our special knowledge with all those who are eager to learn. The best guarantee of better rehabilitation is not criticism but enlightenment, not professionally guarded secrets but shared experiences.

CHAPTER 15

Integration
of Services

A SEEMING PARADOX IN THE REHABILITATION process is found in the concentration of each service upon the handicapped individual as the focal point, such services being entirely geared to his medical, social, and economic welfare, and at the same time this concentration, if it is to be effective, must allow for a combination and unification of all services. Thus rehabilitation assumes both an individualistic and a communal pattern. Yet, in this seeming inconsistency lies the uniqueness and the challenge of rehabilitation programs for each community. Finding the way to organize and develop specific areas of service for the patient and then welding them into a unified program is often a frustrating but vitally neces·sary task.

The words "coordination" and "integration" are sometimes used by workers in the field as interchangeable; actually they are quite distinct in their meaning, yet both properly applied to the organization and utilization of rehabilitation services. Coordination, in its accepted usage, means the act of bringing into common action, the state of harmonious adjustment or functioning. Integration is defined as the act or process of forming into a whole, of uniting so as to form a complete or perfect whole, of unification. In their mathematical applications, coordinate relates to the determination of position whereas integrate infers the finding of an equation among variables. So, too, in their social application, coordination demands an efficient working of the parties in relation to one another, but integration becomes the seeking of ways and means to unite the parties in a functional whole. As applied to community rehabilitation services, coordination of those services would require a process of understanding and agreement between individuals and agencies which would permit them to function effectively together. This harmony of action would make for better working relationships and, therefore, a somewhat better opportunity to secure a more promising result for the disabled person. On the other hand, integration of these same rehabilitation services implies not merely the understanding and harmony as between services but the uniting of those services for a common purpose and to a common end.

Although coordination is both necessary and important among community rehabilitation agencies, the keystone in the development of successful rehabilitation of the handicapped is integration of aims and services. This idea of integration applies not only to the need for agencies working together to develop a complete rehabilitation program for the disabled individual, nor only to the various individuals involved functioning cooperatively for the benefit of the handicapped person, but also to recognition by all disciplines that the patient requires a total program, i.e., an application of all services necessary to insure his restoration to fullest capacity.

The National Foundation for Infantile Paralysis produced a cartoon film several years ago which all too graphically demonstrated the plight of a small boy afflicted with polio who thereafter was literally torn apart by each of the several parties to the treatment and rehabilitation process, all in the blind concentration upon their own particular and limited field of care, without recognition of the total needs of the patient. The truth of the assertion made by this visual means has been all too evident in the approach of certain segments of the professional and technical staffs as well as some agencies involved in attempts at rehabilitation.

The words "teamwork," "team effort," and "team approach" have been used so frequently that they seem trite and meaningless at times, yet they constitute the essence of rehabilitation both as philosophy and practice. Oddly enough, it is easy to forget that the patient himself is the most important member of the team. It is essential that the patient be thoroughly understood by all the other team members both as to his reactions and his needs. The best judge of rehabilitation attempts and the truest test of their effectiveness is the disabled person upon whom they are made. One of the penalties of our age of specialization, particularly in the medical and paramedical fields, is the ease with which the patient as a whole may be forgotten in professional concentration upon applying specialized services in a limited sense. Mr. William F. Stearns, executive director of the Saranac Lake Rehabilitation Guild, has pinpointed this tendency in the following way:

> In developing respect for the role of the specialist in rehabilitation, are we in danger of losing respect for the patient? In the splitting up of his needs into categories, are we disregarding the strongest force we have for his rehabilitation, his sense of importance as a unique combination of mind, body, and spirit? Moreover, in dividing his treatment into special areas, are we really using professional staff to the best advantage? Are they not, too, limited in their effectiveness by the very virtue of their specialization? Do they not also have more to offer than their particular skills?
>
> Rehabilitation, if accomplished at all, is accomplished by the handicapped human being himself, with assistance from other human beings who, by natural sympathy, understanding, and training, develop in him the will and strength and skill to surmount obstacles.
>
> . . . Are we looking at people, or merely medical, social, psychological, and vocational problems? [1]

Most handicapped persons have multiple rather than single needs in relation to rehabilitation. No one of these can be handled effectively without knowledge of and consideration for the others. This means that any tendency on the part of the patient, or the professional staffs attempting his rehabilitation, to regard any one aspect such as medical care, physical therapy, or vocational guidance as constituting the whole of rehabilitation is inherently wrong. Such conclusions deny the concept of the "whole man" and the inclusiveness of rehabilitation as a process. No disabled person is less than the sum total of his needs; the amputee is not only a man who has lost his leg, he is also a fearful and worried human being, the head of a disrupted family, a wage-earner who is out of a job.

The need of joint effort on the part of the various disciplines involved in the rehabilitation process is important not only to the understanding of the patient and his own concept of the full program, it is also vital to the practical success of the entire effort. The teamwork never becomes a reality so long as the physical therapist does not understand and even resents the supposed encroachment of the corrective therapist, so long as the doctor sees no reason for asking the advice of the prosthetist on limb-fitting problems, so long as any one member of a discipline regards the work of other professional or technical people as unwarranted intrusion upon his or her domain. By the same token, the worker in one field of rehabilita-

[1] Stearns, W. F., "Effective Use of Rehabilitation Personnel," *J. Rehabilitation,* **XXII**, No. 3, pp. 4 and 5, National Rehabilitation Association, Washington, (May–June, 1956).

tion cannot consider himself an expert in the areas properly handled by others. Teamwork or team effort is creative and positive action; it is not inherent in similar function. Teams of horses pulled in different directions to accomplish the brutal quartering of a man in the Middle Ages but four horses pulling as one could haul the heavily loaded wagons of our grandfather's era.

The rehabilitation center functions as one of the best testing grounds for this kind of cooperative endeavor. Although no one would be naive enough to proclaim that the centers have not had their share of professional jealousies, disciplinary rigidity, and organizational barriers, the center has nonetheless provided a practical concentration of rehabilitation activities by various disciplines in a localized area and under conditions which necessarily make for greater community of interests and ideas. It is easy for the physician or therapist in the treatment wards of a general hospital to be disinterested in and even resistant to the methods and requirements of vocational rehabilitation or of family counseling as practiced elsewhere in the community. It is much harder for such disinterest and resistance to thrive in the close, personal relationships of a center with constant exchange of ideas, joint staff evaluations, and administrative pressure for communication. It is in this sense that the rehabilitation center movement has contributed markedly toward demonstrating in a practical way the signal advantages of team effort in the successful rehabilitation of the disabled.

While considering the individual parties to the rehabilitation process, it is well not to overlook the voluntary lay worker. It is easy for the professional to decry the efforts of these dedicated people who give countless hours of their personal time to many kinds of rehabilitation activities. Terms such as "do-gooders," "well-meaners," and the like are used glibly to characterize those who try to help in worthy causes. But it is estimated that about 35,000,000 persons in the United States are engaged in volunteer work of all kinds. Volunteer effort is basic to our American way of life and it is one of the reassuring and distinctive parts of our democratic thinking and action. Not only can such persons fill the tremendous gap in the number of available trained personnel in rehabilitation but also the more important contribution of these voluntary workers relates to integration of the rehabilitation services with the community, with the general public. True community understanding of rehabilitation can never be achieved by isolated units of professional competency; it necessarily must involve as many people through as many ways as is practically possible. A sincere lay worker can be a real "booster" for rehabilitation.

There has been hardly a discussion group, convention, speaker, or author of printed material in the last fifteen years, attempting to deal with the subject of rehabilitation, who has not stressed the necessity for integration of community services and agencies. Yet a vast amount still remains to be done in demonstrating the essential worth of such a basic idea. Community organizations and agencies, particularly those related to health, welfare, and recreation, have come into being as the result of real or imagined needs at a particular time. Seldom has there been much regard for those already in existence or those planned by others to meet similar needs. Vested interests frequently prevent what would otherwise be practical coordination or elimination of duplication. Although research, studious evaluation, and professional discussion arrive at the same conclusion, as far as the desirability of integrated community planning is concerned, there are few communities which have made any such thoughtful approach to their human welfare endeavors.

One of the significant research studies in community planning was done by Bradley Buell and Associates in 1948 in St. Paul, Minn. It revealed that about 6% of the city's families suffered from multiple problems in the welfare, correctional, health, social, and recreational areas. This small percentage of families was receiving over one-half the combined services of the community agencies dealing with these areas. Despite the fact that such a large part of the time, service and money of these agencies was expended on this group, there was little organization of joint effort and still less opportunity for any comprehensive solution to the over-all family needs.[2]

This is a typical picture in most sizable communities. In public agencies, there are frequently barriers of legislative definitions of responsibility and over-zealous adherence to "the book," combined with lack of knowledge and disinterest in the work of other agency people. In private agencies, there may be sheer ignorance as to the efforts of other groups but more often it is competitive rivalry for recognition. Such competition arises partly on the basis of individual self-interest, the "we started it" type, but more commonly because of the fund-raising methods of these agencies. The deadly earnest race for their share of the publicly subscribed monies blinds many agencies to any thought of real cooperation with others. We

[2] Bradley Buell and Associates, *Community Planning for Human Services*, Columbia University Press, New York, 1952.

advertise and retail many of our private community services just as we do any other salable commodity. Supposedly it would be fatal to fail to claim that one agency was not doing as good as or better than some others; we have not learned to merchandise cooperative effort.

Of equal importance to community integration of services is integration of those services with the community, i.e., with public opinion and action. Rehabilitation staffs have inherited some of the scorn of the professional for public relations. There has been an underlying tendency to provide services *to* people rather than *for* people. Although there have been some deplorable aspects to public fund-raising endeavors or legislative appropriation attempts by health service agencies in recent years, one of the benefits of such activities has been the emerging consciousness of the value of telling the agency story effectively to the general public. People understand, use, and support rehabilitation facilities and programs only insofar as they know the story and appreciate the worth. Those few rehabilitation centers and more generalized programs which have done the best job of public relations have contributed most to the community because of increased acceptance. The best public education lies in the "success story" of the patient who has been satisfactorily and fully rehabilitated. As the facilities, staff, and services develop and improve in the field, the number of such stories and the impact upon the public will be increased accordingly.

Basic to the community effort toward integration is communications. Within the community area this can be achieved through councils of rehabilitation agencies and organizations, utilization of common facilities or buildings, group meetings, and joint planning efforts. As between individuals, it can be achieved through staff meetings and discussions, exchange visits to agencies, educational interpretation, publications, and working agreements or affiliations. Communication to the general public by newspapers, radio, television, distributed material, open house invitations, and exhibits is decidedly effective. Lay participation through volunteer workers in agencies and fund-raising assignments are other methods of establishing rapport with the "man in the street."

In this consideration of the need of integration of patient with service, of staffs and disciplines, of organizations and agencies, of services with the general public, it might appear on the surface that achievement of such a goal is a well-nigh hopeless task. There are those who feel it is just that, and who advocate the creation of some giant governmental authority, functioning at federal, state, and local levels, which would encompass all rehabilitation activities. The proponents of such an idea argue that it would provide a comprehensive and centralized attack upon the whole problem of disability. Impatience at delays and local lack of coordination can sometimes make this idea look like an easy and prompt answer. Such an answer would be a denial of the essential right of the individual to select his own program of care, would constitute a refutation of the pioneering effort and tremendous accomplishments of the private agencies over the years, and would vitally affect the philosophy of rehabilitation as a combination of community forces dedicated to the betterment of the individual.

Integration does not imply uninspiring standardization or stifling conformity. It should develop ideally in a climate of free communication and with a pattern of exchange between all disciplines. Contrary to what is sometimes feared, integration need not involve surrender of initiative, individual accomplishment, or agency respect. In actuality, few agencies indeed are geared to handle the total rehabilitation needs of the people it serves and can scarcely count on a completely satisfactory job of rehabilitation unless it has the active cooperation of others. The best insurance for the kind of success which not only benefits the patient but also redounds to the credit of the agency is to be found in proper integration of its efforts with those of its fellow agencies or organizations.

Difficult and frustrating as integration of rehabilitation activities may be within the community, there are many hopeful signs that substantial progress has been made. Regionalization projects for the establishment of facilities and personnel which can be utilized by smaller communities on a joint basis, information and referral services to provide knowledge about and use of rehabilitation services in the community, and combined planning for new or improved facilities offer practical proof of such progress. Recognition by legislative groups, agency personnel, professional associations, community councils, fraternal organizations, and labor and management representatives that this sort of cooperative effort is at the root of successful rehabilitation holds great promise for the future. The education of rehabilitation personnel, not only in the techniques of their own discipline but also in the need for integrated effort and services, may eventually make the present-day discussions completely academic. The executive director of the National Rehabilitation Association poses the question straightforwardly:

It may be that the real challenge we face during the next ten years is to see whether it is going to be possible for a multitude of agencies and a multitude of professional disciplines to work together effectively for the meeting of human needs.[3]

[3] Whitten, E. B., "How Big Is the Rehabilitation Problem," *J. Rehabilitation*, **XXIII**, No. 1, p. 20, National Rehabilitation Association, Washington (January–February 1957).

CHAPTER 16

Social Laws
and Rehabilitation

SINCE A FUNDAMENTAL CONCERN OF ALL REHA-
bilitation is the improvement of the lot of the disabled individual
in society, it is not surprising that an increasing amount of attention
has been given to the impact of rehabilitation upon the administration of the social legislation which has dominated the U. S. scene
during the last quarter century. The president of a large corporation
recently remarked that the most significant thing that has happened
in this country since 1900 is that people have become more important.
This is a simple and perceptive way of saying that the attention of
government, business, labor, education, religion, and even the arts
has been increasingly directed toward the needs of the individual.
Critics of the trend toward centralized authority and broadening governmental control complain bitterly of the loss of individual liberties
and rights. Yet, amidst the cries that denounce our alleged progress
toward the "welfare state," there stands the self-evident fact that the
medical, social, psychological, and economic needs of the average man
have become a major concern of all our social institutions. Particularly is this true of that segment of our population which may
be characterized as less fortunate financially.

However, in the rush to provide for the welfare of the American
public, there has been perhaps an understandable tendency to con-
centrate on financial benefits to the exclusion, or at best the neglect,
of rehabilitation to self-sufficiency. Only in the past few years has
there grown a recognition of the fact that it makes more sense socially
and economically to restore a disabled individual to a responsible

role in society than to pay him indefinitely for his disability. This trend of thinking and practice implies a vast expansion of the necessary rehabilitation services and it will constitute a challenge to many groups to effectively harness the service to the need.

The most important social laws with which existing or future programs of rehabilitation must establish a working harmony of purpose are the workmen's compensation acts, the Social Security Act (particularly those provisions dealing with the Old Age and Survivor's Insurance), public assistance laws, and the mandatory disability insurance enactments. All of these categories of social legislation incorporated no provision initially for any rehabilitation of the disabled or handicapped person who might be the recipient of their benefits; yet all are the subject of much speculation and discussion today about the necessity for applying our present knowledge in this field to such beneficiaries.

The workmen's compensation laws, like most social or welfare legislation, were remedial in purpose. Their adoption was rooted in the uncertainty, cost, and delays of tort actions against the employer under the old common law. Their aim was to provide a prompt, simple, and inexpensive method of paying benefits, in like manner as wages, to the injured worker during his period of incapacity from work and to his dependents in the event of his death. The earliest laws were enacted in Germany and England; to be followed in the United States by the Civil Employees Act, passed by the federal government in 1908. The first of the states to enact a workmen's compensation law were Kansas and Washington in 1911, although New York had attempted a compulsory law in 1910 which was ruled unconstitutional by the Court of Appeals in that state. The first law to actually take effect was the Wisconsin act on May 3, 1911. In the succeeding years between 1911 and 1920, all but six states had passed this kind of legislation. The last of the forty-eight states to enact such a law was Mississippi in 1948. Alaska, Hawaii, Puerto Rico, and three federal jurisdictions are also covered by similar workmen's compensation laws.

Although the exact number is unknown, it is reasonable to assume that over 40,000,000 workers are now entitled to the benefits of such laws, if they meet with industrial accident or suffer from occupational disease.[1] Benefits paid in 1954, the latest year for which statistics are available, amounted to $880,000,000, of which more than $300,-

[1] Somers, H. M., and Somers, A. R., *Workmen's Compensation—Prevention, Insurance and Rehabilitation of Occupational Disability*, John Wiley & Sons, New York, 1954, p. 38.

000,000 was for medical care and the balance in the form of indemnity payments to disabled workers or their dependents. Over 60% of the insurance losses were paid by private insurance carriers, about 25% by state insurance funds and the rest by self-insured employers.[2]

Rehabilitation of the disabled worker was not embodied, either as a legislative purpose or administrative practice, in the early compensation laws or, indeed, in the numerous revisions of those laws until recent years. In fact, the administration of medical care to the injured or diseased worker has never been a point of emphasis in the state workmen's compensation systems. It has always been what Marshall Dawson called "a blind spot." The statutes have assumed that the administration of medical care by carriers and employers would be an accomplished fact and that the compensation commission or board would need to act only when there was a dispute over medical questions. The state laws have not stimulated initiative on the part of compensation authorities as far as supervision of medical care is concerned. Having little or no statutory authority to supervise medical care and being therefore reluctant to initiate inquiry into the arrangements made by carriers, state funds, or employers as to the furnishing of medical care as required under the laws, it is not surprising that, until recently, the workmen's compensation administrative bodies in each state have not exhibited great interest in the practical application of rehabilitation concepts and methods to disabled workers. The Medical Committee of the International Association of Industrial Accident Boards and Commissions in 1952 reported that "little, if any, progress has been made to date, in the vast unexplored field of compensation medical care and administration."[3]

The employers and insurance carriers responsible for the provision of medical care have been, for the most part, even less alert to the possibilities of sound rehabilitation methods. Carriers and employers have largely visualized their responsibilities under the laws and to their policyholders as limited to a legal and financial operation. Investigate, pay benefits or contest on liability issues, move case toward disposition by final award or settlement—these were the fixed pattern of handling of workmen's compensation claims. There was little real acceptance of a more positive approach to the removal of the causes of continued disability and the restoration of the employee to full

[2] U. S. Dept. of Commerce, Bureau of the Census, *Statistical Abstract of the United States—1956*, 77th annual edition, Washington, D. C., 1956, p. 275.

[3] U. S. Bureau of Labor Standards, Bulletin 167, Proceedings of 1952 Annual Convention of International Association of Industrial Accident Boards and Commissions, Washington, 1953, pp. 81–82.

work capacity. Professor and Mrs. Somers have indicated in their comprehensive study that rehabilitation is "something apart from the normal claims administration rather than an integral function of the program." They state, "at worst, claims procedures involve built-in conflicts between indemnity rights and rehabilitation possibilities."[4]

Bar associations and individual attorneys have shown no appreciable interest in rehabilitation as a desirable practice and goal in the disposition of workmen's compensation cases. Rehabilitation, which represents a concerted effort to reduce the disability and thereby lessen the consequences of injury, has seemed to be the antithesis of the attorney's efforts to develop a picture of continuing or permanent disability which may result in larger awards, settlements and fees. The National Association of Claimant's Compensation Attorneys is dedicated to developing methods and skills which can more graphically present disability to commissions and courts; as an organization it is supporting the idea of reintroducing the elements of damages and court actions into the disposition of workmen's compensation cases. Such ideas are predicated upon remuneration rather than restoration as the purpose of the workmen's compensation laws and their administration.

There have been powerful forces at work, however, in the direction of highlighting rehabilitation as a necessary component of the workmen's compensation system. These forces are (1) individual and organizational recognition, (2) scientific and economic developments, and (3) legislative and administrative action.

As far back as 1930, Commissioner Duxbury of Minnesota, formerly president of the International Association of Industrial Accident Boards and Commissions, in an address to the national convention of that body, declared that the object of the compensation law was "the economic rehabilitation of the employee."[5] In a similar scholarly analysis of the workmen's compensation laws before the 1950 meeting of the same group, Marshall Dawson indicated that such "economic rehabilitation" presupposed the employee's physical restoration. He stated further that:

> Attention is again being directed to rehabilitation as the goal of workmen's compensation—the word is used in its broad meaning as contrasting with indemnity. Success in rehabilitation is necessarily the culmination of the performance of the workmen's compensation system as a whole.[6]

4 Somers, H. M., and Somers, A. R., *op. cit.*, pp. 275–276.

5 Bureau of Labor Statistics, Bulletin 536, Proceedings of the 1930 Convention of International Association of Industrial Accident Boards and Commissions, Washington, 1931, p. 129.

6 Bureau of Labor Standards, Bulletin No. 142, Proceedings of 36th Annual

The later deliberations of the I.A.I.A.B.C. on the subject led to its going on record to the effect that

> Rehabilitation is the end result of the compensation process. If we, as compensation administrators, fail to realize this important fundamental, and are satisfied merely to sit back and dole out to the injured workman a certain percentage of his wage, according to our various laws, then the entire compensation process becomes archaic and outmoded. Assisting and helping the injured workman to regain his former physical fitness following injury or industrial disease, in order that he may again become a productive, useful member of society is, in our considered opinion, the responsibility of compensation administrators.[7]

A rehabilitation committee has now been established by this group and in its report at the 1956 meeting the committee stated that

> Rehabilitation, in the sense of a complete and integrated physical restoration and vocational placement program, offers our best chance for immediate and direct opportunity to bring a greater degree of justice to those suffering severe, traumatic injuries in the prime of life. We can never compensate, in a monetary sense, for the self-respect and self-reliance they have lost if their injury deprives them of the opportunity to be productive workers meeting their responsibilities to their families and their community. We can possibly restore them physically and vocationally if we bring all our resources and recently developed techniques and attitudes to bear on the problem.[8]

Medical groups began to exhibit marked interest in the subject of rehabilitation as it applied to workmen's compensation procedures. The first of these was the American College of Surgeons which in 1950 appointed a Subcommittee on Industrial Relations comprised of representatives from labor, insurance carriers and federal government as well as the medical profession. One of the five basic principles set forth by this subcommittee reads as follows:

> Full utilization of all our potential manpower is essential to the welfare and strength of the country at all times. The discarding of disabled workers is an economic extravagance detrimental to the welfare of our country, wholly aside from the personal effect on the worker and his family. Solution of the problems of trauma requires cooperation and not competition, between all interested groups and agencies. We must therefore improve and expand all activities, public and private, that aid in rehabilitation of the disabled worker.[9]

Convention of International Association of Industrial Accident Boards and Commissions, Washington, 1950, pp. 61–62.

[7] Bureau of Labor Standards, Bulletin No. 167, Proceedings of 38th Annual Convention of International Association of Industrial Accident Boards and Commissions, Washington, 1953, p. 83.

[8] Bureau of Labor Standards, Bulletin No. 192, Proceedings of the 42nd Annual Convention of the International Association of Industrial Accident Boards and Commission, Washington, 1956, p. 219.

[9] *Bull. Am. Coll. Surgeons*, pp. 167–168 (July–August 1952).

In the same report a portion of another basic principle was that "rehabilitation and restoration to gainful employment of the injured worker must begin with first aid and continue through the period of disability. The physician must bring to bear on these problems all the skills and disciplines that science and society can offer, and utilize all community resources which can assist him in the accomplishment of these objectives."

The principles were endorsed by the Board of Regents of the College in April, 1952. By November, 1954, a critical review of the current practices in workmen's compensation, medical care, and medical and vocational rehabilitation resulted in presentation to the College of a set of operating principles which stated that "rehabilitation of the injured worker and his return to gainful employment is one of the basic concepts of workmen's compensation." It was further stated that ways and means must be found to insure the provision of medical and vocational rehabilitation by the establishment of standards for such services. State workmen's compensation administrative groups should be endowed with authority to supervise the medical care of workmen's compensation cases and to utilize the assistance of impartial medical experts which could insure the adequacy and continuity of medical care and rehabilitation from the date of injury to maximal restoration. These operating principles were formally adopted by the College and additional investigation is now being undertaken which may lead toward the stated goal of

> A compensation system so constituted would restore more efficiently and completely far more individuals to gainful employment and would at the same time eliminate the present highly controversial and expensive procedures and in the end would be far less expensive to industry, labor, the insurance carriers and the community as a whole.[10]

The American Medical Association, through its Council on Industrial Health, in session at Boston in December, 1955, adopted a report on "Medical Relations in Workmen's Compensation," which stressed as one of the basic goals of workmen's compensation today the "establishment of workable rehabilitation programs" which, "aside from great benefit to the disabled, their families and to society," demonstrates "that the provision of rehabilitation services results in substantial savings in both medical and indemnity costs, just as the development of medical care provisions has resulted in savings in indemnity payments."[11] Later on in the report the fact is stressed that:

[10] *Bull. Am. Coll. Surgeons,* pp. 57–58 (January–February 1955).

[11] American Medical Association, "Medical Relations in Workmen's Compensation," December, 1955, pp. 3–4.

The primary obligation of the individual physician is to see that his patient is restored as nearly as possible to the economic and personal effectiveness which he possessed before he was disabled. This requires not only competent and impartial medical care but also that the physician use or recommend the use of other technical skills and resources available, whether in the community or not.[12]

Individual doctors such as Rusk and Kessler had repeatedly emphasized the desirability of incorporating rehabilitation practices into the handling of workmen's compensation cases. The latter, in the 1953 edition of his book, has a chapter dealing with the injured worker in which he refers to a third phase in the evolution of workmen's compensation as being "the restoration of the worker to full earning capacity." Dr. Kessler states further that

Workmen's compensation laws fall short of this goal by failing to include restoration of the worker to his former social and economic position. The monetary benefits provided by them are soon squandered, and the injured man is left without money and in many cases without the physical means to earn a living.[13]

and again in his summarization of the challenges to national action concludes that:

We see then that rehabilitation is different not in technique but in principle. It means team work, as compared to the one-dimensional approach in which the physician, claim adjuster, and industrial commission operate independently without any appreciation of the value of their joined efforts. Each of these agents has much to contribute, but the combined and integrated efforts would yield a greater harvest. How can these ideas be implemented? How can we fulfill the promises implied in the workers' bill of rights? To do so requires primarily a change in attitude, with the emphasis of compensation administration shifting from litigation to rehabilitation.[14]

The impact of President Eisenhower's message to the Congress in January, 1954, on the development of rehabilitation interest has already been outlined in an earlier chapter. In this message, he ably highlighted the aims and interests of the country in relation to the rehabilitation of the injured worker as well as other types of handicapped people. Other executive committees and key individuals in the federal government have endorsed and enlarged on the need. The Task Force on the Handicapped of the Manpower Policy Committee (Office of Defense Mobilization), in its January, 1952 report indicated that "compensation should cover all the constituents of rehabilitation, including prosthetic devices if necessary, as well as income maintenance during the rehabilitation process."[15]   In another portion of the report, it was stated that:

> In all the ramifications of existing state laws, there does not appear to be any clear responsibility on the part of anyone concerned to aid and encourage the individual to return to work as soon as reasonably possible. In fact, while claims are pending, and in any other situation where the degree of demonstrable disability affects the amount of compensation the individual may receive, our compensation machinery often seems to discourage the individual's interest in rehabilitation and return to employment.[16]

Arthur Larson, during his term as Under Secretary of Labor, repeatedly emphasized the need for a complete re-orientation of the basic approach to workmen's compensation insurance and even suggested that the name "workmen's compensation" be changed to "workmen's restoration." His idea was to place the principal emphasis on medical care and rehabilitation as a means to restore an injured worker to full work capacity rather than limiting administrative concern to indemnity benefits. With the help of an advisory committee, he recently prepared a model workmen's compensation act which has been distributed to many of the interested groups for consideration and criticism with the hope that, following constructive revision, it can then be utilized by the several states as a model for improvement of their own laws. This model act stressed the supervision of medical care and the utilization of rehabilitation techniques and facilities.

Educators and research scholars in the several fields of economics, social sciences, and education (particularly vocational education) have recognized and charted the problems. The Somers' book, one of the most definitive works in the field of workmen's compensation, has, as one of its prime focal points, the theme that rehabilitation is manifestly of great significance in the further progress of our system of workmen's compensation. After noting that "rehabilitation is obviously in the interest of both the injured worker and the employer,"[17] the book goes on to point out that:

> Successful orientation toward this new goal will require many difficult legislative and administrative adjustments. In addition to universalizing full medical benefits and providing the necessary facilities for effective

15 Office of Defense Mobilization, Manpower Policy Committee, "Report of the Task Force on the Handicapped," Washington, January 24, 1952, p. 39.
16 Ibid., p. 38.
17 Somers, H. M., and Somers, A. R., op. cit., p. 275.

medical rehabilitation, it will necessitate profound adjustment in the administrative relations of the agencies to the medical and legal professions and the insurance industry.

The strongest potential asset of the compensation program is that it can make possible a cohesive and continuous medical and maintenance program for the injured worker leading to maximum physical adjustment and a return to economic productivity at highest capacity. This is a job of such conspicuous importance that a program which effected it efficiently would be hailed and unchallenged. Workmen's compensation has a unique opportunity to achieve this goal.[18]

The labor unions, who have constituted one of the most outspoken critics of the workmen's compensation system as presently operated, in addition to emphasizing the low level of benefits in comparison to wages and living costs, have consistently maintained that incomplete medical care and inadequate rehabilitation have been the rule rather than the exception. Their firm convictions on the shortcomings of the system in these major areas have resulted in some attempts to establish and operate medical and rehabilitation facilities of their own; the most notable accomplishment in this regard being that of the United Mine Workers. One of the clearest thinkers in the labor field on the subject of workmen's compensation is Jerome Pollack. In his speech before the Medical Care and Industrial Hygiene Sections of the American Public Health Association in October, 1954, he stated that

> . . . rehabilitation is not a recent miracle but the aggregate of means available at any given time for restoring disabled people to optimal physical, mental, social and economic well being. Acceptance of this heroic goal is recent as is the great progress in the effectiveness of rehabilitation. . . . This development was bound to become one of the major goals of the compensation process. . . . But although rehabilitation is essential to a proper compensation system it is not part of workmen's compensation in most states and is not even reasonably well coordinated with compensation.[19]

In his testimony before the Senate Subcommittee on Health of the Committee on Labor and Public Welfare, April 8, 1954, when that subcommittee was considering the President's recommendations on rehabilitation, Walter J. Mason, a member of the national legislative committee of the American Federation of Labor, stated for the record:

> Our first and foremost need is to greatly strengthen the machinery established by States under workmen's compensation laws and to integrate

[18] *Ibid.*, p. 276.
[19] Pollack, J., "Medical Care and Rehabilitation Under Workmen's Compensation—Present Status and Critique," *Public Health*, 45, No. 5, p. 648 (May 1955).

the necessary medical care with vocational training, education, and other means for the industrial rehabilitation of the handicapped.[20]

The significance of all these voices which are now raised in the interest of more effective medical services and rehabilitation in the operation and administration of workmen's compensation laws in the United States lies in the fact that it is more clearly recognized than ever before that rehabilitation must be a major objective of all groups interested in the welfare of the working man.

Two factors, one scientific and the other economic, have been mainly responsible for the awakening of keen interest in rehabilitation as a vital adjunct to the improved handling of serious industrial injuries within the framework of workmen's compensation procedure. One of these is the growth of modern surgical techniques and drug therapy, resulting in greatly increased life expectancy following severe injury or disease; the second is the realization of the staggering costs of prolonged disability in terms of both indemnity and medical under many of the state workmen's compensation laws. At the present time, twenty-seven of the workmen's compensation laws provide weekly payments for as long as the worker is disabled or for life, and thirty-six of the laws provide for the payment of medical benefits for as long as they may be needed or for life. The trend toward including the degenerative conditions, such as heart disease, arthritis and the like, under workmen's compensation, together with the recognized aging of our general as well as our working populations, means greater burdens for industry and insurance in the future. Medical and surgical fees, as well as hospital costs, have greatly increased in the past ten years and there is no significant indication that this trend has ended.

Under many state laws, serious industrial injuries to a young man, such as those involving loss of both arms or legs or spinal cord damage resulting in paralysis of arms or legs, can cost between $200,000 and $400,000 for surgery, prolonged hospitalization, and lifetime nursing care. It can readily be appreciated why industrial management, labor union officials, insurance company executives, legislators and administrators regard with grave concern this steadily increasing burden on American business, on the American public and on the individual American working man. Safety engineering of machines and workers (although it has been a valuable contribution) has not provided the complete solution. The steady trend toward broader interpretation

[20] U. S. Senate Hearings before the Subcommittee on Health of the Committee on Labor and Public Welfare, 83rd Congress, 2nd Session, on the President's Health Recommendations and Related Measures, Washington, April 8, 1954, p. 548.

of the workmen's compensation laws and more liberal benefits prescribed by those laws holds no promise of lowering the over-all costs.

Where then can a solution be found which offers some hope for reduction of the costs of injury and resultant disability to industry and at the same time provides the injured worker with the best of medical attention, reduces his time away from work, and lessens the permanent effects of his injury? Many are now becoming convinced that the answer lies in the direction of a sound rehabilitation program. In order to mitigate the high loss costs of present-day industrial injuries, it is important that seriously injured workers receive the very best that medical skill can provide in diagnosis and surgery, as well as the best of hospital care and rehabilitative therapy. Providing these medical and rehabilitation services in addition to the minimal surgical and hospital benefits which are required by the compensation statutes constitutes an investment in the reduction of disability and the restoration of the seriously handicapped to industry.

Some fifteen years ago, Liberty Mutual Insurance Company, the largest private carrier of workmen's compensation in the United States, undertook a research to see where weaknesses might exist in the treatment and care of workmen's compensation cases and what might be done to shorten disability and to bring about more complete restoration. Examination of many cases of long-term disability disclosed that although the reasons for such disability were multiple, they did form a pattern of causes that could be relieved by some of the new developments in medicine if properly applied. A substantial number of the cases had not made early progress toward recovery, owing to complications in the traumatized part, or to complications of the injury being superimposed on some previously existing bodily ailment. In studying these causes of disability it often seemed evident that errors of diagnosis had been made and intensive diagnostic study needed to be applied earlier in some adequate hospital or clinic facility and that the diagnosis and treatment must apply to the man as a whole as well as the injured part.

The study of serious disability cases revealed a second large group that had progressed well through surgery and surgical healing and had been discharged from the hospital as cured, and yet months or even years later the individuals had not returned to any form of work. Again the causes were multiple, but still they formed a pattern of continued disability due to stiff joints, atrophied muscles, fear of recurrent injury, lack of confidence, or combinations of residual disability superimposed upon some previous ailment.

As a part of the research, projects under way in the United States and Canada for the rehabilitation of seriously injured or handicapped people were also studied. From all of these studies, it was evident that a great deal could be done through a planned process of rehabilitation. Liberty Mutual's management believed that it was not enough to protect the general public and employees of policyholders from injury by reducing hazards and by compensating or settling promptly with those who were injured. A major function of a casualty insurance company is to help reduce lost time and lost abilities by speeding the return to work of injured persons—to return them in proper physical and mental condition so that they may again be useful, self-supporting citizens.

As a result of this company's experience, it is apparent that very material savings in loss cost can be effected by increasingly better medical service and the utilization of improved rehabilitation techniques and facilities. The reduction of temporary disability and permanent loss of function by comprehensive, integrated programs offers a real incentive to all concerned to combine ideas and efforts in behalf of a more practical and more widespread medical handling and rehabilitation of all potentially serious disability cases under workmen's compensation. Other carriers, state funds, and self-insured employers have utilized community rehabilitation services or have experimented with development of their own programs to a lesser extent.

Insurance groups such as the National Association of Mutual Casualty Companies have stressed in recent publications that "through experience with this specialized service, carriers have realized the value of providing the best available medical care and of utilizing the rehabilitation services of public and private facilities."[21] Business and trade associations such as Commerce and Industry Association of New York have sponsored research into back and head injuries and have held symposia on workmen's compensation problems which have clearly demonstrated their understanding of the new significance of rehabilitation as a better answer to the cost of industrial disability.

Legislative and administrative action has recently spurred the machinery of workmen's compensation in the direction of rehabilitation. Twenty states, as well as the Federal Employees' Compensation Act and the Longshoremen and Harbor Workers Act (covering District of Columbia also), Hawaii and Alaska, now include some rehabilitation provisions in their workmen's compensation laws in addition to accepting the provisions of the Federal Vocational Rehabilitation

---

[21] National Association of Mutual Casualty Companies, *The Handicapped Man for the Job—the Job for the Handicapped Man,"* Chicago, 1956, pp. 7–8.

Act.[22] These new provisions include such things as a fund for rehabilitation of the industrially disabled, maintenance allowances during vocational training, etc. A few states such as Massachusetts, Minnesota, and Florida have established boards or committees within the framework of their workmen's compensation commissions with the prime purpose of and responsibility for rehabilitation activities. A number of states have interim committees of the state legislature which are considering revisions of the workmen's compensation laws, particularly with respect to including specific provisions as to rehabilitation. Moreland Act Commissioner Joseph Callahan, in his report to New York Governor Averell Harriman, dated January 28, 1957, in speaking of rehabilitation says that

> A more positive approach to the field, which is the means not only of lowering compensation costs, but also of converting injured workers from welfare recipients to productive, wage-earning, tax-paying individuals, will, therefore, be beneficial to employers, employees and the community.[23]

He stresses in his recommendations that there is need for an advisory committee on rehabilitation, use of board medical forms from physician to insure early referral to rehabilitation procedures, and certain definitive measures relating to placement of rehabilitated workers.

Compensation authorities, insurance carriers, self-insured employers have been slow to recognize the value of utilizing rehabilitation facilities for the reduction of disability in cases involving traumatic injury. Most compensation laws do not yet require that either physical or vocational rehabilitation be provided, and only a few employers and carriers have recognized the advantages of providing such services on a voluntary basis. Most have not wished to venture into the sponsorship or support of rehabilitation centers and only a comparatively few cities in the United States have comprehensive rehabilitation facilities that can accomplish practical results in workmen's compensation cases.

There remains a lot to be done if we are to increase the acceptance and use of rehabilitation services by those involved in the workmen's compensation process. An informal study made by a subcommittee of the President's Committee on the Employment of the Physically Handicapped in 1955 of workmen's compensation cases referred to local rehabilitation centers throughout the United States covered replies received from 51 centers out of 62 contacted. Nineteen indi-

[22] U. S. Chamber of Commerce, *Analysis of Workmen's Compensation Laws,* Washington, January, 1956 edition and January, 1957 supplement, p. 45.

[23] Report of Costs, Operations and Procedures under the Workmen's Compensation Law of the State of New York to governor of the State of New York by the Moreland Act Commissioner Joseph M. Callahan, Albany, January 28, 1957, p. 25.

cated no usable statistics. Thirty-two centers (mostly privately operated) reported that during the year they treated a total of 2211 compensation cases, for an average of 69 cases per center.[24] A survey of the number of workmen's compensation cases treated in centers during 1955 was conducted by the International Association of Industrial Accident Boards and Commissions through questionnaires sent from its Rehabilitation Committee to workmen's compensation agencies in forty-eight states and four territorial jurisdictions. Twenty-one states, three territories, and the District of Columbia reported using rehabilitation centers of some type. Twenty-seven states did not report any use of such rehabilitation facilities. Those states using rehabilitation centers reported a total of over 5,000 workmen's compensation cases treated in rehabilitation centers, with four states (Wisc., Va., Ore., and N. Y.) accounting for over 3,100 cases. The number of individual facilities is not shown.[25]

Regardless of the inaccuracies or omissions in either study, it would seem apparent that nowhere near the true potential of rehabilitation in workmen's compensation cases is being realized by the present use of available services. The National Safety Council figures for the same year of 1955 showed an estimated 75,000 work injuries resulting in permanent impairment.[26] Even if only half that number were cases which would be available for rehabilitation under workmen's compensation, that would mean a yearly potential of 37,500 cases for rehabilitation services. The study figures, at their most optimistic, show only about one-seventh of the total potential and this potential takes no account of the backlog of disabled workmen's compensation cases from former years. The Rehabilitation Committee of I.A.I.A.B.C. concluded that "of the twenty-one states operating or utilizing rehabilitation centers not more than two or three states use the centers for as many as 20 per cent of the injured workers off work over 90 days."[27]

Within the next few years there will be marked changes in the application of rehabilitation to workmen's compensation cases. Mandatory provisions in state acts, requiring the employer or carrier to provide rehabilitation in the same way as routine medical care, seem destined to become universal. Reports from carriers and employers to the industrial accident boards or commissions, together with similar

[24] Unpublished data in study by Compensation Benefits Committee of President's Committee on the Employment of the Physically Handicapped, 1956.

[25] U. S. Bureau of Labor Standards, Bulletin No. 192, *op. cit.*, pp. 206–207, 221.

[26] National Safety Council, *Accident Facts—1956 Edition*, Chicago, 1956, p. 13.

[27] U. S. Bureau of Labor Standards, Bulletin No. 192, *op. cit.*, p. 209.

reports from physicians, will provide the machinery for review by administrative bodies as to discovery and early referral of cases for rehabilitation, follow-up, vocational training where needed, and final job placement. Activities of state workmen's compensation authorities and those of vocational rehabilitation divisions, employment security divisions, and public health departments will be more closely coordinated. Some states may experiment with state-operated rehabilitation centers, as Rhode Island, Washington, and Virginia have already done, with the idea of processing workmen's compensation cases directly into such facilities, similar to the Canadian method of operation. Most, however, will probably attempt to expand the use of private facilities with a clear recognition of what is needed to handle the compensation case, as compared with the long-term chronic disability. With the passage of time, there will be a rapid increase in the understanding of administrators, insurance people, industrial executives, and physicians in respect to the role which rehabilitation can play in effecting a more complete and satisfactory recovery for the victim of industrial injury or disease. With this understanding will come an increasing demand upon existing rehabilitation services everywhere.

The Social Security Act of 1935 established two programs of benefits to aged persons. One was the Old Age and Survivors Insurance (OASI), or Social Security, and the other was Old Age Assistance. The former was designed to provide a monthly income to those who would retire in the future from covered occupations; the latter was to provide financial assistance to those already in retirement. OASI is strictly a federal program, whereas Old Age Assistance is a federal–state grant-in-aid arrangement. Both programs have established statutory rights to benefits on the part of individual beneficiaries which are subject to change by Congress at any time. The Old Age Assistance program applicant must undergo a financial means test; OASI has no such requisite. In considering the possible effect of rehabilitation on the program, it will be well to limit the discussion to the OASI.

Social Security, since its inception, has been geared to the protection of the working man; i.e., the deduction or withholding of contributions for payment into the federal trust fund has been clearly related to amount of wages earned and time worked. Amendments to the original act have extended coverage to certain self-employed groups, civil service personnel, etc., have increased amounts of contributions, and have made some changes in the ages at which benefits are payable to certain groups of people.

As of the beginning of 1956 there were some 70,000,000 workers covered, and this total was substantially increased by the later 1956 amendments extending coverage to additional persons.[28]   The total number of people in the United States in 1955 over the age of 65 was estimated as just over 14,000,000.[29]   Of this number, 6,500,000 were receiving OASI benefits and another 2,500,000 were receiving Old Age Assistance benefits.[30]   To give some idea of the import of this program for the future, it is estimated that, by the year 2000, there will be about 28 million persons over age 65 and they will represent between 10 and 13% of the total population.   This could mean a federal trust fund in the neighborhood of 100 billions of dollars as against the present twenty-two billion fund.[31]

Since the introduction of social security legislation in the United States, there has been agitation to include some kind of cash disability insurance.   Such a program would be patterned upon the practice in some Europeon countries and, indeed, the disability benefits payable in this country under the Railroad Retirement Act and other government pension plans.   The basic concept in connection with such proposals is that some form of income maintenance is necessary for persons who are unable to work by reason of disability.   The 1954 Amendments to the Social Security Act were the opening wedge to practical acceptance of the cash disability principle.   Those amendments provided for a so-called "disability freeze" or "maintenance of benefits" program.   In the case of workers on jobs covered by the OASI who became unemployed by reason of disability their benefit rights would be preserved.   In other words, the individual earning record would be "frozen" during the period of disability instead of operating to reduce the amount of future benefits by reason of no reporting of earnings during the disability period.   These amendments did not provide any benefits to workers during the period of disability but preserved their rights to benefits payable at age 65.

In the 1956 Amendments to the Social Security Act the Congress went the rest of the way along the road to the actual establishment of a disability cash benefit.   The new law provided that full Social Security benefits be paid to workers age 50 or over who have been in covered employment and who have become totally and permanently disabled.   As presently constituted, the law sets forth the following

[28] N. Y. World-Telegram and The Sun, *World Almanac and Book of Facts,* 72nd issue, New York, 1957, pp. 664–669.

[29] U. S. Chamber of Commerce, *American Economic Security,* July–August, 1956, Washington, p. 16.

[30] *Ibid.,* p. 15.

[31] *Ibid.,* p. 16.

eligibility requirements for both the "disability freeze" and the disability insurance payments at age 50:

1. 5 years of work in the 10 years before the established beginning date of the disability, and 1½ years of work in the 3 years before that date.

2. Physical or mental disability of such severity that the beneficiary is unable to engage in any substantial work and expectation that the disability will continue indefinitely. Temporary disability or partial disability ineligible. Medical evidence of condition and duration of disability required.

3. Waiting period of six months; i.e., requirement of disability for six months before "freeze" effected or benefits payable.

4. Acceptance of rehabilitation services from state vocational rehabilitation agency. Benefits may be withheld if offered rehabilitation services are refused without "good cause."[32]

The first cash disability benefits will be paid in July, 1957, as provided in the enabling legislation. It is estimated that about 250,000 people will become immediately eligible. There is also a provision for insurance benefits for disabled children, age 18 or over, if such children have been disabled before reaching age 18, are unmarried, and are either dependent on parent entitled to OASI benefits or were dependent on a parent who died after 1939 and who was insured for OASI benefits at the time of death. Children's benefits started in January, 1957.[33]

It has been estimated that the disability benefits program will cost 250 million the first year and by 1975 the cost will have risen to nearly one billion dollars.[34] The passage of the 1956 amendments was preceded by a bitter legislative battle, with medical and business groups opposing the measure and labor and social welfare groups supporting it. Some of the argument lay in the feasibility of the whole idea of a government cash disability benefits program, its difficulty of administration and its vulnerability to abuse, in the danger of nationalization of medical care and socialization of medical practice, and in the alleged prohibitive cost of any such plan. Interestingly enough, however, the principal argument related to whether the availability of cash benefits undermines or deters the rehabilitation of handicapped

---

[32] *Ibid.,* pp. 18–19.

[33] U. S. Dept. of Health, Education and Welfare, Social Security Administration, "The Rights of Disabled People under the Social Security Law as amended in 1956," OASI-1956-4, Washington, August, 1956.

[34] U. S. Chamber of Commerce, *American Economic Security, op. cit.*

persons. The battle of rehabilitation versus pensions has not yet been resolved despite the passage of the 1956 legislation. There are those who contend that official disability determinations under the law and cash benefits to continue during such disability would remove all incentive for recovery or possible employment. Others argue just as vehemently that entitlement to benefits not determinable by a financial means test (not a relief or public assistance type of payment) maintains the morale and will to work of the disabled individual and actually improves his chance to become rehabilitated.

It is true, of course, that the Congress recognized the validity of the contentions regarding rehabilitation in its provision for the referral of both "disability freeze" and cash disability benefit cases to the state vocational rehabilitation divisions. However, the rules and regulations for determination of "disability" are still somewhat vague and subject to interpretation by physician, patient, and administering officials. The "good cause" for refusal of rehabilitation services is compromise language and, again, is open to varying and confusing definition. It is interesting that neither the House nor Senate committees considering this legislation were apparently able to devise any "work test" which would be satisfactory as an authority for the suspension of benefits. It has been interpreted already that a person earning under a rehabilitation program, for instance in a sheltered workshop, will be considered as able to engage in substantial gainful employment, but not until those earnings have continued for one year.

The important element in the whole discussion over the national program of cash disability benefits and their relation to the development of rehabilitation is not so much what the program is at the moment but rather its import for the future. The door has now been opened for later Congressional action to revise and extend the provisions of the Social Security Act as far as disability benefits are concerned. It is interesting to note that the new instructional pamphlets issued by the Department of Health, Education and Welfare refer to the program as "disability insurance payments."[35] There is an aura of permanency, entitlement, and administration continuity to that phrase. If later Congressional amendments should lower the age of eligibility for disability benefits, increase the amount, or remove the restrictive interpretation on the severity and duration of disability, there will be, in truth, a national pension plan for disabled persons. This would raise grave questions as to rehabilitation continuing to be an effective instrument in our national planning for the ill and injured. John H. Miller has pointed out one possible effect:

[35] "The Rights of Disabled People under the Social Security Law as amended in 1956," op. cit.

Much progress has been made in encouraging employers in the employment of the handicapped. If the government, through OASI benefits, should assume primary responsibility for maintenance of the disabled, it seems likely that many employers would consider themselves to be relieved from any social or community responsibility to workers who become disabled or who slow down as they approach retirement age. As a result, many handicapped or aged workers might be deprived of an opportunity to remain self-supporting until normal retirement.[36]

On the other hand, E. B. Whitten has interpreted the trend in a somewhat different way:

We fully believe that nearly all handicapped people prefer to earn their livelihood rather than be dependent upon pensions, even though they have contributed to the fund that makes the pension possible. We believe they will respond to the opportunity to be rehabilitated, when such is explained and made available to them. The relatively small sum spent on careful screening and professional evaluation of disability and rehabilitation potential will result in a saving to the trust fund and make an important contribution to human dignity and social usefulness. In our judgment, the manner in which this program is administered in the years immediately ahead may very well determine whether this country, in the long run, will turn to rehabilitation or to cash benefits as the major solution to the problems of disability.[37]

Public assistance laws, commonly referred to as "welfare" or "relief" programs, function at federal, state, and local levels. Historically, the first responsibility for medical care of needy people has been assumed by the local community. From community to community there have been great differences in both the quantity and quality of services as well as the availability of the services to needy persons. For many years, doctors, hospitals, and other medical services rendered care to the indigent without charge as a public service or community responsibility. During the 1930's, when the economic depression was rampant, the Federal Emergency Relief Administration started a fee-for-service program which became a pattern for steady enlargement of the payment by federal, state and local government agencies for medical care of the needy. Payments were usually fixed and not at the private care level, but at least there was a clear recognition of the responsibility of public assistance for support of medically indigent care programs as against complete dependence of the needy individual upon free service. At the same time, the doctor, hospital, or other medical service could reasonably expect some financial return for

---

[36] Miller, J. H., "Meeting the Needs of the Disabled Worker," *Am. Economic Security*, p. 17 (Sept.–Nov. 1955), U. S. Chamber of Commerce, Washington.

[37] Whitten, E. B., "Cash Benefits for the Handicapped," *J. Rehabilitation*, p. 28 (Sept.–Oct. 1956).

the care of those in the community who were less fortunate financially.

The Social Security Act of 1935 authorized the federal government to make grants to the states to help them finance public assistance in three areas—those dealing with old age assistance, aid to the blind, and aid to dependent children. However, there was no specific provision for medical care of these groups except in the allowance for medical requirements in determining the total needs of the person applying for assistance, upon which the cash payment to the needy person would be based. In the 1950 amendments to the Social Security Act, definite provision was made for so-called "vendor" payments; i.e., payments directly to doctor, clinic, hospital, or other medical service in connection with medical care of a person on public assistance. States were encouraged to establish a "pooled fund" out of which these expenses would be paid and the federal government shared in the expense. A new category was added to the previous three which were subject to federal assistance, that being the aid to the permanently and totally disabled, between the ages of 16 and 65 (excluding the blind). Also included was a provision for grants to persons residing in public medical institutions. All of the indicated legislation developed new resources for the financing of medical care programs by the state and local public welfare agencies.

Present-day programs at the community level vary widely from the comprehensive pattern involving a variety of medical services, including rehabilitation, to the sharply limited type with little more than emergency hospital and doctor care. Broad criticism has been leveled at inadequacy of service, lack of continuity, lack of professional supervision, chronic fund shortages, and the barrier of the means test. There has been argument for bringing the public health agencies into the administration of medical care to the needy. Some areas have experimented in development of joint plans with local medical societies, providing for flat monthly fees to the medical society for each recipient of public assistance with all care to be provided under a plan worked out by the society. There is probably a real need for revision of certain applications of the means test and integration of public assistance medical care programs with voluntary or governmental pre-paid medical plans.

The total cost of public assistance programs in the United States in 1955 was nearly $2,757,000,000, of which only $214,288,000, or less than 8%, was paid out in the general assistance programs and the balance in the federally aided programs.[38] More than 3 million peo-

38 U. S. Dept. of Commerce, *op. cit.*, p. 275.

ple were recipients of the various types of public assistance. No valid figures are available on the amounts expended in vendor payments for medical care.

The relationship of disability to dependency upon public assistance and the possibilities of rehabilitation in reducing both disability and dependency have intrigued many who have studied the problem. It is known that in 1954 for example, of all the persons rehabilitated through the public programs 20% were receiving some form of public assistance at the time they applied for rehabilitation services or at some time during their rehabilitation.[39] At the same time, it is evident from a study made in 1951 by the Bureau of Public Assistance of the Social Security Administration of 13,200 persons receiving aid to the permanently and totally disabled that only 10% were known by or referred to the state vocational rehabilitation division.[40] There obviously exists a huge and untapped segment of rehabilitation potential on the public assistance rolls. There is great need for coordination of effort between public agencies, for integration with private agency operations, and for understanding and perceptive use of medical and rehabilitation facilities or programs, if any perceptible inroads are to be made on the backlog of such cases in any community.

Mandatory, non-occupational disability insurance is a newcomer in the field of social laws. Such laws are now in operation in one federal jurisdiction and four states. They provide for payment of cash benefits in case of loss of income due to nonoccupational sickness or disability. The federal Railroad Retirement Act covers railroad employees only and the benefits are comprised of age annuities, permanent and total disability annuities, and occupational disability annuities, as well as pension and spouse benefit provisions. The state programs began in Rhode Island in 1942, followed by California in 1946, New Jersey in 1948 and New York in 1949. Both Rhode Island and California plans provide for employee contributions only with the former operating a state fund for payment of benefits and the latter having optional arrangement for employers to subscribe to state fund or make arrangements with private carrier. The New Jersey law requires employer contribution as well as that by employees, permits election of private insurance plan or self-insurance, and bases benefits on recent wage record of the employee. The New York plan is very similar to New Jersey except that it permits other types of plans

[39] U. S. Dept. of Health, Education and Welfare, Reprint from Annual Report, Section on Office of Vocational Rehabilitation, Washington, 1954, p. 237.

[40] U. S. Dept. of Health, Education and Welfare, "Characteristics of Recipients of Aid to the Permanently and Totally Disabled," Washington, 1951.

than the statutory one and it has tied the administration of the law into the Workmen's Compensation Act.

In general, these laws are an enforcement of compulsory group disability insurance. They are essentially income maintenance programs with benefits ranging from $10 minimum to $35 maximum weekly payments, the duration of payment period limited to 26 weeks. No particular provision is made for medical care but, since three of the state laws permit the employer to place the insurance with private carriers or to self-insure, this means that selected plans may very well be more extensive than the statutory limitations, not only as to disability benefits but also as to inclusion of medical and surgical coverages. This kind of legislation is clearly indicative of the trend toward public and private concern as to broad planning for prepaid disability insurance which will cover income loss and also medical care costs. Rehabilitation from the effects of illness or non-occupational injury would become a factor only if the plan selected by the employer were broad enough to include medical benefits which would provide an opportunity to apply rehabilitation services. More will be mentioned about this subject in the chapter on health insurance.

Nothing has been said in this chapter about unemployment insurance, which constitutes the other big category in what Arthur Larson calls "Income Insurance." The reason for this omission lies in the fact that those laws, which began in Wisconsin in 1931 and are now in force in every state, the District of Columbia, Alaska, and Hawaii, bear no direct relationship to rehabilitation possibilities. The laws are designed to provide cash benefits for limited periods of non-employment, entirely unrelated to disability. They make no provision for medical care.

Social laws and insurance of the kinds described have been the most marked social and economic trend of the twentieth century. A concerted attack has been mounted on each of these progressive measures, as they have come before the Congress or the state legislatures, by those who believe that all these programs are moves toward socialism and "the welfare state." Most thoughtful people, however, now realize that social insurance is here to stay and that we had better get on with the job of making it effective for our population in the areas of real need. It may reasonably be argued that social insurance is the alternative to vast expenditures for public assistance. In our community programs of public assistance there is probably a need for more effort in the direction of rehabilitating persons to productive employment. It is not only possible but also probable that the years ahead of us will see a further extension of public disability programs, through revisions of laws and new insurance provisions, to a point where there will be a meshing of the many disparate federal–state programs with the private medical plans and disability insurance for the purpose of meeting the need for all classes of people, but particularly of those who are aged or disabled. It is the job of those dedicated to rehabilitation to make its philosophy and practice an integral part of national and local planning; to remove a handicap rather than reward it.

CHAPTER 17

Health Insurance
and Medical
Care Plans

ONE OF THE PHENOMENAL DEVELOPMENTS IN the twentieth century United States has been the rapid growth of a comprehensive system for the financing of health care. Three of the major components of this system have been (1) the evolution of voluntary health insurance, through both group and individual coverages; (2) the organization of the health and welfare plans of the labor unions; and (3) the government plans for medical care. Fifteen years ago, voluntary health insurance was comparatively unknown to the majority of American people; at that same time, labor unions were more concerned with pay increases, working conditions, and preferential legislation than with the "fringe benefits," insurance coverages, and union welfare planning of today. The government was concerned with little other than the medical care of veterans.

Terminology in the mushrooming voluntary health insurance field has often been confusing. We hear of "pre-paid medical plans," "group accident and health insurance," "hospital pre-payment plans," "sickness insurance," "medical and surgical plans," "catastrophe coverage," and the like. This confusion has come about largely through the evolution in the many different types of coverages and the fact that some original insurance plans have been combined or improved, as the result of the new demands for more complete protection. Probably the best over-all term for the whole field is voluntary health insurance; the contrast with the government plans is obvious from the word "voluntary" and the words "health insurance" are broad enough to include all the manifold types of coverage which are characterized by individual terminology.

In order to fully appreciate the magnitude and scope of health insurance protection, and to later consider its implication for those in the rehabilitation field, it would be well to consider the dramatic figures on present coverage in this type of insurance. An estimated 118,000,000 persons, as of May, 1957, were protected against hospital expenses (the most popular form of health insurance), 103,000,000 were covered for surgical expenses, 67,000,000 had policies covering regular medical care expenses, and 10,000,000 were insured against major medical expense.[1] Although there is obviously some overlapping and duplication of coverages involving the same person, the total picture means essentially that over 70% of the civilian population of the United States is today protected from the expense of medical care by some form of voluntary health coverage. In addition, nearly two-thirds of all gainfully employed civilians in the country participate in some plan of insurance or other fund which protects them against loss of income during a period of disability.[2] Considering both the premiums charged by insurance companies and the income from subscriptions of the Blue Cross–Blue Shield or other organized hospital and medical-surgical plans, the total payments for health insurance in the year 1956 were almost five billion dollars.[3] This figure includes the premium on loss of income coverages as well as the medical care coverages. Just under three billion dollars were paid out in benefits for hospital, surgical, and medical care during the same year.[1] In the year 1957, it is estimated that this payment figure will go over the three billion mark, or a rate of almost ten million dollars a day. Compared with the year 1941, the percentage increase in the various categories of health insurance is almost fantastic; hospital 600%, surgical 1300%, general medical 1700%, and major medical (only introduced in 1949) has multiplied 50 times.[2] Indeed a convincing demonstration of the importance which the American public has placed upon individual and group protection against the cost of illness and injury.

The contributing factors in this tremendous growth of health insurance have been (1) increasing complexity and cost of medical care;

---

[1] Press Release on findings of 11th annual survey of Health Insurance Council on Extent of Voluntary Health Insurance Coverage in U. S., May 27, 1957, New York.

[2] Public Interest Advertisement of Health Insurance Association of America—April, 1957 issues of *Harper's Magazine* and *Atlantic*.

[3] *Newsletter*, Health Insurance Association of America, No. 18-57, May 3, 1957, Chicago.

(2) public interest in protection against unexpected personal and family expenses, particularly income loss and medical expense, involved in sickness or injury; (3) business interest in health plans as a means of developing better employer–employee relationships; (4) labor union use of health plans and insurance as "fringe benefits" and a desirable bargaining objective; (5) the impact of veterans' and other government plans for health services and benefits; (6) interest and support of the medical profession for pre-paid medical plans on a private basis; and (7) the ability of the insurance companies to devise and offer for sale new and broader forms of health insurance protection.

In general, health insurance may be divided into two categories; the income loss or disability payment insurance and the hospitalization, surgical, or medical care insurance. It should be obvious that the first pays cash benefits, usually in weekly amounts, for loss of income during disability due to sickness or injury. The second provides stipulated benefits, in varying amounts and for limited periods, toward the payment of all or some of the bills rendered for hospital, surgical or general medical care. Some types of health insurance policies provide both kinds of benefits in the same policy. The health insurance policies may be written on either a group or individual basis, and may cover both policyholder and his dependents.

More specific breakdown of health insurance coverages would be as follows:

1. Hospital expense insurance—room, board and ancillary charges.
2. Surgical expense insurance—fees for operations.
3. General medical expense insurance—doctor's care at hospital, office, home.
4. Major medical expense insurance—serious and prolonged expense of major illness or injury, in excess of those covered by other health insurance.
5. Loss of income insurance—weekly benefit in stated cash amount.

The earliest form of accident and health insurance was that written by commercial insurance companies about 1850 to cover travel accidents; usually a stated cash sum for bodily injury which disabled the policyholder more than a stipulated period. In 1863 one carrier was empowered to issue policies protecting against accidents generally, not merely those incurred while traveling. By 1890, the accident insurance companies began to move into the sickness field, at first protecting only against a limited list of serious illnesses. Group accident and health insurance, as an extension of group life coverages, began in

1919 and opened the door to a lower premium cost for health coverages. Both the hospital and surgical expense types of coverage grew out of the original loss-of-income coverages and by the 'thirties were evolving into separate forms of protection. Major medical expense protection developed in 1949 as the newest and fastest growing form of health insurance.

As of the year 1956, of the total amounts paid for health insurance, close to two-thirds went to insurance companies and the balance to the Blue Cross–Blue Shield plans. The differences between these two major providers of health insurance protection lie in the methods of payment and the nature of the organization. Insurance company policies ordinarily provide for payment of benefits to the policyholder or insured person while the Blue Cross–Blue Shield plans provide for payment to the persons or institutions who provide the medical service, as for instance, the doctor or hospital. The insurance companies are commercial organizations operating for a profit and the Blue Cross–Blue Shield plans are nonprofit in character. The commercial companies have ventured into all the fields of health insurance coverage and have been especially concerned with the development of the major medical expense coverage, while the Blue Cross–Blue Shield plans have limited their operations pretty much to the hospital, surgical, and general medical expense categories.

In addition to the startling growth in amount and extent of health insurance coverages, the most significant developments in the field have been the steady broadening of benefits payable and a rising concept of health security rather than merely payment for specific accident or illness. In the earlier days of individual or group health and accident protection, the income loss or disability benefits were often limited to 13 weeks or 26 weeks, medical benefits to small amounts for long lists of specific surgical or medical care procedures, with over-all limits frequently not in excess of $500. The trend at present is toward two-year maximums on hospital care and much more realistic fee schedules on surgical and medical care procedures are in the offing. The major medical expense insurance policies are a big step toward insuring the risk of serious illness or accident and severe disability in the average family. Limits on benefits in such policies may run to $5,000, $10,000, and even larger amounts. This kind of coverage has been made possible through the application of the principles of "deductibles" (specific amounts such as $50 or $100 which the policyholder will assume himself or cover through other insurance plans) and "co-insurance" (a means of limiting the expense which the insurance company will assume and expecting the policyholder or insured person to pay a percentage of the cost of medical care, often a 75-25% ratio). These limiting factors on major medical expense payments can lead toward more adequate coverage of substantial medical expense at a rate that the majority of people can afford.

The rising concept of health security rather than payment only for specific illness or accident is a new approach to insurance coverages. In the past, health insurance has been visualized as primarily an attempt to provide protection against income lost and medical bills paid by reason of actual disability from illness or accident. The present plans and coverages are including more of the kind of medical care which is not the result of acute illness or injury but the preventive and curative care which, because it is soundly recommended and needed from a long-range point of view, may well contribute to better health and less chance for future sickness or accident. This is an area in which insurance carriers, private plans, physicians, and hospitals have grave questions. It could be subject to open abuse but it may offer even greater opportunities for constructive health planning and better long-range medical care for all except the medically indigent, who must still be cared for under public welfare or private charity programs.

The labor unions have played a very significant role in the progressive development of health insurance as well as in the organization of union or other health and medical welfare plans and services. In the year 1955, employer contributions to social insurance and related programs were almost seven billion dollars. Employee contributions were more than five billion. Private pension and welfare plans were financed by industry to the tune of over five billions.[4] Many of the gains in these areas have been made by the unions in collective bargaining negotiations, sometimes as the result of foregoing wage increases in order to obtain increases in these "fringe benefits."

Some unions, notably the United Mine Workers, have directly sponsored, organized and operated welfare or health plans which are geared to pay for or even to directly provide medical and rehabilitation services. These plans, for the most part, are not insurance plans comparable to the commercial or Blue Cross–Blue Shield protection but are more in the nature of "service benefit" plans which provide hospital, surgical, and medical care in institutions or by doctors directly supported or even under the ownership and employment of the union organization. The United Mine Workers, for instance, has operated

4 Pollack, J., "Responsibility for Rehabilitation," *Best's Insurance News*, fire and casualty edition, **58**, No. 2, p. 22 (June 1957).

its own health and welfare fund, into which the mine owners pay an agreed amount per ton of coal produced, which has not only provided excellent medical and rehabilitation services on a purchased basis but has also enabled the union to build, equip, and staff its own series of hospitals in the coal-mining country. The International Longshoremen's Association has recently opened its own medical center in Brooklyn, N. Y.

The third major component of the system for financing medical care is the government medical care plans. In addition to the "disability freeze" provision and the amendments to the Social Security Act calling for benefit payments at age 50 to those incapacitated by physical or mental disability, both of which make allowance for rehabilitation activity, the principal government medical care plans are those relating to members of the armed forces, veterans, and the "medicare" plan for dependents of those in the armed forces. In the military and veterans hospitals, comprehensive rehabilitation programs are well integrated into the medical care program. Liaison is maintained with community services which may be utilized when the service man or veteran returns to his home town. Veterans' Administration medical care is available for service-connected disabilities at any time and for nonservice connected disabilities under certain financial means limitations.

The so-called "Medicare" plan for dependents of those in the armed forces is the result of legislation (Public Law 569 of the 84th Congress) which was signed into law by the President on June 7, 1956, and put into effect December 7, of that year.

The basis for the Dependents' Medical Care Act is the provision of medical care to the dependents of those serving in the armed forces through the use of civilian medical care facilities under circumstances in which military facilities are not reasonably available. The state medical societies and hospital associations are asked by the federal government to select an agency to administer the plan in each state. This agency may be an insurance company, an organized health and medical care plan such as Blue Cross–Blue Shield, or a medical society itself in some instances. The dependents have free choice between civilian medical facilities and military medical facilities, except where such dependents reside with the serviceman and the Secretary of the particular branch of the service has restricted dependent medical care to the military facility. Even such a restriction does not apply in an emergency involving accident or illness requiring immediate treatment at the nearest available facility. Dependents are furnished with an authorization and identification card and the hospitals or physicians rendering service report on a form provided for that purpose to the agency administering the state plan.

The medical, surgical, and hospitalization services provided under the "Medicare" program may be rendered for a wide range of *acute* medical and surgical conditions which result from either injury or illness. Complete maternity care is covered. No treatment for chronic disease and nervous or mental disorders (except for acute, emergency complication) is included. No provision is made for medical care at home (except under a few particular and limited conditions) or in a nursing home. Drugs, medical supplies, and ambulance charges are not covered, except under special circumstances. The program is designed primarily for in-patient hospital care and makes provision for out-patient care only under very limited circumstances; mostly for initial treatment of bodily injury and certain pre-operative or post-operative and diagnostic tests, including pre- and post-natal care. Elective medical and surgical procedures requested by the patient but not medically indicated are ruled out under the plans.

Hospital and physician charges for medical care are governed as to amount by agreements negotiated in each state between the federal government and the state hospital associations or state medical societies. The agreements establish an agreed basis for daily hospital room charges and ancillary hospital charges as well as for specific surgical procedures, diagnostic tests, per-visit doctor charges, and the like. These charge agreements may vary from state to state.

Bills for care are rendered by hospital or doctor to the administering agent for the state plan and direct payment is made by that agent to the provider of the medical service. The agent is then periodically reimbursed by the federal government on the basis of a prescribed formula. In connection with the limited out-patient services and procedures permitted under the program, and also in connection with allowable hospitalization, the dependent patient must pay a certain minimal amount himself, as a deductible provision of the plan.

Legislation now before the Congress would provide a comprehensive plan of health insurance for federal civilian employees and their families. The proposed plan would provide basic and major medical coverage; the government would pay one-third of the premium cost. Employees would select any locally available group health insurance or plan meeting minimum standards set up in the law. New York state is considering similar legislation for its state employees.

Little has been understood and still less said about the possibilities of rehabilitation in connection with health insurance and organized medical plans. This has been true in the past because of the limited amounts available in the various categories under most policies and plans. When a group plan or policy provided only twenty-six weeks of disability payments and only $500 maximum medical expense, there was nothing left for rehabilitation purposes by the time the patient recovered from surgery and was ready to leave the hospital. However, with the broadened benefits emerging today in the health insurance field, and particularly with the great increase in major medical expense coverage, there should be an ever greater opportunity to provide and pay for rehabilitation services.

At this time, as far as insurance coverages are concerned, it is evident that there is no real opportunity to provide rehabilitation services under the standard group hospital, surgical, and general medical care insurance policies. The policy language and the benefit limitations are too restrictive. There may be a change in this regard in the future for this type of policy, although it seems likely that there will be more of a trend toward the combination of the group and individual hospital, surgical, and regular medical care coverages with the new major medical expense protection. Under the present major medical policies, there is ample opportunity to provide rehabilitation services, of a medical nature, under the "therapeutic service and supply" section of the policy and listed benefits. This could include services rendered by a rehabilitation department in a general hospital, a rehabilitation center, evaluation and follow-up by physicians in this area, etc. If the insurance carrier wishes to recommend, or if the physician prescribes, rehabilitation, it can be properly provided under this type of policy. A distinction must be made, however, in that this would apply only to medical rehabilitation—vocational training, testing, and placement would not be included under the present policy language. One carrier has already experimented with the writing of a special provision in such a policy that would provide vocational rehabilitation with a prescribed maximum expenditure for this purpose. This might well be a pattern for extension of the idea into an operating program of both medical and vocational rehabilitation services under the major medical coverages. It is quite probable that future policies, both group and individual, in the health insurance field will include the word "rehabilitation" as a specific part of the over-all medical care provided by such policies.

Jerome Pollack has concluded that

> In addition, health insurance should be made to share the burden of medical rehabilitation means as far as possible. As the medical costs of rehabilitation exceed the means of most people with extended or major disability, the only alternative to meeting much of the cost through tax-

supported programs is through group efforts to share these costs and pay for them in advance by people when they are well.[5]

As we move steadily into an era of pre-paid planning for medical care, the extension of insurance and other voluntary plans to cover long-term and major illness seems a sound aim. An integral part of these advances ought to be a specific attempt to include payment for rehabilitation services in the extended coverages. Such attempt, however, must be realistic in its understanding of the vital importance of early rehabilitation activity. Limiting language or practice which would defer payments for rehabilitative care until one year, eighteen months, or two years after onset of illness or disability would defeat the whole purpose of rehabilitation. A way must be found to include not only medical but vocational rehabilitation, to provide out-patient and home care in the various rehabilitation processes and services. Loss of income or disability insurance should be alerted to the potential of rehabilitation; private insurance and other organized plans must take into consideration and complement the public programs in this area.

Those who plan, operate, or are interested in rehabilitation programs, services, or facilities in their respective communities would do well to learn something of the character and scope of health insurance and organized medical care plans, the benefits provided, the operating policies, and the changes which have characterized this facet of the medical care picture in recent years. Their understanding and practical assistance to physicians, insurers, agency personnel, and covered patients may contribute directly to the incorporation of rehabilitation into the medical care planning and insurance administration during the years ahead.

[5] *Ibid.*, pp. 23–24.

CHAPTER 18

Economic Values
of Rehabilitation

THE HUMANITARIAN AND SOCIAL VALUES OF rehabilitation are obvious; the economic values are less well understood yet no less tangible. There are at least four valid methods by which the economic factors in the rehabilitation process can be measured. One relates to the more efficient manpower utilization made possible by both habilitation and rehabilitation. The second deals with the economic gains in restoring workers to earning power. The third stresses the tax savings made by removal from public assistance rolls, and the fourth concerns the reduction of the cost of disability.

One of the great spurs to rehabilitation and the employment of the handicapped was the acute shortage of workers for the industrial production lines of World War II. The demand for help, coupled with the advances in rehabilitation techniques, resulted in a substantially greater number of handicapped persons being absorbed by industry. As a nation, we learned that we could not afford the extravagance of an unused segment of our work force, many of whom were suffering from a remediable disability. The Baruch Committee estimated that during the war 83% of the nation's industries employed handicapped workers, presumably of varying types and in varying numbers.[1] With the end of the war, the return of millions of veterans, the steady increase of our population, and the mechanization of our industrial processes has this need for manpower ceased to be an influencing factor in our national rehabilitation picture?

[1] Baruch Committee on Physical Medicine, "Report on a Community Rehabilitation Service and Center," New York, 1945, p. 5.

Quite the contrary; the expanding economy, the rising standard of living, the continued diversification and specialization in industry, the continued alert defense effort have all contributed to a progressively greater need for efficient use of our maximum labor force. In 1956, private business had plans to invest about 35 billion dollars in new plants and equipment.[2]   In the year 1955 around 55 billion dollars was spent on new construction of all kinds, residential, commercial, and institutional.[3]   Individual business concerns are planning for expansion anywhere from 4 to 25 years ahead.   All of these plans must take into account not only the materials, transportation, and markets but also the availability of manpower.

In 1956, the Bureau of the Census indicated that the total labor force of the nation (14 years of age and over), including those in the armed forces, amounted to approximately 69 million.[4]   The Bureau of Labor Standards has estimated that by 1965 the number will be around 77 million.[5]   There is going to be an influx of young workers (the beginnings of the effect of the high birth rates during the war), the middle age group will be static, there may be a decline in the numbers of older workers, particularly those over 65.   Women workers have increased; three men for every woman in 1940, two for one by 1965.[6]

The tremendous production of goods and the even greater demand for those goods makes it evident that there is going to be a continued need for workers of all kinds.   But there is clear evidence of a change in the character and emphasis of our work force.   With no appreciable fanfare, 1956 marked a milestone in the distribution of the labor force.   In that year, the steady growth of our economy had accomplished more than a doubling of the number of workers in the service industries and, for the first time in our nation's history, the number employed in service businesses (utilities, banks, insurance, government work, retail stores, etc.) exceeded those working in the productive industries (factories, farms, mines, fisheries, etc.).

Along with this trend, we have witnessed the rapid development of more complex machines and processes—automation.   Earlier in

---

[2] U. S. Dept. of Commerce, Bureau of the Census, *Statistical Abstract of the U. S.*, 1956, 77th Annual Edition, Washington, 1956, p. 498.

[3] *Ibid.*, p. 757.

[4] *Ibid.*, p. 197.

[5] Clague, E., "Workers—Our greatest Natural Resource," article in *Am. Economic Security*, **XIII**, No. 3, p. 7, published by U. S. Chamber of Commerce, Washington, May–June, 1956.

[6] *Ibid.*, pp. 9–10.

the century there was much furor over "labor-saving devices," with the positive assertion that they were going to put everyone out of work. Today, the trend toward "automation" is regarded somewhat more calmly. There is little likelihood that increased mechanization, electronic computation, and similar technological advances will result in less need for manpower. On the contrary, it may require more help in the long run.

However, the true significance of the changes now taking place in business and industry lies in the kind of worker who will be required in the future. Both the phenomenal growth of the service businesses and the automation of the industrial processing routines mean that the demand for the skilled worker, the technician, and the well-trained employee will steadily increase. The present generation of young children may well live to see the day when "laboring work" and the "common laborer" are a thing of the past. Unskilled work and untrained workers will be obsolete. Work days and work weeks will be shorter, more shifts of workers putting in less actual time and using much more efficient methods and machines will produce even more goods and services than is now the case.

Donations to colleges, heavy recruitment expenditures, subsidized technical education, internal training, and advancement programs are all attempts on the part of big business to attract, train, and hold their necessary manpower. Yet the demand continues to grow; competition for skilled help increases. Industry recognizes that it is good business to hire the handicapped and that it would be good for our national economy to make the disabled productive. They need help and cooperation in the discovery of good rehabilitation methods and effective placement procedures. The dominance of the service job, of skilled work, and the gradual decline of the heavy work and the laboring job, should mean an ever increasing opportunity for absorption of the disabled into the work force. But, at the same time, it will require the more effective testing, training, and counseling of the handicapped and more compulsion than ever before to sell industry on the man's skill rather than his disability.

The economic gains made possible by the restoration of disabled workers, or handicapped persons who have never worked, to a real earning capacity has never been carefully measured, and, admittedly, it is a difficult matter in which to draw statistical conclusions. In regard to workers who become disabled through disease or injury, either occupational or non-occupational, the survey figures show that somewhere between one million and one and one-half million persons

in the labor force are unable to work on an average work day.[7] This
means a loss of about a billion man-days from industry each year
because of disability.[8] If we relate this loss of man-hours to the
average hourly earnings for the principal production and service businesses of about $2.00,[9] it becomes apparent that there are about two
billions of dollars in earning power "going down the drain" each
year by reason of disability. It is likely that less than a quarter
of this loss is made up by workmen's compensation, group disability
or private accident and sickness benefits. The cost to industry, aside
from the wage loss to the worker himself, is impossible to compute
but obviously would run into the billions of dollars. Granted that
much of this disability is temporary and not needful of rehabilitation efforts, probably 5 to 10% involves disability of a character
and duration which would benefit from rehabilitation services. Effective restoration of earning power for even such a percentage would
constitute a very significant contribution to the national economy.
Earning power is spending power and tax-paying power; its preservation is vital to our way of life.

In the case of handicapped persons who have never worked, it
is particularly difficult to estimate the possible economic effect of their
habilitation. Educated guesses as to the size of this group, which is
comprised of the severe, chronic, physical and mental disabilities,
vary from the figure of one million to nearly five million. Probably
the former figure is more nearly correct. It is interesting that the
tabulation of the Chronic Illness Commission for the ages 15 to 54
(in the composite of non-institutional, civilian individuals disabled
over three months) showed slightly more than one million in this
category, probably the best age group for employment potential.[10]
If we may properly assume that the earning power of this group is
somewhat less per week than the average for the workers already
in industry, because of technical as well as disability limitations, perhaps a figure of $35.00 per week would be justified. It would be
logical to further assume that application of the best available reha-

[7] Woolsey, T. D., "Estimates of Disabling Illness Prevalence in the U. S.,"
Federal Security Agency, Public Health Service, Public Health Monograph No. 4,
Washington, 1952, p. 6.

[8] Report of President's Commission on Health Needs of Nation, *America's
Health Status, Needs and Resources*, Vol. 2, *Building America's Health*, Washington,
1953, p. 75.

[9] U. S. Dept. of Commerce, *op. cit.*, pp. 221–223.

[10] Commission on Chronic Illness, *Care of the Long-Term Patient*, Vol. II of
"Chronic Illness in the U. S.," Commonwealth Fund, Harvard University Press,
Cambridge, p. 476.

bilitation methods to this group could not hope for more than a 50% "batting average" in terms of successful placement in employment. Even with such a limited accomplishment, the effect of rehabilitating and placing 500,000 severely disabled, who had never worked previously, on jobs paying an average of $35.00 weekly, would be to add $17,500,000 each week or $910,000,000 a year to the purchasing power and the tax-paying power of this nation. This would have a potent effect upon the yearly production of goods and services.

Figures publicized by the Office of Vocational Rehabilitation and by the divisions of vocational rehabilitation in several states have dramatically highlighted the savings in taxes through the removal of rehabilitated individuals from public assistance rolls as well as the increased ability of those rehabilitated to earn wages and to pay taxes themselves. As indicated previously, nearly 20% (or about 11,-600) of the persons rehabilitated in the state programs in 1955 were found to have been receiving public assistance. The total cost of such welfare assistance annually has been estimated at more than $11,000,000. They and the others rehabilitated during 1955 have increased their annual earnings from an estimated $15,000,000 to $105,000,000. The disabled persons rehabilitated for gainful employment in 1955 are now paying about $8,500,000 in federal taxes and in less than three years they will have repaid the equivalent of the entire federal investment of over $25 million expended on their rehabilitation. It is further estimated that this group will, during their working lives, pay $10 in federal income taxes for every federal dollar invested in their rehabilitation. The increased earning power will also be reflected at the state and local tax levels. The vending stand program for the blind showed net earnings to over 1700 blind persons of more than five million dollars.[11]

The Department of Rehabilitation in New York similarly reports that in the year 1952 it was able to rehabilitate 1017 persons at a cost of $197,000 to an extent sufficient to increase their total income from $433,000 to $2,336,000.[12] A study conducted by a faculty member of the University of Washington Graduate School of Social Work on 321 rehabilitation cases handled by the state division of vocational rehabilitation in the year 1951, with follow-up on employment histories in 1953, showed 92% to be self-supporting as wage-

[11] U. S. Dept. of Health, Education and Welfare, 1955, *Annual Report,* Section on Office of Vocational Rehabilitation, Washington, 1957, pp. 183, 186, and 194.

[12] Report to Gov. Averell Harriman of N. Y. by Commissioner Joseph M. Callahan, "Costs, Operations and Procedures under the Workmen's Compensation Law of the State of New York," January 28, 1957, Albany, p. 25.

earners or housewives and, whereas 53% had been receiving public assistance at the time accepted for rehabilitation, only 3% were dependent on such assistance at the time of follow-up.[13] In a series of 284 cases in the District of Columbia in 1954 their aggregate earnings of less than $41,000 a year had increased more than fifteen-fold.[14]

A series of paraplegic and other severely disabled miners rehabilitated and returned to employment prior to June 1952 indicated that the cost of maintaining them (and their dependents) on relief for the balance of their lives would probably have totaled over six million dollars. On the basis of their expected earnings following rehabilitation, nearly seven million dollars would be added to the income picture at the federal, state and local level, instead of a continuing drain on tax rolls.[15]

A comparison between the cost of rehabilitation as against the cost of public assistance is most graphic in its implications. In 1954, for instance, the average cost per individual rehabilitated in the federal–state program was $634; in that same year, the Bureau of Public Assistance reported 244,000 persons, in the aid to the permanently and totally disabled category, were receiving benefits at a rate of $156,456,000, an average of $641 each. Since the rehabilitation cost is normally a "one shot" proposition and the public assistance is a continuing and even increasing expense, the investment worth is obviously on the side of the former.

Individual instances of the comparative economy of rehabilitating as against public welfare support are equally demonstrative. A California project involving 73 parents receiving aid to dependent children resulted in rehabilitation of the parents and removal of some 300 persons from relief rolls, with a total cost of $46,000, equal to the amount which would be expended for assistance in less than five months. One of the cases involved a man, wife, and nine children to whom a total of $11,000 had been paid in three years all because surgery for a hernia had not been provided, thus enabling the father to work and support his family.[16]

These statistics on the comparative value of rehabilitation are not always easy to interpret in a personal way, even for those interested in

13 U. S. Dept. of Health, Education and Welfare, 1955, *Annual Report*, Section on Office of Vocational Rehabilitation, Washington, 1955, pp. 236–237.

14 *Ibid.*, p. 238.

15 Pohlmann, K., *Am. J. Public Health*, pp. 448, 451 (April, 1953).

16 California State Dept. of Education, Bureau of Vocational Rehabilitation, "Rehabilitation of Disabled Parents in the Aid to Needy Children Program," Sacramento, August, 1954.

or active in the field. Certainly they should be of direct importance to the community planner and the public administrator. It is less certain that they are of concern to the business man or industrialist, whether in connection with the operation of his business or the financial support of community activity in rehabilitation. The Somers have suggested that these comparisons have not proved particularly effective in influencing national policy. They go on to state that

> Except during periods of conspicuous manpower shortage and, in a few instances, in the field of compensation, the sound economics of rehabilitation does not appear to have had much effect on public policy. The value of human resources is not yet widely understood.[17]

There is, however, an area of real vulnerability in the armor of resistance to the practical economic value of rehabilitation. The increasing cost of disability has been a strong motivating factor in the search of public agencies, industry, and private insurance for ways and means to prevent and reduce loss cost. National Safety Council statistical compilations for the past several years have revealed that close to 2,000,000 work accidents occur each year, with a total production loss of 40,000,000 man-days and a total cost in loss of wages, medical expense, compensation benefits, and other administrative expenses of over one and one-half billions of dollars. If the so-called hidden, or indirect, costs of lost production time are added, the total estimated cost of work accidents exceeds three billion dollars annually.

The growth of modern surgical techniques and drug therapy has resulted in greatly increased life expectancy following serious injury or disease. The prolonged disability which now becomes a possibility as the result of such medical advances can result in staggering costs as far as both indemnity and medical benefits payable under state workmen's compensation laws are concerned.

The accepted principle in workmen's compensation has been that the employer and, hence, his insurance carrier would be responsible for providing benefits to injured and diseased workmen, regardless of fault, and that the cost would be charged off against production. Industry and insurance were thus supplied with a concrete incentive to reduce costs by eliminating hazards (loss prevention through machine guarding, industrial hygiene, general safety instruction, plant medical programs). Since every accident or occupational disease cannot be prevented, the next concern of industry and insurance must be to minimize the consequences of the disability resulting from such

[17] Somers, H. M., and Somers, A. R., *Workmen's Compensation—Prevention, Insurance and Rehabilitation of Occupational Disability*, John Wiley & Sons, New York, 1954, p. 254.

injury and disease. Workmen's compensation premiums paid by the employer are predicated upon his basic rate (which differs with inherent hazards of the industry) and upon his own accident experience (the more frequent or more severe the accidents, the greater the effect on the premium). These rates are computed through a factor applied to each hundred dollars of the business payroll. Loss costs and premiums are affected by benefit increases, legislative changes and court interpretations, and the local administrative procedures on case handling to some extent, but basically the experience is the important element.

The most effective method of controlling and reducing disability is through a good medical care program and good rehabilitation service. By such a planned operation, a worker can be returned to the dignity of self-support and to gainful employment. By effecting a reduction in either the time lost from work or the permanent loss of function in the injured part the cost to both employer and insurance carrier is reduced. Economic gain thus coincides with social gain.

Demonstrations of the savings to be made by rehabilitation of industrial injuries have been made in various areas and by several methods. One of the earliest was Thompson's study in England in 1949 wherein he indicated substantial reductions, in number of days away from work, provided by a suitable rehabilitation program. Following operation for internal derangement of the knee, patients receiving rehabilitation averaged slightly more than 18 days away from work, whereas those who did not have the program averaged over 31 days.[18]

Flax in 1951 reported on a study of hand injury cases rehabilitated in the state insurance fund center in Puerto Rico. In a series of 814 patients there was a saving of $251 per case due to "a complete surgical and medical program, including modern methods of physical medicine and rehabilitation."[19]

The Liberty Mutual Insurance Company, the largest private carrier of workmen's compensation insurance in the United States and a pioneer in the adaptation of rehabilitation techniques and services to the advantage of the injured industrial worker, has produced some very significant statistics in support of the economic values to be derived from rehabilitation. In their own two centers at Boston and Chicago, the first operated since 1943 and the second since 1951, it has

18 Thompson, A. R., "An Industrial Accident and Rehabilitation Service: Engineering Methods in Occupational Therapy," *Brit. J. Physical Medicine,* **12,** p. 114, 1949.

19 Flax, H. J., "Physical Medicine and Rehabilitation Therapy of Hand Injuries," *Arch. Ind. Hygiene,* **3,** p. 236, 1951.

been found that 85% of all cases could be improved to the point of being physically able to work and, of that number, about 82% actually did return to work. A survey made of thirty typical, routine industrial injury cases, ranging from simple fractures to post-operative discs, processed by the Boston center indicated an average estimated saving in workmen's compensation benefits of slightly over $1000 per case. In the rehabilitation of the more dramatic and complicated spinal cord injury cases by this company, the statistics are even more impressive. On a series of 86 completed cases, in which almost 50% were returned to employment and 95% were divorced from the need of continued hospital care or the continuation of expensive attendant care, the total net estimated saving in indemnity and medical cost (after deduction of the cost of rehabilitation procedures) is $2,719,200. Although any estimate of monetary savings such as these and even the speculation on the effect of rehabilitation upon the future life of a given individual are necessarily theoretical to some extent, they are based on careful review and evaluation of each case in each year of its active existence and are based also on sound technical judgment of costs, actual and potential, in the workmen's compensation jurisdictions involved.

The New York State Insurance Fund has had similar experience in the referral of its cases to community rehabilitation facilities. In a series of 40 workmen's compensation patients referred for rehabilitation the Fund estimated a total saving in compensation costs of $170,000, an average of $4250 per case.[20]

In the area of nonindustrial injury and illness, the costs of disability are even greater. The cost of automobile and public liability accidents and the disabilities resulting therefrom are in excess of the total costs of work accidents. The cost of illness, much of which now comes under voluntary pre-paid medical plans (i.e., individual or group accident and health policies), cannot even be guessed at with any degree of accuracy. Like the increase of indemnity and medical benefits in the workmen's compensation field, recent years have witnessed the steady growth of jury verdicts, settlement prices, increasing physician and hospital charges, broader group insurance coverages, and greater benefits under those coverages. All of this has led to the same kind of spiraling cost of disability as that which has characterized the workmen's compensation case.

Once an accident has happened the probability of loss depends upon two things—the liability and the disability. In the control

[20] Report to Gov. Averell Harriman of N. Y. by Commissioner Joseph M. Callahan, *op. cit.*, p. 25.

of liability fairly set patterns have been established. Over the years many decisions have been handed down; compensation law and negligence law have become settled. Only a very small percentage of the accidents reported can be successfully controverted or defended. Insurance companies are generally alert and well trained to recognize those cases that should be controverted or defended and, except for a few jurisdictions and in selected circumstances, there exists no great potential of saving through more and better trials. The very major part of the loss dollar goes out on cases of clear legal responsibility to pay for disability. The future possibilities of control of compensation or other insurance loss, therefore, lie to a large extent in the control of disability.

The effectiveness of rehabilitation upon the residuals of traumatic injury or disabling illness in these other areas can be as striking as in the field of workmen's compensation. In the new and rapidly expanding health insurance coverages and plans there is a challenge to all concerned. Are we going to be content with cash benefits for disability and medical treatment or can the services of medical and rehabilitation personnel and facilities be utilized to control and minimize disability? More than twice the number of industrially injured are maimed in automobile accidents each year. Our present system of common law liability and insurance does not encourage rehabilitation—in fact, the monetary advantage to the injured party is often in the direction of trying to show maximal disability and minimal recovery at the time of settlement or trial.

The whole idea of direct and positive interest in the personal welfare, particularly the medical welfare, of the victim of accident or illness holds many economic ramifications. The endorsement of and utilization of modern rehabilitation techniques and facilities by doctors, lawyers, and insurance representatives could lead to substantial reduction of disagreements on the end result obtained following traumatic injury and contribute directly to the medical, social, and vocational welfare of the injured person. In the Liberty Mutual program, it has been demonstrated that the same rehabilitation methods which have proved so helpful on reducing temporary and permanent disability in cases involving industrial accident are equally effective in reducing similar effects from accidents occurring as the result of automobile or public liability hazards.

It is worthy of note that much of the economic saving in compensation cases and other types of prolonged disability cases is accomplished through the elimination of continuing, expensive, medical care. In the Liberty Mutual study of spinal cord injuries, previously cited, the average estimated saving in medical cost on the completed cases was $38,344. Dr. Rusk has quoted similar figures for paraplegic cases referred to The Institute for Physical Medicine and Rehabilitation in New York by insurance carriers. He has estimated the cost of maintaining these people in a general hospital as running at a possible rate of $50 to $60 daily for an indefinite period, possibly the rest of their lives.[21] The rehabilitation of 120 veterans, who had been hospitalized at a cost of $12 per patient per day, realized an estimated saving for the federal government of $1,125,000.[22] Prolonged hospitalization is costly; any expenditure for rehabilitation is almost certain to be substantially cheaper in the long run.

Business people genuinely interested in the practical application of methods by which new techniques and facilities can help their injured or sick workers now have both the opportunity and the challenge to make contributions to the humanitarian and economic goals which characterize the whole philosophy and practice of rehabilitation. Much remains to be done in the years ahead if jointly we are to meet the public demand for increased medical services of all kinds. The accomplishments of new scientific research, improved medical teaching, and better treatment or therapy techniques will mean increased responsibility, increased cost for such services, and new challenges for all concerned if we are to truly lead the way toward greater alleviation of human suffering and economic distress.

Even in this age of automation, the individual American working man is still our country's real strength and its most important commodity. The working man represents the bulwark of our national income, our purchasing power, our standard of living, the basic unit of our tax structure. Any social law or insurance system which is to prove its worth must be geared to his welfare and especially to his medical welfare.

The tragedy of human and economic waste resulting from prolonged disability of an individual worker is ironic in this day and age. The restoration of a disabled individual to a useful and productive life is a goal which is both economically and socially sound.

[21] Rusk, H. A., "Application of Rehabilitation to Workmen's Compensation Cases," published address in *Medical Aspects of Workmen's Compensation*, Commerce and Industry Association of New York, Inc., N. Y., 1953, p. 67.

[22] U. S. Senate Committee on Labor and Public Welfare, 83rd Congress, Report on Hearings Before the Subcommittee on Health on President's Health Recommendations and Related Matters, Washington, April 5, 1954, p. 412.

CHAPTER 19

The Community
Responsibility

COMMUNITY RESPONSIBILITY FOR REHABILITA-
tion is basic to both its philosophy and practice. If we believe in the
immeasurable worth of human life and spirit, then the most important contribution of society is its concern for and efforts on behalf of
the individual. The medical, social, and economic welfare of each
person in the community becomes, in truth, a compound which constitutes the welfare of the whole community. The collective strength
of the community lies in what it does for its people; it can be good
or bad, progressive or backward, a "live" or "dead" town, depending
upon the degree of its concerted action toward benefits for its resi-
dents. At the same time, it is a reciprocal relationship; we each make
our community a better place in which to live and work by our own
interest and participation in its institutions, organizations and
services.

According to the 1950 census figures, there are over 4700 urban areas
in the United States; 106 of these are 100,000 population or over, the
balance having between 2500 and 100,000 people. These include
the cities, towns, villages, and boroughs, either incorporated or unin-
corporated. There are just over 13,800 so-called rural territories,
with slightly more than 4000 of these being 1000 to 2500 in population
and the rest below the latter figure.[1] Contrary to what is sometimes
the prevalent thinking in program planning at a national level, we
are still a nation of smaller communities.

[1] U. S. Dept. of Commerce, Bureau of the Census, *Statistical Abstract of the
United States*, 77th Edition, Washington, 1956, p. 19.

The recognition of the community's importance in service to its people is certainly no new concept. It is as old as the first gatherings of man in communal groups for hunting food and protection against a common enemy. But much of the contribution of the community in the ancient civilizations and, indeed, in the later European cultures or our own pioneer days was related to military, political and economic considerations. It was only with the rise of the big cities, the increased complexity of social relationships, and the greatly intensified interest in the welfare of the individual, all products of the twentieth century, that the community began to understand and to exercise its modern role in relation to its people. The deliberate effort to deal effectively with poverty, health, education, housing, and employment are all a part of the later concept of the nation, the state, and the community as responsible for public and private programs devoted to improvement in all such areas of human existence.

The recognition of community responsibility for progressive action in these areas of human welfare has not always received perceptive and personalized attention. There has often been a tendency to abdicate community responsibility in favor of dependence on some national agency or program. Sometimes this is because of fanciful ideas about the size of the problem or the cost of doing anything about it. Yet there has been repeated emphasis on the fact that no national program can succeed without community interpretation, support and action.

General Omar Bradley in December, 1945, when he was Director of Veterans' Administration, had this to say:

> To those who would look to Washington when they hear of veterans' problems, there's a thought I'd like to leave. Washington alone can no more help the veteran than Washington alone could win the war. For although government can tell you what the veteran wants—and perhaps suggest some ways to help him—it is America that must do the job.

> Veterans want the chance, first, to show they're good civilians. They want jobs, homes, loans—the breaks they need to get going again where they left off for war. We can write the checks, but the man needs more than checks. He needs the intelligent counsel, the neighborly advice, the friendly assistance that can be given him down in the town where he lives. This is a job for America—for the people who want to make good on the promises we've made.[2]

Oscar R. Ewing, former Federal Security Administrator, and often criticized as a proponent of a completely nationalized health pro-

---

[2] Booklet, *Reintegration of the Veteran into His Community*, notes on meeting held at Mitchel Field, L. I., N. Y., December 5, 1945.

gram, in his detailed report to President Truman of Sept. 2, 1948, repeatedly emphasized that

> All of the help the nation can give, however, will prove insufficient unless the communities themselves enter wholeheartedly into the work.[3]

Later in the same report he stated

> The community effort is the spearhead of all federal and state action for health. It is the local front that national, state and community planning fuses into a single program, into a joint drive to improve conditions, to prevent individual sickness and disability and to save individual lives.[4]

Rehabilitation of the physically handicapped is inherently a community problem. Although the assistance of private and public agencies, at the state and national levels, is both valuable and desirable, the basic need is community understanding of the problems of the physically and mentally handicapped and for concerted action based upon that understanding. There is often an unfortunate tendency to regard problems in the field of social or human relations in the larger sense; i.e., on the basis of a national scale of thinking which many times presents a discouraging aspect. A statement that some 28 million people in the U. S. are disabled or that between five and six million persons of working age in this country have disabilities serious enough to present difficulties in finding suitable jobs is a pretty awesome statistic. A request to the Congress for $30,000,000 for expansion of rehabilitation services can be equally dismaying. To the organization or community contemplating action on any of the several aspects of the problem of the handicapped, review of such statistics and the making of comparisons between the over-all need and the pitiful shortage of existing facilities for dealing with the problem may lead to understandable discouragement in considering the huge financial backing, and the education of industry, labor, medicine, and administrative agencies which seem necessary to attack the problem. Actually, realization of the number of handicapped in a given community, utilization of existing and planned facilities, together with the specific support of interested parties, offers real opportunity for success.

Sheer inertia and "the easy way out" may often imbue the comprehensive national or state program in rehabilitation with unjustified attractiveness. The tough job of daily efforts at coordination between

---

[3] Ewing, O. R., *The Nation's Health—a Ten Year Program*, a report to the President by the Federal Security Administrator, Washington, 1948, foreword, p. xii.

[4] *Ibid.*, p. 161.

agencies and programs, the difficulty of integration of a community-wide service, the barriers of personalities, petty jealousies and competitive drives for funds, and the failure to "sell" rehabilitation at all levels and all at once make the compulsory and wholly centralized authority in rehabilitation seem like the long-range answer. "Besides —the government has all the money to do this job." Such hazy thinking overlooks the basic fact that, in a democratic society and form of government, improvement in human affairs and relationships is accomplished through existing and local institutions, organizations, and individuals. The government may sketch the plan, suggest the means, assist with the financing, even provide leadership or technical assistance; but, fundamentally, the job is done by community understanding, support, and action. The local blueprint for rehabilitation, the facilities, the personnel, the services, the recreational opportunities, the job possibilities, the public attitude, will all be created in the community—not synthetically in some master plan, speech, or publication.

Community responsibility for rehabilitation services reaps its reward in several ways. First, the services will inevitably become what the community is willing for them to be and expects them to be. Limited imagination, unsound planning, insufficient financing, and lack of public understanding will point unerringly to inadequate services.

Second, the character and size of the facilities for rehabilitation will be more likely to fit the particular needs of the community. Illogical location, lack of proper medical supervision, faulty staff organization, or limited function or service are more likely to follow in the wake of unrealistic individual planning or the suggestions of uninformed outsiders.

Third, community teamwork is in itself the working heart of effective rehabilitation. The fact that community interests, both individual and organizational, have combined to bring about a sound community program of rehabilitation increases the probability of better relationships between groups working in the field, of more effective integration throughout the entire program.

Fourth, public relations are shaped largely by community effort and individual reaction. Contributions of an active rehabilitation program are reflected in willingness of individuals to participate through money or service. "If the program is worthy of the time and effort of respected people in the community, it is worth my interest and support." "If they can take the time to come into my factory to outline this man's skills and capabilities, I can take the time to find him a job he can do." These might be typical reactions. The average man is more impressed by the complete restoration of his crippled neighbor than by some appeal on the basis of tax savings or the theoretical benefits of mass rehabilitation.

Fifth, the individual patient is most vitally influenced in his attempt to rehabilitate himself by the attitude of the community. In the final analysis, his neighbors, his friends, his employer, his family will determine the success or failure of the community investment in this rehabilitated person. Community efforts at rehabilitation which fail to involve as many persons as possible are defeating the opportunity to develop community concern and understanding, thereby weakening the chances of successful adjustment of the rehabilitated person to that community.

Sixth, public education on what rehabilitation is and does depends to a large extent on community interest and action. Rehabilitation is a complex and confusing process to many; it needs explanation and interpretation over and over and over through every possible personal and visual media. Rehabilitation should become valuable for its own sake as a philosophy and practice within the whole community, not the isolated and exclusive property of one agency or organization, not a glamorous "gimmick" or "catchword" used to elicit funds or to make the public think that this or that individual or organization has jumped "on the bandwagon" of medical progress.

Seventh, the community is necessarily the source of rehabilitation personnel. The success of almost every rehabilitation venture in this country depends on developing interest in young people toward entering one of the several professions or disciplines involved in the rehabilitation process. This cannot be done simply by publishing statistics on shortages nor by the tempting bait of subsidized education; it must be accomplished by clear and convincing evidence that there is a material and spiritual satisfaction to work in the rehabilitation field. It must become rewarding not only as a contributive career but also in monetary compensation and in recognition by the community as a practical and valuable job.

Eighth, the community is the best research medium and the most needful of the fruits of that research. Rehabilitation is a rapidly changing body of knowledge and experience. In order to discover the most effective program for the community, basic evaluation of need must be done, not by some mysterious formula evolved by a national body, but by hard and perceptive work in the community, by those who know the problem best. Follow-up research will have to be done to keep the community informed of needed changes in emphasis or character of service. Other agencies or organizations in the community can also benefit from research done by the community rehabilitation services—just one example would be the welfare agencies utilizing accumulated data on the practical value of rehabilitation services to re-orient their own programs in the direction of getting people off the welfare rolls by medical or vocational rehabilitation.

These, then, are some of the fruits of community organization for rehabilitation. The problems of disability, chronic disease, and aging all have a very significant relationship to community welfare. Maintaining any appreciable number of disabled in institutions, either medical or custodial, or supporting them in idleness at home, on the basis of present-day costs, is a real economic drain on the community. Of greater significance, however, is the social import of our neglect of the right of all the disabled to independent living, if modern science and skill can make it possible for them.

One of the distinctive features of our approach to rehabilitation in the United States, as in the case of our other social and welfare endeavors, has been the emphasis upon voluntary effort. In the many discussions of rehabilitation organization at the international conferences on the subject, it is evident from the remarks of the representatives from other countries that they conceive of the rehabilitation of disabled persons as properly organized and developed almost wholly within the general administrative framework of the national government. Seldom are the words "voluntary agencies," "community planning," and "private fund support" heard in the discussions or seen in the record of those meetings. One of the most revealing comments made by a number of different members of technical assistance teams from European countries, during their visits to a Boston rehabilitation center, was to the effect that "You mean to say that these patients don't have to come here for treatment, that they have an individual choice in the matter?—you don't realize how important that right of choice is: do all you can to preserve it—we have seen it taken away and we now realize its true importance." There is no substitute for and there should be no compromise with our native faith in community organization and the inherent rights of the individual, in medical care, and in social welfare as well as in the realm of political and religious liberties.

The most effective rehabilitation programs, whether comprehensive or limited in scope, are found in those communities which have recognized and taken full advantage of the community-wide approach. The "Miami Plan," "Operation Knoxville," the Crossroads program in Indianapolis, the Binghamton (N.Y.) program, the Stamford (Conn.)

success story, the big-city planning in Cleveland, Detroit, New York, and Boston are all testimonials to the value and, indeed, necessity of broad planning and integration of community services. As a citizen's committee in Pittsburgh concluded in its 1955 report:

> There are four courses that a community may take in dealing with the handicapped problem. It may: ignore the problem, insist that present social service and government agencies do a better job of helping the handicapped find employment, count on periodic bursts of publicity to do the job, recognize that the problem basically is a community problem that can be solved by action at the community level. After examining all of the available evidence, the Survey Committee chose the last course because it was the only practical solution.[5]

Selective studies such as those now being made in Kansas City will increasingly document the field of rehabilitation within the community, both in terms of results and unmet needs. Such studies already conclusively demonstrate that one of the most important aspects of a total rehabilitation program is concerted community interest and participation.

Dr. Whitehouse of the American Heart Association has truly said that

> Rehabilitation is a social problem—one that has its roots set firmly in the life of the community. It is the community that spawns, nurtures and produces the human being that is its raw material. It is to the community that the person returns a success or failure by community standards.[6]

The effects of community neglect of its responsibility toward the disabled insinuate themselves into many other elements of our community life—taxes, insurance costs, commodity prices, availability of physician time, lost manpower, crime rate, broken homes. Only understanding and responsible activity within the community can attack the situation with any hope of success.

Kenneth Hamilton has phrased the demand neatly:

> Community organization is no gadget of legerdemain. It is not a panacea. It is a precondition to the slow process of evolution of organized effort. Its purpose is to convince rather than to coerce. It seeks to educate rather than legislate. It presupposes group understanding. Assuming the mutuality of the group as its basis, it attempts group planning and group building. Community organization does not seek to solidify, perpetuate, or reinforce agency or personal status. The necessity for

5 Health and Welfare Federation of Allegheny County, Family and Child Welfare Division, "Survey of Handicapped Workers—Report of a Citizens' Committee," Pittsburgh, 1955, p. 5.

6 Whitehouse, F. A., "The Rehabilitation Center—Some Aspects of a Philosophy," *Am. J. Occupational Therapy*, **VII**, No. 6 (Nov.–Dec. 1953).

organization is recognized when it is accepted that needs change, that people and communities are dynamic, and that resources must be viewed accordingly.

Without organization, the myriads of specialized services available to the handicapped are like the streets lacking names in a strange city. Unless the perspective underlying organization is truly community-wide rather than just services-to-the-handicapped-wide, rehabilitation agencies may try to organize independently of the other necessary welfare resources of the community, like the star athlete playing independently of his team.[7]

There are those who become vastly impatient with our progress in rehabilitation, who lament that community understanding and support are lacking, that its goals are appreciated only by a few and then in a narrow sense. This situation, if it be true, will not be cured by polemics or surveys, by criticism or legislation. Like any program whose basic ingredients are people, it will be solved by the common sense, factual knowledge, human interest, and imagination of other people. Leadership in a community plan for rehabilitation may come from a dedicated individual, from one agency, or a group of interested organizations or from public or private sources. All these components are located in the community; its responsibility for better rehabilitation services rests squarely upon them. Their devotion to the effort of slowly changing human thought and practice are the best guarantee of success.

[7] Hamilton, K. W., *Counseling the Handicapped in the Rehabilitation Process*, Ronald Press, New York, 1950, p. 188.

CHAPTER 20

Surveying
the Need

NO DEFINITIVE PLANNING FOR COMMUNITY
rehabilitation can be done without a careful survey of the need. Such
a survey is not merely an estimate of the probable number of persons
needing rehabilitation services in the community; it also includes the
number and character of existing services, their adequacy in terms
of effect upon the total picture, the level of understanding and cooperation among public and private agencies, the degree of acceptance
of rehabilitation and, finally, the existing "market" for any enlarged
plan of rehabilitation service.

There are three principal methods of determining the extent of
disability in a given area. The first is the abstract method of applying a formula based on the estimated or known national figures for
specific types of disabilities, or the composite figures and percentages
for broad classes of disability obtained from national or regional surveys, to the local population. The second is the pooling of available
data from local agencies and services to form the basis for an "educated guess" on the total disability picture. The third method is the
house-to-house survey or canvass type of personal contact, carried
out on either a broad or limited segment of the community.

Opinions vary considerably as to the efficacy of these respective
methods. Perhaps a combination of all three would be the most
informative. In any event, the individuals and groups interested in
analysis of the local disability situation will necessarily have to decide
which method or what combination of methods they want to utilize.
Their decision will also have to answer the question of whether they

wish to try to carry out their survey themselves (using local people
and facilities) or retain the services (either voluntary or paid) of outside professional researchers.

There are some advantages to the use of the professional research
person in the areas of practiced organization, skilled preparation of
forms or questionnaires, cooperation from agencies, qualitative analysis of data, objective approach and, possibly, shortened time schedule
for the survey. On the other hand, there is a tremendous cost differential. The fee for a professional on a six-month to one-year time
schedule might run as high as fifteen to twenty thousand dollars.
Use of voluntary, local effort might not run more than a few hundred
dollars, since the principal costs under such circumstances would be
for printing, telephone, transportation, and similar incidentals. Many
communities have carried out effective surveys to obtain various
kinds of rehabilitation data using entirely local people. Most of
the smaller communities will probably prefer to utilize this method.
Helpful published data on how to carry out surveys, local talent
who may have had some experience in research, local educational or
research institutions, national foundations who can make research
and statistical information available without charge, and government
technicians from interested agencies can all be tapped to great advantage and with little or no cost for the organization and completion of
surveys.

There is probably an intangible benefit to the self-organized survey
group in the community and its attempt to carry out its own study.
That benefit lies in the area of necessary communication between
agencies and individuals and the fact that conclusions and recommendations will be the product of local effort and the practical
ground for local improvement. There is always some resistance to
what the outsider concludes or recommends; he necessarily has to
make some comparisons with other localities, programs, or standards.
This frequently results in local resentment or disregard on the grounds
that what is a proper plan for Cincinnati may not be the right one
for Dallas. There is great merit in "a survey and plan of our own,
tailored to local conditions and needs." This does not mean that all
available data and the experiences of others cannot be used to
advantage but rather that the locally organized and operated survey
probably has some real benefits as against the professional survey conducted by outside individuals or organizations.

Assuming that the community group has decided on running its
own survey, the selection of the method for determining extent of
disability then becomes of paramount importance. In considering

the three possibilities previously mentioned, the community must have some available facts on the nature and scope of each method. In the case of the abstract formula on disability percentages applied to local population, it would be necessary to obtain certain guide material already in use. Since determination of the number of handicapped in a given community will probably be subdivided into age groups, sex, and type of disability, it becomes apparent that several sources of guide material on the national incidence estimates for specific disabilities will be needed. The definitive general surveys such as the National Health Survey, the Hunterdon County study, the Baltimore study, the Public Health Service estimates by Woolsey based on the 1949 and 1950 current population survey, the 1954 estimate prepared by Dr. Moore for the Office of Vocational Rehabilitation, and the preliminary data from the comprehensive study in Kansas City, all of which were previously discussed in the chapter on "The Size of the Problem," are basic to any consideration of general formulas and percentages on disability incidence. The National Society for Crippled Children and Adults, the Conference on Rehabilitation Centers, Inc., the American Foundation for the Blind, the National Foundation for Infantile Paralysis, and many similar national groups dealing with specific disabilities have accumulated helpful data on estimated incidence of disability. On the basis of analysis of these accumulated incidence figures in the general population and in specified areas of study, the appropriate percentages for each kind of disability and for broad general categories can then be applied to the local community population. Census figures on the community area or determined percentage of total U.S. population applicable to the community area, properly sub-divided into children under 21 and adults, are used for the computation of the local community population.

The pooling of the data available from local agencies and services is important to true determination of the need for rehabilitation in the community. Such a method of obtaining information on the rehabilitation potential of the community should not be limited to a case load study; it should also include an informed opinion of agency representatives as to how many cases there are in the community which are not presently being served. Small case loads in given agencies do not necessarily mean a small number of potential cases; it may mean inadequate facilities, poor referral procedures, or many undiscovered cases. Even allowing for agency exaggeration as to case load or potential of a given disability in the community, it is probable that local agency people are in a better position to leaven the national incidence figures with common-sense evaluation of the local situation. The gathering of these local estimates need not be limited to the facilities or agencies already rendering rehabilitation services. They may constitute only a minor portion of total available services for the handicapped in the community.

For instance, a personalized schedule intended to discover information about blind persons in the Greater Boston area went to some 300 different agencies and institutions. Many of these were not established to serve the blind and many were not specifically rehabilitation services but all played some part in the total adjustment of the blind person to the community. The fact that some were not rendering any real service to this particular type of disability was in itself significant, because they should have been doing so if the program were completely effective. Needs of the disabled are not limited to merely the health, rehabilitation, and welfare agencies; the broad scope of community services, recreational, industrial, civic, educational, are all involved in the participation of each person in his community environment. The disabled are entitled to the opportunity to share in all such activities; otherwise rehabilitation in a community sense does not exist.

Information can be gleaned from such sources as the workmen's compensation authority, insurance carriers, local committees on the aging or chronic disease, public school systems, family service agencies, employers, nursing groups, and medical societies, as well as the more obvious services normally involved in rehabilitation. More involvement of a greater number of people will be likely to result in a more meaningful measurement.

The most personalized of all methods is the house-to-house survey. It is time-consuming, expensive, and just plain hard work. If well done, it can be very informative; if poorly done, it can be almost useless. The validity of data gathered in a personal call depends to a large extent on the reliability of the informant and the basic knowledge and perception of the interviewer. Technical description of injury or illness, its handicapping effect, amenability to rehabilitation, and possibility of self-care or employment are very difficult to obtain by verbal interview. The importance placed on the Kansas City, El Paso (Colorado), Baltimore and Hunterdon County studies, however, clearly indicates the significant contribution of the door-to-door process in factual determination of disability incidence and the over-all evaluation of needs.

Review of the number and character of existing rehabilitation services is the next part of the comprehensive survey of need. It has become almost a truism among rehabilitation researchers that a surprisingly large number of people actively working in the field are very poorly informed about the other services in the community, outside those rendered by or closely connected with their own agency or professional discipline.   Lack of good communication is largely responsible and it forms a very real barrier to obtaining a comprehensive picture of local rehabilitation services from one or a limited number of sources.   It takes a lot of digging to get the complete picture and more often than not there is a lot more going on and being done in the general area of rehabilitation than most people suspect. Any community directory of such services is a good starting point, but this should be supplemented by discussions with many knowledgeable persons in the field and visits to facilities and agency headquarters to see at first hand what is being done and how effective it may be.

The adequacy of services is, to some extent, a difficult area in which to involve any community group conducting a survey of need.   No individual, agency, or institution likes to be criticized, even by inference, on the basis of real or fancied shortcomings in its own program. One way of overcoming possible individual prejudices and hasty or ill-advised conclusions in the evaluation of adequate provision for rehabilitation is through sizable working committees to review the programs of particular agencies or groups of agencies serving particular types of disability.   The Marion County (Indiana) survey has effectively used this method.   Carefully selected advisory groups or study clinics are other means of tackling this problem of agency and program evaluation.   Not all the evaluation results will be critical; another element is the planned or desirable expansion of existing programs.

The level of understanding and cooperation among public and private agencies in the community is prerequisite to any sound conclusions on the need for rehabilitation services and the practical opportunity to develop them.   The necessity for integration of services has been stressed in an earlier chapter.   Emphasis in many health and welfare programs has been on the role of the particular discipline or the individual agency.   Only now is the "team concept" being evolved as a "must" in rehabilitation planning and action.   The best planning for the patient and the community is not always what will redound to the greatest recognition and publicity for any one agency.   One of the great benefits from any comprehensive survey will be the increased recognition of the need for integration by many who were unaware of or indifferent to its importance.   To the degree that the community surveyors feel that integration and cooperation can be obtained, as a practical matter, will the horizons of rehabilitation planning broaden and brighten.

The acceptance of rehabilitation by the community and its component services becomes a focal point for any group surveying the need. No rehabilitation plan or program, however well intended, can hope to prosper in an aura of defeatism, limited understanding, and reactionary attitudes. One of the more important areas of understanding and support must be the local medical profession. Since the doctor is the moving force in most referrals to rehabilitation facilities, his cooperation is integral to success in maximum case service. Is there a passive approach to rehabilitation in which no disabled person gets into the rehabilitation process until or unless he presents himself to an agency? Are the services now operating in rehabilitation limited to only one or a few of the many kinds of disability? Is there any appreciation of the mental and emotional aspects of disability? Have fund drives for medical, health, or rehabilitation programs been well understood and supported in the community? The answer to these questions and many more can help to form a picture of community attitude toward rehabilitation which, in the evaluation and planning for unmet needs and increased services, can strongly affect final action.

The "market" for rehabilitation services and the determination of that market has not been well understood by planning groups. In the emotional enthusiasm and almost blind conviction that motivates some individuals who are in a position to supply funds or leadership to rehabilitation programs, there lurks the very real possibility of tragic mistakes in expensive facilities, highly publicized services, and grandiose plans which never "get off the ground." More often than not, at the root of these miscues there lies a failure to determine and attract users or consumers of the service. Impractical location, financial distress, inability to attract professional personnel, and limited or inadequate program may all be eventual reflections of the initial failure to measure the practical possibilities for use of the service as opposed to theoretical belief in potential cases. In surveying the need within the community, the prospective use or "market" for any actual or proposed rehabilitation service rates top priority in serious consideration of the community planning group. Rehabilitation has to be sold like any new idea or practice. The principles of successful merchandising hold true for this non-commercial enterprise.

Community groups undertaking to survey the needs of the disabled and the need for rehabilitation services can look for constructive support from some of the new administrative developments growing out of the rehabilitation legislation of 1954. The amendments to the Hill–Burton Act provide for assistance to the states in determining needed facilities. Federal grants, to be matched by state funds, are made available to the state authorities having responsibility for the allocation of Hill–Burton construction funds. The survey and planning provisions of the amendments follow the provisions of the original Hill–Burton Act in that a state plan is to be evolved by which hospitals and other facilities that render rehabilitation service will be inventoried in order to provide a base for appraisal of rehabilitation needs in the state and the proper allocation of federal-state funds to applicants wishing to construct rehabilitation facilities. The nature of the information required in these inventories and in any applications for construction funds is such that it would be most helpful to community planning groups.

Project grants under the amendments to the Vocational Rehabilitation Act also permit the allocation of monies to communities or community groups wishing to carry out definitive surveys as a precedent to the development of more effective rehabilitation services. Funds and even technical assistance available under these grants might substantially ease the job of surveying the need.

No survey of need in any community is completely effective merely as a series of statistics which seem to justify action, nor as a seemingly authoritative set of conclusions about the community programs in rehabilitation. The survey is but the first step in development of a community plan. More will be said about such a plan in a subsequent chapter. The survey itself, if it is to be truly meaningful, should conclude with an evaluation session by a sizable group representing all the agencies and services which are or would be involved in later specific rehabilitation planning. At such a session, the outline of significant findings revealed by the survey can be presented in such a way that exceptions, criticisms, and omissions can be noted and all those present can make constructive suggestions. Only after this kind of evaluation or analysis should the final report of the survey be made public and distributed to those agencies or individuals interested. This kind of advisory participation by community agencies leads to better acceptance of the survey, and any later plan based on the survey.

CHAPTER 21

The Cost
of Rehabilitation

LIKE ANY SPECIALIZED PROGRAM OF CARE, rehabilitation is expensive. Many parts of the process require the establishment and maintenance of facilities which, in themselves, constitute a sizable investment. Personnel is varied and multiple, equipment extensive, programming cost considerable. For these reasons, any community group contemplating the development of a rehabilitation program needs to carefully scrutinize their ideas, plans, and financing possibilities before embarking on specific ventures in the field. Poorly planned or insufficiently financed operations in rehabilitation can immeasurably harm the cause in any community, as well as tying up badly needed personnel and funds.

There have been no really definitive studies as to the cost of providing rehabilitation services. A few have been attempted, but the variances in program have been so great that little has been clearly recorded for the assistance of community planning groups. Until certain accepted standards of staffing, required floor space for facilities, and basic equipment are established in the various component services of the rehabilitation process, it is going to be difficult for any meaningful cost analysis to be made. Realizing this to be true, it would be brash of this author to attempt any clear-cut delineation of rehabilitation costs on a comprehensive or conclusive basis. However, there may be some value in bringing to the attention of the community planning groups certain aspects of the problem, if for no other reason than that of emphasizing the necessity for careful evaluation of needed services in the light of available financial support.

Taking the four main categories of expense for initiating rehabilitation program operation: (1) administrative costs (executive staff, clerical, office space, office equipment, public relations, fund-raising, etc.), (2) facilities, (3) personnel, (4) equipment; there are developments in each category which give some clues to the trend in rehabilitation cost. It should be borne in mind that comments made and figures given are based on a community program of rehabilitation. There has been no attempt to evaluate the scope or cost of national or regional programs since the variances there could be from thousands to millions and the efforts are often more heavily concerned with public information, fund-raising, and the like; with purchase rather than direct provision of services.

Administrative expense is a nebulous element in rehabilitation cost since it will vary widely dependent upon the factors included in such expense and the possible maintenance of office facilities, headquarters staff and general programming as physically separated from the local operation of facilities and specific services in rehabilitation. Assuming for the moment that we are talking about the kind of rehabilitation service in which the administration is contained in the same essential unit as the service facility, then it would probably be fair to state that the over-all expense of the administrative portion should constitute about 15% of the total annual cost of operation. On the basis of a $250,000 annual operating expense, this would mean that approximately $37,500 could properly be anticipated as falling in the category of administrative expense.

Costs of building and operating a facility, of course, will fluctuate according to the size and character of the particular facility. Since one of the most typical of rehabilitation facilities is the rehabilitation center, with most communities studying the need for initiating or expanding this kind of service, it would be pertinent to review the cost picture involved in this particular facet of a community program. Differentiation must be made between the type of facility which is an adjunct to a general hospital or the so-called rehabilitation institute type, both of which ordinarily include in-patient as well as out-patient service, and the regular comprehensive community center which is entirely on an out-patient basis.

As to the former, one estimate of the amount of floor space which should properly be allotted to a hypothetical, comprehensive, multiple-disability facility, handling average case load of 43 in-patients and 105 out-patients (with average daily attendance of some 40 out-patients) was a figure of 41,230 square feet.[1] If this figure is multi-

[1] Desjardins, E. J., "Adaptation of Plant and Equipment to Potential Case Load, Financial Resources and Personnel," address and paper included in *Proceedings of*

plied by the latest available construction cost figures for the year 1955 involving hospital and institutional type of construction, which amounts to $20.50 per square foot,[2] the resultant total would be $845,215. In round figures it would appear that something in the neighborhood of $750,000 to $1,000,000 must be considered when planners are contemplating the building, expansion, or development of the larger facility which will include both in-patient and out-patient care. In the less elaborate type of community center, providing service on an out-patient basis only, a comprehensive, modern facility can be built for $200,000 to $250,000, on the basis of current experience in several parts of the country. Figures for both types of facilities are exclusive of the cost of any land purchase. Naturally, there are many variances in cost as the ideas of the planners find expression. Construction costs may be expected to increase over original estimates. One large rehabilitation facility now being constructed in Boston has found the actual building cost to be running 20% higher than original estimates. If many elaborate kinds of vocational shops, extensive sheltered workshop areas, extra space for certain kinds of therapy, added residential, dormitory-type space, or recreational facilities are included in the plans, then there is really no limit to the amount which can be spent. Several state and private groups are currently considering or actually building multimillion dollar facilities. Most of these are designed to serve much more than one localized community area. If suitable space can be rented, it will save substantially on initial expense of launching a program.

In earlier chapters, emphasis was placed on the drastic shortages of professional and technical personnel in the rehabilitation field. This has often made it difficult for community planning groups to recruit a capable staff of sufficient size to properly operate established or planned facilities and services. The salary problem of such a staff is a major concern in the planning for rehabilitation programs. To attract and hold competent people, the planned and continued salary policies must be realistic in the light of rapidly changing conditions.

Basically, we must all face up to the fact that rehabilitation personnel have been underpaid, in comparison with similar professional and technical skills in other fields of endeavor and even with business or industrial work requiring less education and special training. A recent, informative report prepared by the Seventh Company, Inc., of New York on the salaries of rehabilitation workers indicates that,

---

The Institute on Rehabilitation Center Planning sponsored by Conference of Rehabilitation Centers, Inc., Feb. 25–March 1, 1957, Chicago.

[2] U. S. Dept. of Commerce, Bureau of the Census, *Statistical Abstract of the United States,* 77th Edition, Washington, 1956, p. 763.

except for the top administrative or consulting positions where the range may be from $10,000 to $15,000, the amounts paid run between $4000 and $5200 a year. Salaries to federal government workers in the field rank as highest, followed by private organizations specifically devoted to rehabilitation and with private and state hospitals at the bottom of the ladder. These ranges compare unfavorably with private secretaries, skilled mechanical jobs in industry and even public school teachers in the larger cities. The report concludes that "our research indicates that a major reason for the shortage of personnel in the rehabilitation field is—inadequate salaries."[3] It further states

> But if rehabilitation is to meet its own manpower needs, it will have to compete with other industries, other occupations, other professions, other competing demands for able, competent people.
>
> . . . But the need for professional rehabilitation personnel is already so great, and promises to become so much greater, that the nation simply cannot much longer rely upon the sense of satisfaction that motivates a small group of dedicated people.
>
> . . . The facts in this report lead to the conclusion that unless action is taken soon, our country will suffer from the consequences of an inadequate supply of professionally trained people in rehabilitation. By "an inadequate supply," we mean an insufficiency of trained people who can rehabilitate the thousands of handicapped Americans who can be trained and returned to work as self-sustaining citizens.[4]

The organizers of community rehabilitation programs need to bear these discouraging facts clearly in mind and, in the initial development of specific facilities or services, attempt to peg starting salaries in brackets which more truly represent the considerable skills of rehabilitation personnel. In the example given previously of the requirements for a comprehensive, multiple disability unit for both in-patient and out-patient care, the estimate of needed staff was 72 persons, with 62 of these being full-time and 10 part-time.[5] Since the part-time help would be mostly the medical and psychological consultants, together with nurses' aids and domestics, one may reasonably conclude that the balance of the staff were in the various therapy, technical, nursing, supervisory, administrative, and clerical groups. If at least 50 of the staff fell in the $5000 range to start and the total for the balance was in the neighborhood of $150,000, this would make an initial hiring budget of $400,000 for the operation of this kind of

[3] Tickton, S. G., "Rebuilding Human Lives: The Rehabilitation of the Handicapped—Part One, Trained Rehabilitation Workers: How Much Are They Paid?" The Seventh Company, Inc., New York, 1957, p. 12.

[4] *Ibid.*, pp. 12–13.

[5] Desjardins, E. J., *op. cit.*

facility. As to the regular, out-patient rehabilitation center for a community, the staff would probably amount to between 25 and 30 with a consequent expenditure of around $125,000 in salaries.

Equipping a rehabilitation center is subject to tremendous variances in cost, due to different ideas of planners in the types, quantity, and quality of equipment needed. Some equipment will be built to specification as a part of the construction of the center, whereas other items will be purchased through commercial channels. Office furnishings and practical furniture for recreation and visiting areas, drapes, floor coverings, and other decoration items are necessarily included as a part of the over-all equipment in the center. Granting the possibility of great individual differences in this part of the planning, perhaps a reasonable figure for the combined in-patient, out-patient facility would be between $150,000 and $200,000 while the expenditure for the community, out-patient only center would be around $35,000 to $50,000.

Once the plans for actual construction, staffing, and equipping of a rehabilitation facility have been made, the community planning group must necessarily cope with the matter of annual operating expense and the establishment of a sensible budget, considering all continuing expenses of operation and their relation to income from all sources. Standard operating expense, like that of construction, staff, and equipment, will vary according to the size of the facility, the amount and character of service, and the number and type of staff. The Institute for the Crippled and Disabled in New York reports gross expenditures of operation for the year ending June 30, 1955 of $866,187 (including wages paid to disabled workers in the sheltered workshop).[6] The Crossroads Rehabilitation Center of Indianapolis, in its financial statement for the year ending August 31, 1956, reported expenditures of $253,354. The latter facility, certainly one of the most proficiently and efficiently operated centers in the United States, has provided a very interesting breakdown of its annual expenditures. This runs as follows:

[6] Institute for the Crippled and Disabled, *Rehabilitation Trends—Midcentury to 1956*, New York, 1956, pp. 94–95.

Medical direction and supervision	$ 3,856.00	1.52%
Physical therapy (P.T.) service		
(9,521 P.T. treatments to 256 patients)	14,370.67	5.68
Occupational (O.T.) therapy service		
(4,988 O.T. treatments to 321 patients)	11,740.93	4.64
Speech therapy service		
(2,491 treatments to 38 patients)	4,468.40	1.77
Curative shop service		
(66 employed and trained)	26,182.00	10.33
Vocational training and blind adjustment		
(2,572 treatments given 14 blind and		
severely disabled)	5,220.30	2.06
Model nursery service		
(3,395 hours to 20 crippled children—		
47 parents counseled)	3,390.49	1.34
Recreational service		
(270 enrolled in camps and clubs)	2,402.65	.96
Social Service		
(752 individuals served)	6,639.75	2.62
Rehabilitation and individual service		
(117 returned to productive employment)	6,258.64	2.57
Education and counseling service	7,819.90	3.08
Public information	11,909.98	4.70
Transportation service	8,710.08	3.44
Maintenance of buildings and grounds	9,141.49	3.61
Fund raising service		
(520 volunteers—8,000 hours of service)	7,674.49	3.03
Administration service	7,762.26	3.06
State and national societies	5,716.37	2.26
Building fund service	5,445.45	2.15
Loss of assets depreciated and disposed of	3,930.79	1.55
Building funds (new quarters)	94,584.15	37.33
Junior League funds (for Speech		
Department)	2,500.00	0.98
Funds reserved (for Vocational Department)	3,000.00	1.18
Checking account—balance	359.12	0.14
Total collected and accounted for[7]	$253,353.88	100 %

[7] 19th Annual Report, Crossroads Rehabilitation Center, Indianapolis, 1956.

The amounts shown include salaries as well as other expenditures. It is increasingly evident, of course, that salaries of personnel form a larger and larger part of the annual expense of operation for rehabilitation services, as in business and professional activities generally. The Institute for the Crippled and Disabled, for instance, reports that in 1951 staff salaries amounted to slightly more than 50% of total expense, whereas in 1955 they accounted for over two-thirds of over-all cost of operation.[8] This represents about a 17% increase in four years and, as indicated previously in the comments on salaries of rehabilitation workers, this upward trend will and must continue.

Estimates of average costs of rehabilitation based on patients served or cases treated are not reliable indices of the principal factors in rehabilitation expense. Such figures are subject to tremendous range due to types of cases treated, kind of program, facilities used, length of treatment, and similar variables. It can be stated, for instance, that the Institute for the Crippled and Disabled had a per-person-served cost of $398 for the years 1954–55.[9] The Liberty Mutual publishes an average cost per industrial case treated at their centers of $594 but an average of more than $10,000 for comprehensive rehabilitation of the severe disability cases resulting from spinal cord injury.[10] The Office of Vocational Rehabilitation cites an average cost per person rehabilitated of $666 for the year 1955.[11] Although all these figures are of interest to the particular agency or organization operating a program as well as purchasers of the service, they are of little significance for planners, either in connection with establishing operating budget norms, setting fees, or considering financial support.

If initial costs of construction, staff, and equipment, together with costs of maintenance and operation, are important to the planners of community programs, the sources of income to meet these expenses are of equal, if not greater, concern. There is little purpose to elaborate plans for rehabilitation services if adequate financing is not readily available. The measurement of sources of revenue is too often hastily and inaccurately approached, with the result that well-intentioned programs fail or struggle along under intolerable burdens of operating deficit. Although rehabilitation may be one of the most dedicated and altruistic of human endeavors and although no rehabilitation program is designed as a money-making proposition, there is still great appeal to sponsors, workers, and contributors in the well-managed facility or service which essentially matches income with expenditures and is not always in the midst of a desperate appeal for extra funds to salvage the whole operation.

[8] Institute for the Crippled and Disabled, *op. cit.*, p. 42.

[9] *Ibid.*

[10] Hanson, S. L., "Results of Rehabilitation in the Field of Workmen's Compensation," article in *J. Chronic Diseases*, **3**, No. 3, pp. 323–330 (March 1956).

[11] U. S. Dept. of Health, Education and Welfare, *Annual Report*, Section on Office of Vocational Rehabilitation, 1955, p. 183.

A logical and positive approach to financing, with the assistance of the most capable persons having financial experience in the community who can be interested in the project, seems basic to good community planning in this area. Charles E. Caniff, executive director of the rehabilitation center in Evansville, Indiana, has perceptively indicated:

> There is no royal road to success in raising funds. Nor are there any guaranteed techniques that are sure to work in every community. A sound, well-planned service program, an effective community education program, a strong organization guided by respected and responsible leaders coupled with hard work is the best guarantee of financial success.[12]

Realizing that there are somewhat different sources of financing for the building or construction phase (together with the equipping, staffing, and starting of the proposed service) and the continued operational expense of the going service, it may be well to consider them separately. Insofar as the capital fund or building fund portion of the planning is concerned, the prime sources of financing would appear to be (1) individual gifts of major size, (2) local, private foundations, (3) fraternal or charitable community groups, (4) grants under the federal-state programs established by Public Laws 482 and 565, (5) business firms, and (6) public fund-raising drives. There is no set pattern as to which of the sources may be most effective in any one community. The planning group should carefully study and weigh the merits of any or all methods before embarking on the actual fund-raising.

In regard to the financing of the regular operating expense of an established program, facility, or service, it should be realized at the outset that any broad community service is not going to realize all of its operational expenses from fees charged for services rendered. This means that there will be definite and continuing need for "subsidy" from other sources. This community "subsidy" will cover primarily the charity or partial payment cases and the extra costs of educational, informational activities, and the like with which every rehabilitation activity becomes involved. One estimate for guidance purposes, frequently cited, is to the effect that half of the income should be derived from fee charges to consumers or purchasers of the service (public or private agencies, insurance carriers, employers, etc.), one-quarter from fee charges to individual patients, and one-quarter from voluntary

12 Caniff, C. E., "Estimating Financial Resources for Support of the Center," address and paper included in Proceedings of the Institute on Rehabilitation Center Planning sponsored by Conference of Rehabilitation Centers, Inc., Feb. 25–Mar. 1, 1957, Chicago.

contributions or donations from various sources.[12] There is no assurance that this kind of formula is statistically accurate or that it would be valid for every community or service. Certainly no service should be established on the basis of iron-clad adherence to any such rule, with resultant refusal of care to any excess percentage of the charity or non-payment cases. The principal aim is to provide the needed service and to accommodate the financing to the facts of that need.

Since income is related to fees charged for service, there is great interest in the whole subject of how to establish a fair and adequate charge. One method is to take the total annual expense of operation—for example, $200,000—and divide it by the annual number of treatments or patients handled per day (this figure is obtained by multiplying the daily treatment total or patient load by five for a week's operation and multiplying again by fifty-two), as for instance, $75 \times 5 = 375 \times 52 = 19,500$, in order to determine the per treatment or per patient-day cost and fee to be charged; in the example, this would amount to $10.25 on an all inclusive fee basis. This method is most satisfactory for those services which operate on the basis of the patients being in a comprehensive facility, program, or service every day for practically a full day.

Many community services, of course, do not operate in this fashion and render care on an hourly basis for portions of the day and not necessarily every day. Under such circumstances, community rehabilitation services seek to determine a fair hourly charge, sometimes varying the charge for the particular kind of therapy or other service rendered. This greatly complicates the whole process of determining proper charges and is one of the reasons why the fee situation in rehabilitation is in a state of complete confusion at the moment. In rehabilitation centers, for instance, the per diem charges throughout the country run from as little as $4.50 to as much as $35.00 and many make additional charges for medical examinations, special diagnostic or treatment procedures, counseling, prosthetic fitting and training, etc. There is great need for detailed study of the measurement of and proper fee allocation to services rendered in rehabilitation, with the hope of developing some uniformity and possibly finding more efficient operating methods.

Assuming that no open community service in rehabilitation can expect to meet operating expense entirely from fee charges, the "deficit" must then be covered by the voluntary contributions and donations derived from available community sources. Such sources would include the community chest or united fund support, national health organizations (with which the rehabilitation service may be directly affiliated), local civic, fraternal, religious or charitable groups, individual gifts and bequests, business or educational interests, direct annual public fund appeal. It should be obvious that the development of as many of these as possible on a fixed basis, clearly understood and supported by the community, will be to the distinct advantage of the rehabilitation program. The more definite and permanent its knowledge and expectation of this area of non-fee financial support, the more secure and progressive will be its management and contribution.

Administrative people concerned with rehabilitation programs are much worried over the rising cost of rehabilitation services. It is perfectly true that hospital and medical care costs have risen tremendously during the last fifteen years and that any service as complex and specialized as rehabilitation could not escape a similar trend. However, there is no belying the fact that, despite all protestations of the need for rehabilitation becoming an integral part of routine medical care, it still is in the nature of an "extra" or added service. With the staggering costs of hospital care, surgery, definitive medical treatment in the process of recovery from illness or injury, the provision of rehabilitation as the ultimate step in that recovery process must be kept within the bounds of reasonable cost. The attack on this problem may be mounted on several fronts:

1. Wider recognition of the utilization of rehabilitation as a means of reducing the length of hospital or institutional confinement, thereby lowering the over-all cost of medical care either on a private, insured or publically supported basis.

2. Better integration of community services to avoid duplication and consequent added expense.

3. Additional studies on measurement of rehabilitation services in the light of proper and more uniform allocation of fees.

4. Additional exploration of more efficient operating procedures in those programs providing rehabilitation service, with particular emphasis on possible purchase of part-time consulting services in the community rather than incorporation of all possible services in one facility.

5. Further examination of salary levels with eye to most attractive career possibilities, yet at the same time insuring the maximum utilization of staff, perhaps involving voluntary, part-time and consulting assistance as alternatives to full-time, permanent employees at every level and in every discipline.

6. Recognition of the effectiveness of smaller, less-expensive units

in the several distinct areas of community rehabilitation activity rather than huge facilities attempting to serve every rehabilitation need in the most expensive fashion. Development of complementing rather than all-inclusive services in every facility.

7. Regional utilization of centrally located and existing facilities as an alternative to construction of duplicate units in smaller communities.

8. Concentrated drive on more general understanding and acceptance of rehabilitation as a philosophy and practice. In wider use lies lower treatment or case cost for every type of service.

Every community planning group and all administrators in the field have the obligation to face up to the hard facts of rehabilitation cost and financing. The worst criticism which could possibly be leveled at the rehabilitation efforts in this country would be to the effect that "rehabilitation is wonderful but who can afford it?" If the understanding and cooperation of physicians, patients, administrative authorities in workmen's compensation and pre-paid medical plans, labor unions, and private or public health and welfare agencies is to be solicited and expected, the expense of the services rendered must not out-range the obvious individual, social, and economic benefits. Practical evaluation, research, and combined effort can provide the knowledge to meet and solve the issue.

CHAPTER 22

Community
Organization
for Rehabilitation

THE TASK FORCE ON THE HANDICAPPED IN ITS
1952 report, at the start of the portion containing the summary and
recommendations, made the crisp and forceful observation that
"because the problems of disability cover practically all the problems
which one might expect to encounter in human affairs, their solution
requires community action."[1] Phrased in a different way, one might
reasonably conclude that rehabilitation is too broad a concept, too
big a challenge, and too complex an operation for any one authority
or agency. Nothing less than community-wide thinking, planning,
and action can hope to approach the task with any real chance of
success.

Good community organization for rehabilitation, like other areas
of human endeavor, does not come about by chance. It cannot be
evolved from single agency authority, disciplinary competition, governmental authority, impractical humanitarianism, or selective disability interest. The old patterns of "the greatest good for the greatest
number," of progressive thinking and constructive action, are emphat-
ically applicable.

A sound plan for community organization would include the
following 11 definitive components:

1 Office of Defense Mobilization, Manpower Policy Committee, "Report of the
Task Force on the Handicapped," Washington, January 24, 1952, p. 58.

1. Imaginative leadership
2. Survey of need
3. Master plan
4. Broad involvement
5. Program orientation
6. Facility development
7. Integration of services
8. Financial support
9. Public relations
10. Education and research
11. Permanent organization

Imaginative leadership in rehabilitation planning, as in other kinds of community planning, is ideally broad in scope and representative in its composition. Usually, a single organization or small group of dedicated individuals is the spur behind the focusing of attention on rehabilitation as a point of needed activity within the community. This is commendable as a start, but worthwhile efforts in rehabilitation, if they are to benefit all the handicapped in the community, cannot long remain the province of one isolated group in the area, however sincere. The penetration of rehabilitation thinking and practice into so many areas of community effort and responsibility precludes any continued organization and planning on a limited basis. If it is to broaden and strengthen its purposes and activities, it must involve a community leadership on a base which includes all the interested, active, and needed people or organizations. The best answer to this need would seem to be some sort of community committee, council, or federation which is designed to function as the leader, planner, and organizer of an approved program.

Even though fundamentally sound in theory, this idea is not simple of accomplishment. Individuals or groups who arouse thinking and action, who perhaps regard themselves as pioneers in the community attempts at rehabilitation, are loathe to relinquish fancied authority and attendant publicity value in favor of a wider, joint effort. Yet the inherently democratic nature of rehabilitation seems to require broad representation and planning which is oriented to community needs of the disabled, not the specialized problems of one aspect of rehabilitation. In setting up and using a committee, council, or federation, in endowing it with sufficient stature and authority to get the job done, there will, of necessity, be some "noses out of joint," some "stepping on toes," certain individuals or agencies that will regard such action as an unwarranted intrusion into the sacrosanct sphere of their own interest and activity. However, the dividends of joint understanding and organization will be so marked that the jurisdictional difficulties will seem minor in comparison.

Sometimes an already existing community health, welfare, or social service can be utilized as a focal point for the organization of the rehabilitation committee, council, or federation. This often has the advantage of immediately providing a practical source of meeting place, staff help, and existent services for publicity, mailing, research, and the like. Under other circumstances, the organization might have to be started almost from scratch and evolve its working plan through contributed effort by participating agencies. In any event, it is not necessary to establish an expensive, new organization with paid staff, rented quarters, and fancy publicity programs. Relatively little expense can accomplish a great deal through effective use of voluntary effort and the staff services of existing member groups.

Whatever the nature of the central leadership, it will function most effectively if its power is not dictatorial but suggestive, not arbitrary but persuasive. Sincerity and common interest in the cause of the handicapped can be the working lever to insure cooperative effort and integrated service. There will sometimes occur the belief that a broad council type of direction can result only in indefinite and nonspecific function. This criticism can be avoided by the establishment of working subcommittees in specialized areas of concern. By participation on these subcommittees, the member agencies will gain a sense of direct contribution, especially in areas which are their particular interest.

Under no circumstances should the central community group be attempting to provide actual service in any aspect of rehabilitation. To do so would remove it from the realm of impartial and cooperative planning and place it in competition with existing agencies or services in the community. Its proper function is to review, plan, suggest, and influence all of the community effort toward rehabilitation of the disabled but to leave to the member or cooperating organizations the actual provision of service, present or planned.

Ideally, the committee, council, or federation concerned with community rehabilitation effort would be comprised of representatives from the following types of agencies, organizations, and institutions:

County or city medical society
Welfare department
Individual physicians interested in
　rehabilitation

Nursing association
Therapy associations
Social service groups
Special schools for handicapped

Rehabilitation centers
State and local health services
Veterans Administration
Local chapters of national voluntary agencies (polio, heart, cancer, cerebral palsy, tuberculosis, multiple sclerosis, and the like)
Veterans' posts
Church councils or charities
Women's clubs
Parent-teacher association
Organized parent groups (often for particular handicap)
Newspapers, radio, and television
Community voluntary service groups like Red Feather
Medical specialty societies
Limb and brace fitters
Chamber of Commerce
Fraternal organizations
Hospitals
Universities and colleges (departments of education, psychology, medicine, nursing, therapy, social work)
Public and private educational systems
Workmen's compensation authority
Division of Vocational Rehabilitation
State Employment Service
Insurance carriers
Blue Cross–Blue Shield or other prepaid medical plans
Labor unions
Employer groups or individual firms with record of interest in handicapped
Research institutes
Local bar association
Sheltered workshops
Training schools for handicapped
Financial foundations and trusts
Pertinent legislative committees
Lay individuals concerned or interested in rehabilitation
Legislative commissions or committees

The chairmanship of the community planning group in rehabilitation is most effectively vested in a person not only vitally interested in the broad field of rehabilitation but primarily a good organizer and administrator, one who can get people to work together. He or she need not necessarily be a professionally trained person and, in fact, a knowledgeable layman may be able to bring less prejudice and more objectivity to such an assignment. The working arm of the group will be an executive council or committee, the membership of which may best be developed from the competent specialists serving as chairmen of the respective working subcommittees. Special advisory groups may be set up from time to time for purposes of selected research projects or particular contact assignments.

The *survey of community needs* of the disabled as a precedent to development of a sound plan for rehabilitation was discussed in an earlier chapter. Insofar as possible, this survey should form a working blueprint for the community rehabilitation planning group in connection with its practical consideration of what areas of local difficulty can best be improved by group action or appropriate suggestion to the agencies concerned.

Like most civic improvements, the development of proper rehabilitation facilities and services in a community is dependent on the formulation of a *master plan*. Such a plan would not be a limited outline of needs in one area of rehabilitation, such as jobs for the handicapped or special classes for pre-school children with hearing defects, but would cover the whole picture of the community's needs in the many ramifications of rehabilitation generally. Neither would such a plan be a budget outline of what the community could presently afford in the way of facilities and services. A master plan is necessarily a goal, an incentive, even a "dream." It is the synthesis of all the obtainable opinion from the best informed people in the community on this particular subject. It has taken into careful consideration the survey already made of the numbers of the disabled, the present rehabilitation programs in operation and the measurement of their adequacy, the general atmosphere of rehabilitation in the community. On the solid facts of that survey, the rehabilitation committee, council, or federation would attempt to erect a practical structure of needed services. No account would be taken at this stage of cost, financing possibilities or details of final operation. Those would become the concern of later implementing procedures by agencies and organizations involved, at the urging of the central committee.

The master plan thus becomes a practical and a positive evaluation of what the community should be doing in rehabilitation, if it is to truly meet the needs of its handicapped people. It cannot and should not be merely a critical comment on shortcomings of community agencies and programs, although the clear recognition of those deficiencies may have led directly to the more constructive recommendations in the plan. Without this kind of over-all plan, the community has little chance to influence and channel the rehabilitation activities of its institutions, organizations, and individuals. Possessed of an objectively written plan, authored by the joint effort of all those participating in the planning group, the community can have some hope of steady progress toward attainable and worthwhile goals.

Broad involvement of persons in the community interested in, responsible for, or learning about rehabilitation activities will continue to be a primary responsibility of the community planning and coordinating group. In the listing above of representation on the central committee itself, it is obvious that there is a tremendous range of activity and interest in this field. The involvement extends not only to the committee or council but also to the work of the agencies and institutions. They must learn the benefits of getting maximum participation and cooperation if rehabilitation is to become an accepted part of our community lives. One writer laments the fact that reha-bilitation has almost been a cult of a relatively few dedicated leaders and their followers and that the message has not really permeated the thinking and action of the general public. The validity of such state-ments may reasonably be questioned on the grounds that the "general public," a too often undefined generality, is sometimes more aware of and responsive to the message of the dignity of man and his right to modern techniques of restoration to the "full life" than the many poorly informed professional, technical, and business people. In any event, the answer to the plea for more information on rehabilitation is, to a great extent, involvement. Too often we have seen the glowing plans for a rehabilitation service come to fruition without any attempt at involvement of the local medical society or other medi-cal groups in the community, only to later witness bitter complaints by the service staff on the failure of the local doctors to know about or to use the rehabilitation service. Edward Lindeman once stated perceptively that "the key word of democracy is participation."[2] No expression could be closer to the basic need of rehabilitation involve-ment for people from all walks of life.

Proper *program orientation* is important to the eventual success of any rehabilitation venture. There are at least four pre-requisites to any development of a sound community rehabilitation program. These apply not only to the broad program planning but equally to the individual activities of agencies and institutions making up the program. First and foremost the program concerns the interests of the patient—it must be patient-centered. Rehabilitation is *for* the patient, not *to* the patient. Interest, understanding, and motivation are the qualities in rehabilitation programs which serve to arouse the patient's cooperation and insure his getting the most from a program. Cold insistence on routine, over-attention to publicity schemes, rivalry between staff departments or disciplines, or lack of continuity can all stifle the patient in a blanket of confusion. The planning group must find a common denominator of concern for the patient in all its considerations of a final program. Prestige for the community and "keeping up with the Joneses" through the latest equipment, tech-niques, and facilities is much less important than planning around the needs of your community and your people as prospective patients. Seldom do we ever see a patient or former patient on an advisory board nor do we hear of rehabilitation administrators meeting reg-

2 Lindeman, Edward C., *The Democratic Man, Selected Writings,* Beacon Press, Boston, 1956, p. 167.

ularly with patients to obtain their ideas on possible improvements in programming.

Secondly, the integrated program of rehabilitation offers a diagnostic and evaluation procedure as one of its principal components. Dr. Shands has remarked that "with insufficient information and inaccurate diagnosis a patient may start a program of rehabilitation totally unsuited to his handicap."[3]   It is not enough to rely on original medical records at the time of injury or onset of disease; neither is it sufficient to ask a referring physician to spell out the prescription for further rehabilitative care.   Although both of these types of information are necessary and desirable to completion of the patient's history, there is basic need for a careful evaluation, preferably by the team of rehabilitation professional staff and technicians who can consider the status of the patient and define his needs at the time of the beginning of his rehabilitation program and periodically thereafter. This pattern is valid not only in connection with the physical restoration phases of his case but also in the psychological, personal counseling, and vocational aspects of patient progress.   Rehabilitation is no automatic process in which the patient is referred to the facility or the agency and a streamlined, guaranteed product comes out at the other end.   It is a complex process of constant re-evaluation to determine successes and failures, to permit changes and reconsiderations, to adapt goals to practical possibilities.

Comprehensiveness is the third pre-requisite in program orientation. Few knowledgeable people in the field now dispute the premise that little is gained by erratic stabs at rehabilitating a handicapped individual.   A dab of physical therapy here, a bit of vocational training there is not a logical approach to successful end results.   Comprehensiveness must permeate not only the program outlined for each patient but it should also be characteristic of the facilities and agencies in that they are willing to tackle a wide variety of disabilities in order to more effectively meet the community need.   The comprehensive community rehabilitation center is becoming the accepted standard of community planning and expenditure rather than the facility for a specialized disability.   The Office of Vocational Rehabilitation and the state divisions of vocational rehabilitation have assumed responsibility for a comprehensive series of rehabilitation activities under the broadening concept of rehabilitation initiated by the 1954 legislation.

The last component of program development is continuity.   Much has been said in rehabilitation literature and discussions about the

---

[3] Shands, A. R., "Diagnostic Clinic for Rehabilitation," *J. Am. Med. Assoc.*, **140**, No. 11, p. 937 (July 16, 1949).

detrimental aspects of a helter-skelter process of rehabilitation in the community. The doubts, fears, and discouragements which often lead to failure of a patient to finish or to succeed in a program of rehabilitation can often be attributed to breakdown in continuity. Time lags and significant gaps in one agency finishing its part of the process and another agency taking up the slack reveal real weakness in the program planning and execution. Successful rehabilitation is much like the old Chinese block puzzle. One little wooden section put into place at the wrong time or in the wrong sequence meant inability to form the smooth cube or sphere which was the objective.

Development of good rehabilitation facilities is part of the community plan for effective service to its disabled. Although facilities in themselves do not guarantee successful end results, they constitute a powerful means of coordinating and localizing the professional and technical procedures for physical restoration, prevocational testing and evaluation, measurement of self-care activity, vocational training, sheltered employment, and the like. It is difficult to visualize any community sincerely interested in developing a sound program of rehabilitation not considering some sort of rehabilitation center or institute as a basic part of its initial plan. Ideally for the smaller cities and towns, the center should probably be comprehensive in nature, of a multidisability type, and incorporating some or all of the features and services of the sheltered workshop. The standards for such centers as outlined by interested professional groups, by the Vocational Rehabilitation Act, and Hill–Burton Act amendments have been previously discussed and need no repetition here. Expansion and utilization of hospital physical medicine and rehabilitation departments, psychiatric clinics, and vocational training schools are other aspects of the community development of facilities to perform the necessary roles in the rehabilitation process.

Integration of services was the subject of an earlier chapter and therefore needs no detailed consideration at this juncture. It seems obvious that such integration, both as to the service rendered the patient within a facility or by an agency and as to the multitude of various rehabilitation services in the community, would become a meaningful goal for any planning group. One of the key details of such integration would rest in the planning group or rehabilitation council itself. Its own existence, membership and deliberations would be integration in practice—its plans, if well prepared and genuinely representative of the best interests of the disabled, would constitute further evidence of the integrated approach. A central information and referral service, perhaps operated by the community rehabilitation council or committee, can form an effective instrument of purposeful integration for all the agencies and institutions involved.

Financial support of a rehabilitation program or facility is not always recognized as one of the responsibilities of a community planning group. In the chapter dealing with the cost of rehabilitation there is ample evidence of the fact that rehabilitation is an expensive process. Methods of fund raising and sources of financial support are briefly outlined. It is incumbent upon any community planning organization to develop a workable design for proper fund raising in connection with the improvement, expansion, or creation of rehabilitation programs and facilities. This design may take the form of assisting the agencies already active in the field to discover and tap new sources of funds or it may be a basic plan for the financial structure of a whole community rehabilitation program. In either event, federal, state, local fund sources are prime subjects for exploration. Private foundations, business firms, national health organizations, government agencies, fraternal or charitable groups, public subscription drives, and individual contributions all constitute potentials for partial or total financing.

Grandiose plans involving massive initial expenditures have less chance of sound financing than the projects which perhaps start modestly and grow as the need is demonstrated. Financing plans need to include not only the expense of establishing, equipping, staffing, and housing the program or facility but also the continuing expense and anticipated income. Sources of case payments, possibilities of later grants and gifts, long-range plans for growth, and increased capital are all as much a part of the necessary consideration of what a community can support as the initial expenses of getting started.

Rehabilitation programs have a lot to learn and practice in the realm of establishing good *public relations*. The national health and specific disease drives have become past masters of the appeal to public imagination but, except for isolated instances, local rehabilitation programs and facilities have lagged badly in capturing the interest of the public and of the professions, technical people, business interests, educational systems, or community organizations. Yet it is basically a subject with tremendous personal and dramatic appeal. There are few dramas which can compare with that of man's conquest over his own disabilities—it touches the heart strings, it stimulates the imagination, it fires the enthusiasm and activity of the most callous of men. The pen of the most skillful author could scarcely conjure up the defeats and triumphs, the grim determination, and the pain-wracked struggles which are commonplace in the files of nearly every rehabilitation agency or institution. It is interesting that no great novel has yet been written on the subject of rehabilitation.

It has been demonstrated that rehabilitation has to be "sold" to patients and to participating professional or technical groups or individuals. It also has to be "sold" to the general public and to the community as a whole from the point of view of understanding, use and financial support. Many professional people in the field talk glibly of "public education" as the great need for the future growth of rehabilitation. No adult, least of all the professional, executive, or administrative person, relishes the idea of "being educated" to something. Need for education implies ignorance, carelessness, inertia, resistance. How much more positive is the concept of public relations, of a need to develop common understanding, sympathy, involvement. It is ever so much easier to "sell" a graphic portrayal of human need than condescending effort to teach or impress the values of rehabilitation.

All the avenues to public knowledge and specialized appreciation are open to effective use by rehabilitation planners or involved groups. Radio, television, newspapers, magazines, speeches to conventions and group meetings, exhibits, demonstrations, visits to facilities, published literature, all constitute effective media of information readily available and often without great expense. The community rehabilitation council or committee can organize, develop and carry out a program of public information very effectively and, in this way, can publicize the efforts of many community services which could not otherwise afford or execute such programs on their own.

Education of professional and technical personnel for work in the rehabilitation field is part of the community responsibility. If we are to seek and find competent young people to learn the techniques of rehabilitation, in any of the several professions and disciplines involved, some method of developing basic interest in and training for the job is of paramount importance. Public and private school systems, universities and colleges, need encouragement to learn of the opportunities for humanitarian service and individual achievement in these areas. A close working relationship, to the point of actual affiliation in some instances, with practical rehabilitation programs in the community can provide excellent training for later entry into the various fields of activity in rehabilitation. Even those who may never contemplate actual work in this area would gain appreciably in understanding and development of personal attitudes by some exposure to the challenges of disability for those who suffer its affliction and those who attempt its conquest. Educational institutions are wont to regard rehabilitation as a practical, unacademic process which might be better left to the apprenticeship in the outside world. There is little understanding yet of the broad spread of human thought and activity which is inherent in the very concept of rehabilitation. If democracy is worthy of study and analysis as a focal philosophy and practice in daily life, surely the attempt of man to overcome the ravages of crippling disease, injury, or congenital defect through a systematic, restorative process and thus to achieve independence in his social and economic world, can deserve no less consideration from the educators.

Research into the effectiveness of any community rehabilitation program is basic to its hope of improvement and to its contribution in terms of a lesson for others. The project grants made by the Office of Vocational Rehabilitation, the sponsored research on the part of private foundations and interested groups, have greatly stimulated the initiation of studies in many different areas of rehabilitation activity. It is not sufficient, however, to await the completion of national surveys or broadly definitive studies. Much more practical value can be gained from the development of sound local follow-up and accumulation of statistics within the various components of a community rehabilitation program. A community rehabilitation council or committee can take leadership in planning, staffing, and financing such research to the mutual benefit of all community groups. Far too little is known of what causes failures in some cases of attempted rehabilitation; too few studies are made on what happens to cases after they have assumedly been rehabilitated (did it stick?); information is scarce on practical methods of measuring cooperation by agencies involved in rehabilitation. All sorts of definitive information could be uncovered in any community by carefully planned and executed studies along these and similar lines. Rehabilitation without measurement of results leads to static processes, to limited accomplishments, to ineffective "selling" of a service to the community. It is surprising that so many rehabilitation programs and facilities pay so little attention to this phase of their activity. They may plead a lack of funds for this purpose or ignorance of methodology. It takes no professional to obtain and study the simpler statistics and practical facts which can be woven into a most telling demonstration of strength or weakness. The benefits of such demonstrations are more than worth the effort involved.

Successful community organization for rehabilitation is not merely a matter of initial planning and launching of a project or a program. Too many community groups, sincerely interested and inspirationally motivated, have been born in a burst of civic enthusiasm, dynamically driven to substantial accomplishments in launching a rehabilitation venture, only to wither on the vine once the project was actually under way. From its inception, a soundly developed community plan should contemplate a continuing, *permanent organization* which will act as the nucleus of rehabilitation interest and activity for that particular community. Representation on the continuing council or committee should be sufficiently broad to insure the cooperation of both public and private agencies. Its demonstration of dedicated effort can become the pattern for all the community planning, the prime force for integration of effort, the source of practical assistance and inspiration toward greater accomplishments in the field by all components of the rehabilitation process. In organizing and developing a community rehabilitation council or committee to carry on this kind of centralized sharing of ideas and activity there is sometimes a fear on the part of individual agencies or institutions that they will lose their identity and surrender their prerogatives; that some kind of super-authority will dominate their efforts. The truth of the matter is rather that the combination of promotional and developmental activities will strengthen each agency program and help it to be more effective in its own particular area of rehabilitation.

The Inter-Agency Committee on Rehabilitation Service for Severely Disabled Persons, appointed by the Retraining and Reemployment Administration of the U. S. Dept. of Labor, in its report on a community program format, makes this astute observation on the subject of community organization:

> The needs of the severely disabled are so varied, occur in such unique combinations, and require appropriate services over such an extended period of time that their rehabilitation cannot be accomplished in a single agency. It is only through the mobilization and coordination of the efforts of voluntary and public agencies, and the integration and expansion of their services, that the community can discharge its responsibility to the severely handicapped. The conservation of human resources, like that of our natural resources, is a community responsibility. The community with its services and resources and their effective coordination becomes a rehabilitation center.[4]

Community organization for rehabilitation, or for any other worthy purpose, is never an easy task. It is fraught with frustrations, disap-

[4] Porter, E. B., "Community Organization—the Dynamics of Community Action," *J. Rehabilitation*, **XIX**, No. 4, pp. 416–418 (July–Aug. 1953).

pointments and defeats. Edgar Porter has truly said "I can assure you that helping a community to organize its thoughts and actions in behalf of the handicapped is the hardest work you can hope to do, but it is the most satisfying in its results."[4] Because of its many ramifications, its varied interests, its broad spectrum of concern, successful community rehabilitation is democracy in action—a combination of spirit and purpose vital to the modern attack upon disability of all kinds.

CHAPTER 23

Rehabilitation
and the World
Community

CRIPPLING DISEASE AND INJURY RESPECT NO
international boundaries. The afflictions of mankind and the social
or economic consequences of those afflictions are as common to Pak-
istan as to Great Britain. The back strain of the worker in the tin
mines of Bolivia or the crippling effects of spinal meningitis upon the
schoolchild in Turkey wreak their disturbing influences upon individual, family, and community in much the same fashion as would be
expected in Davenport, Iowa. Pain, doubt, fear, anxiety, discouragement, and the final surrender to disability are universal emotions
and experiences.

Just as rehabilitation seems to call forth the best in individual and
community understanding and effort, so the challenge of man's attempt
to conquer his own handicaps appears to strike a chord of deep
response in the area of international concern and cooperation. The
United States, while developing more resources and expending more
funds in recent years, has no monopoly on either the philosophy or
practice of rehabilitation. As a matter of fact, many of the pioneering
programs were in other countries and, even today, some facets of the
rehabilitation process have found greater social and political acceptance outside our own national boundaries.

It is notable that the first institution which devoted its entire
resources to the care of the crippled was established in Switzerland in
the year 1780. The first known school for the blind was founded

in France in 1786. Earlier chapters have dealt with the programs developed in England, Germany, Canada, and the Scandinavian countries for military casualties, the crippled child, and the elderly handicapped person. From these earlier attempts were derived many of the initial efforts of physicians, social workers, technicians, government agencies, and community planners in the United States. The sound planning and application of rehabilitation programs and techniques in whatever land has found ready acceptance and utilization by others interested in the accomplishment of the same objectives for their own peoples.

The character of rehabilitation services which have been developed in various countries throughout the world is necessarily different by reason of the social, economic, cultural, and political variations and requirements. Nations which have just started to emerge from the cocoon of domination or control by other nations, those which are only beginning to recover from the devastating effects of war, are expending most of their time, effort, and money in the basic organization or re-organization of essential services to their peoples. Although their interest in rehabilitation may be as strong as our own, their need for such services even greater than ours, it has been a simple matter of "first things first" in the development of a political system, a social order, and a business economy which is struggling to survive. The need for encouragement, guidance, cooperation, and financial assistance is literally tremendous and the thirst for knowledge in the rehabilitation field both thought-provoking and inspiring.

Many countries lack the industrial concentrations, the huge city populations, the educational and communication facilities of the larger nations. Diversified, primarily rural populations, lack of general education, ineffective health and sanitation programs, and over-supply of able-bodied workers make rehabilitation a vastly different concept and practice than that which may be typical of our present programs in the United States. But the challenge is all the greater for the difficulties which are present. More and more we are coming to realize that the shrinking boundaries and barriers of our world today are forcing us to the clear appreciation that not only the security but also the welfare of all the peoples depends upon sharing of ideas and knowledge, upon assistance through many avenues toward individual as well as racial or national independence.

Two trends have been evident in the growth and development of international action on the rehabilitation front. One has been the establishment of international groups specifically interested in rehabilitation and the other has been the individual or team "rehabilitation missionaries." Both kinds of activities have led to healthy interchange of ideas and methods with resultant improvement of national and community programs on the part of all participants.

United States' interest in the health and social welfare of other nations had its inception in the recovery aid programs of the United States after World War I, both by governmental and private agencies, and in the organization of the League of Nations. Certain of the activities which were an outgrowth of the League involved certain health and social planning and assistance. Most definitive of these was the International Labor Organization (I.L.O.) which was established in 1919 when its constitution was adopted as Part XIII of the Treaty of Versailles. The purpose of this specialized agency was to contribute to the establishment of lasting peace by the promotion of social justice, to improve labor conditions and living standards through international action, and to promote economic and social stability. From the first, it was interested in the rehabilitation and employment of disabled workers. Much of its activity was in the area of research and published material for many years but more recently it has embarked upon a practical program of cooperation with governmental and voluntary groups. By a series of regional conferences throughout the world and by direct assistance on labor and manpower problems, the I.L.O. is seeking the goal of increased understanding among governmental, labor, and industrial leaders as to the value of rehabilitation. In 1955, its governing body adopted the following policy statement (quoted in part):

> Vocational rehabilitation services should be made available to all disabled persons, whatever the origin and nature of their disability and whatsoever their age, provided they can be prepared for and have reasonable prospects of securing and retaining suitable employment.[1]

Other groups such as the International Health Organization and the Advisory Committee on Social Questions also demonstrated international interest and cooperation on subjects related to certain areas of rehabilitation during the years following World War I. In the same years, the war relief activities of the United States government and the privately financed operations of the Red Cross, International Conference of Social Work, many religious and charitable groups, contributed vastly to the growing concept of international responsibility for world health and welfare.

By the time of World War II, this groundwork of social consciousness had been so well laid that the organization of the President's War

[1] Rusk, H. A., "I.L.O. Aids the Disabled," column in the N. Y. Times, Sunday, August 19, 1956.

Relief Control Board and its administration of war charity work, together with the formation of the United Nations Relief and Rehabilitation Administration, seemed natural expressions of cooperative planning for maintenance of health and direction of rehabilitation efforts in the war-ravaged countries. U.N.R.R.A., particularly, became involved in the plans for providing medical treatment, appliances, occupational retraining, and special vocational training for the great numbers of adults and children in places such as Greece, China, Yugoslavia, and Italy.

Formal declaration by national governments of their vital concern for the economic and social, as well as the political, welfare of their peoples became a reality with the signing of the United Nations Charter on June 26, 1945. That document, in its preamble, cites the determination of the signatory powers to reaffirm their faith in "the dignity and worth of the human person," to "promote social progress and better standards of life in larger freedom," to "employ international machinery for the promotion of the economic and social advancement of all peoples." Under Chapters IX and X of the Charter, provision is made for international economic and social cooperation and for the creation of the Economic and Social Council as an arm of the United Nations to accomplish the defined purposes.[2] At the first regular session of the General Assembly of the United Nations in 1946, upon recommendation of the Economic and Social Council, the Assembly acted favorably upon Resolution 58 (1) which established the program of Advisory Social Welfare Services and mentioned services for the handicapped as an area in which expert advice, demonstration and technical equipment should be made available to governments. A Social Commission was set up as a functional body under the Economic and Social Council. On Dec. 11, 1946, the General Assembly established the United Nations Children's Fund (U.N.I.C.E.F.), which also functions under the direction of the Council. Still another specialized agency of the Council is the United Nations Educational, Scientific and Cultural Organization (U.N.E.S.C.O.), brought into existence in 1946.

At the eleventh session in 1950 of the Economic and Social Council, the Secretary-General of the United Nations was requested to "plan jointly with the specialized agencies and in consultation with the interested non-governmental organizations, a well-coordinated program for the rehabilitation of physically handicapped persons."[3] A

[2] United Nations Charter, San Francisco, 1945.

[3] United Nations Social Welfare Information Series, ST/SOA/Ser. F/11.2, "Rehabilitation of the Handicapped," New York, Sept. 1953, p. 3.

technical working group was created from experts in various organizations working in the international field and the prepared program was adopted by the Social Commission and by the Economic and Social Council in 1952. This document or report is worthy of the careful reading of every person concerned with or interested in the rehabilitation of the handicapped. After emphasizing that the different standards of living and varying levels of basic services in each part of the world require careful and deliberate exploration before attempting any comprehensive rehabilitation program, the report makes the significant point that "there is no country in the world, however underdeveloped, in which the first steps cannot be taken towards alleviating the suffering of the handicapped." Further on in this section dealing with the general principles of the United Nations on this subject, the following comment is made:

> It is generally agreed that facilities for the handicapped must form an integral part of the services in the field of health, education, social welfare and employment which each government is endeavouring to develop, and not as an extraneous service for a particular class of the community. It is the responsibility and privilege of the United Nations and specialized agencies, as well as of the non-governmental organizations working in this field, each group in its own manner, to assist the governments in any way possible in the building up and strengthening of these basic services, in the promulgation of measures to prevent or limit physical disability, in the education of public opinion on the duty of society towards the handicapped, and in the development of modern rehabilitation methods for the reconditioning, the training and the employment of all classes of handicapped persons.[4]

The contributions of the United Nations and its specialized agencies may be said to fall in the areas of (1) publicity and information, (2) research and promotion of standards, (3) preventive health measures, (4) technical advice, (5) training, through fellowships and seminars, (6) technical supplies. The tremendous weight of authority and prestige of relationship carried by the United Nations have proven of immense value in stimulating the coordination of world effort on behalf of the disabled.

Another agency which has played a significant role in the area of international concern for the handicapped is the World Health Organization. An outgrowth of the International Health Conference held in New York in 1946, the W.H.O. came into being in April 1948 when 26 members of the United Nations had accepted its constitution. Its stated purpose is to aid attainment by all peoples of the world of the highest possible level of health. Its program has been especially

4 *Ibid.,* pp. 4–5.

effective in the prevention of disability through campaigns against infectious disease. Sponsorship of training fellowships and technical meetings, use of expert consultants, has done much to improve the medical phases of rehabilitation in many areas of the world. A joint committee on the particular needs of the physically handicapped child has emphasized the need of bringing the professional services and facilities to the child, without disturbing the balance of normal growth and development, and has stressed the need of community integration of services.

In line with the 1950 resolution of the Economic and Social Council of the United Nations, requesting the joint planning with nongovernmental organizations, an immediate dividend of this action was the Conference of World Organizations. Over 25 international groups in scouting, therapy, trade unionism, social work, and veterans' activities met for the first time in 1951 and three times since then. Their aim is to bring about greater understanding and cooperation among the voluntary international organizations which have an immediate interest in the physically and mentally handicapped.

The International Refugee Organization (I.R.O.) faced up to the challenging task of resettling persons who were both displaced and disabled following World War II. The fitting of these "outcasts of the world" for new lives and new jobs in other countries has attracted and deserved the admiration of those in all lands who are dedicated to the task of overcoming the effects of disability.

One of the most significant contributions to international thinking and action on behalf of the handicapped of the world has been made by the International Society for the Welfare of Cripples. Founded in 1922 as the International Society for Crippled Children, it was reconstituted in 1939 under its present name. A quotation from its Secretary General describes its composition and purpose succinctly:

> It is a federation of national, non-governmental organizations in 30 countries maintaining liaison with each other for the inauguration and development of programmes for physically handicapped children and adults. Broad in scope, the purposes of the Society embrace: the compilation and distribution of information concerning services for all the physically disabled other than the blind and deaf; the encouragement of measures for the prevention of physical disability; assistance in the establishment of national voluntary organizations in this field; the holding of international congresses; and aiding in the cultivation of public opinion throughout the world to increase services and opportunities for the physically handicapped.[5]

[5] Wilson, D. V., "International Co-operation for the Handicapped," reprint from *Int. Nursing Rev.,* International Society for the Welfare of Cripples, New York, 1956.

The Society holds a world-wide meeting every three years and maintains one of the foremost film libraries on rehabilitation in the world. It provides information on fellowship opportunities and exchange study between countries; has established an international prosthetics information center in Copenhagen to provide a base for exchange of information in this vital field. It has consultative status with the Economic and Social Council of the United Nations and with U.N.I.C.E.F., cooperates with I.L.O. and U.N.E.S.C.O., and has an official relationship with W.H.O. Under a foundation grant, translations of technical and scientific articles in rehabilitation are made available in several key languages.

Side by side with the activities of the international groups and, indeed, often with their sponsorship or support, have developed the contributions of the team or individual "rehabilitation missionaries." Some of the most practical and far-reaching education and direction in the establishment of rehabilitation services and programs in the countries of the world has been sparked by this kind of personalized "mission." Pioneers in the field of medical rehabilitation such as Howard Rusk, Henry Kessler, key administrators like Bell Greve, teams of physicians, nurses, therapists, and others have given weeks and months of their time in the cause of the handicapped of other lands. Their efforts, together with the knowledge gained by hundreds of professional and technical students or workers from many countries studying our methods in rehabilitation, constitute a bond of international cooperation for the betterment of mankind which will grow ever stronger and more meaningful.

Few of us are in a position to analyze or appreciate, as yet, the significance of our increasing concern for the better medical care and the complete rehabilitation of the disabled individual, in the light of world developments. Some hint can be obtained from the fact that more and more people who are in a position to know something about the matter are convinced that our efforts on behalf of the individual, our sincere interest in his medical, social, and economic welfare, under a democratic form of government, may contribute in large measure to tipping the scales of world opinion in our favor. Very much like the exhibits of the United States at the international trade fairs, the surprising discovery of unsuspected support and friendship for the Western democracies at the Bandung Conference, our practical demonstrations of assistance to the other countries of the world in the areas of preventive, curative and restorative medicine, the social and economic improvement of their lives have served to revitalize a dwindling faith in the "American ideal" and have placed the communist ideology on the defensive.

Dr. Howard Rusk, one of the foremost spokesmen for this international significance of rehabilitation, has stated that "rehabilitation can also provide the understanding between peoples and nations that is the essential foundation of any political effort toward peace."[6]   Dr. Henry Kessler, another leader in the march toward better services for the disabled of the world, says:

> These developments not only mean more and better care for millions of handicapped persons, but, taken together, reflect the international ideal of service which is the hope of a peace-seeking world.[7]

The awesome multitudes of the diseased and the crippled in the nations of Asia, Africa, and the Near East provide a staggering challenge to the medical, social, and financial resources of the Western world.   With the passing of the age of imperialistic dominion, the struggle of nations and races to achieve independence is linked to their desire for social and economic betterment.   High in the order of need, as national strivings find expression in political, social, and economic accomplishments, is the basic urge for recognition of the dignity of the individual—his right to a chance in life.   This concept is the root of all our rehabilitation efforts and its increasing translation to the minds and hearts of the less privileged nations of the world can form a large part of the future guarantee of peace, international understanding, and cooperation, a major impetus toward dedication of the world's peoples to mutual trust and security.   Financial aid, political suggestion, and diplomatic pressures may be resisted or resented but direct and practical concern for and assistance with the sick and disabled of any land touches deeply the hearts and minds of communities, families, and individuals.   Each of us who has a part in this great undertaking of rehabilitating the handicapped, difficult though our temporary problems may often be, can find a sense of deep satisfaction in the knowledge that peoples everywhere are watching, hoping, and reacting favorably to our growing achievements in the field of medical care and rehabilitation.

[6] Rusk, H. A., "Rehabilitation: An International Problem," article in *Arch. Phys. Med. Rehabilitation,* 37, No. 3, p. 136 (March 1956).

[7] Kessler, H. H., *Rehabilitation of the Physically Handicapped,* Revised Edition, Columbia University Press, New York, 1953, preface to second edition, p. xiii.

CHAPTER 24

Challenge for the Future

REHABILITATION IS NOT A STATIC PROCESS. ITS pattern of services and programs will continue to change with the thinking and the practices of future years. No simple blueprint of future development can be readily sketched at this time, yet there are certain obvious challenges presented to all who believe in and are concerned with any of the many aspects of rehabilitation activity.

It is apparent that rehabilitation cannot grow apart from other lines of human endeavor; it is not some separate process imposed upon a select few as sort of an after-thought, nor can it survive as the conviction and practice of a few professionals and technicians. If rehabilitation is to be a meaningful aspect of twentieth century life, it must become an integral part of accepted medical practice, of social welfare activity, of management-labor concern and negotiation, of education, of governmental and private agency function, and of the daily attitudes and knowledge of the people as a whole. Its imprint must be on every reaction and every practical measure connected in any way with the effects of disability upon the lives of our fellow men. The Chinese sage, Laotzu, philosophized that "a good man, before he can help a bad man, finds in himself the matter with the bad man." Transposed into the idiom of rehabilitation, it may be said that any of us who would help those mentally or physically limited must find within ourselves the depths of understanding which are born of the doubts, fears, and despair of all human beings in the face of adversity.

In this era of great political, social, and economic change, we are conditioned to hearing and reading of ideologies, social theories, economic trends, progressive education, communal planning, governmental domination, and the like. Perhaps we have lost sight of what may well be the most significant change of all, the fact that "people have become more important." This simple phrase concisely describes the reason for our present concern with the whole process of rehabilitation, from philosophy to practice. One can hardly advocate or carry on rehabilitation activity unless one is convinced of the importance of human life, of the dignity of man, of the right to full opportunity for all individuals. Imbued with this kind of philosophy, it becomes inconceivable to relegate the handicapped to the seclusion, the aversion, the hopelessness of years past.

Certain specific challenges confront those who are concerned with rehabilitation, whether physician, administrator, therapist, counselor, community planner, or even the so-called man on the street. The following seem to be some of these areas of challenge which could well serve as guidelines for future planning and action:

1. *Weaving the pattern of rehabilitation into the practice of medicine.* There is no exclusive right to rehabilitation knowledge or activity on the part of any one branch or specialty of medicine, nor can the physician relegate the responsibilities in this connection to the technician or the layman. The Commission on Chronic Illness has concluded that "Rehabilitation is an innate element of adequate care and properly begins with diagnosis. It is applicable alike to persons who may become employable and to those whose only realistic hope may be a higher level of self-care. Not only must formal rehabilitation services be supplied as needed, but programs, institutions and personnel must be aggressively rehabilitation-minded."[1] It has become fashionable to berate the medical profession for its presumed lack of interest and uncooperative attitude in rehabilitation. Actually the people in rehabilitation programs and facilities have the obligation of bringing medical groups, institutions, and individuals into the planning, teaching, and servicing activities of rehabilitation. From the undergraduate in medical training to the experienced specialist there is need for understanding, help, and advice along rehabilitation lines. Rehabilitation has little purpose and no direction without medical guidance; the doctor will learn to use and take pride in this new clinical tool for his disabled patient.

[1] Commission on Chronic Illness, *Care of the Long-Term Patient,* Vol. II of *Chronic Illness in the United States,* Commonwealth Fund, Harvard University Press, Cambridge, 1956, p. 24.

2. *Planning for adequate and proper rehabilitation facilities.* The tremendous population growth and the extended life span, with its implication of survival only to incur chronic illness and accidents, the increased understanding of evaluation, conditioning, and retraining (not only for vocational placement but also for self-care and independent living) will mean increasingly heavy demands for facilities. As the demand rises, so does the necessity for careful planning. Nothing is more tragic than money and personnel wasted on impractical schemes for rehabilitation facilities in remote locations, on too specialized a basis, or with inadequate supervision and direction. Self-interest and sentimental motivation must give way to sound community planning directed at achieving the best facility for the most patients. Comprehensiveness rather than specialization seems the desirable aim in facility planning.

3. *Integrating public and private programs.* Nothing would more seriously affect the cause of rehabilitation than for government and voluntary programs to establish duplicate and competing services for the disabled. The size of the job to be done in future years, the complexity of the rehabilitation process and the great cost of establishing programs, facilities, and services clearly emphasizes the importance of cooperative and complementing action. It would appear that the national public rehabilitation programs can be most effective in the research, financing, coordination, and public information areas, whereas the specific state programs in vocational rehabilitation, crippled children's services, etc., can serve to provide direct assistance to the disabled in areas in which the private agencies are not always equipped to function effectively. For the most part, the greater the provision of direct service, particularly in the medical phases, to disabled persons by private organizations the better for the community program. The national government may continue its program for direct benefits and services to veterans, federal employees, and the like, but any further extension of federal funds or services into general medical care or rehabilitation for the disabled civilian, either child or adult, seems undesirable.

4. *Recruiting and training rehabilitation personnel.* The crying need for more trained personnel in all the various professions, disciplines, and technical phases of rehabilitation has been a focal point of emphasis by all research studies and professional associations in the field. There is the unsolved problem of interesting the high school boy or girl in some phase of rehabilitation as a career, providing the opportunity and the financial support for his or her education and then developing realistic and competitive pay scales for rehabilitation

workers. This is an effort in which the combined talents, resources, and money of public and private agencies or organizations, together with the help and advice of educators, rehabilitation experts, and the young people themselves, will be needed to come up with any successful answer.

5. *Improving the social laws to include specific provision for rehabilitation.* Certain steps have already been taken in this direction. The new amendments to the Social Security Act may lead to the discovery of many disabled persons formerly unknown to public or private agencies. There is need for an increasing understanding and administrative supervision of rehabilitation activity under the workmen's compensation acts of the states. This may require certain mandatory provisions similar to those already in effect in a few states. Welfare laws and practices would benefit from the introduction of a rehabilitation rather than a cash benefit philosophy. State programs for the aging and the chronically ill might well be based on rehabilitation facilities and the development of self-care and effective home living rather than more institutions for permanent residence and care.

6. *Gearing insurance and health plan programs toward rehabilitation.* There is little excuse for continuance of our insurance programs and voluntary health plans on a basis of emphasizing monetary reward and cash benefits for disability and medical care occasioned by accident or illness. Whether workmen's compensation, liability, or health insurance, the disabled worker, policyholder, or member of the general public needs the assistance of modern methods and techniques for restoring physical activity, mental competence, psychological balance, and vocational ability just as much as he needs the monetary benefits under the law or the policy. As public and private programs of insurance move steadily in the direction of comprehensive coverage for both illness and injury, either on or off the job (with indemnity as well as medical benefits expanded), the cost of disability to the insurance buyer, whether private individual or corporation, will become prohibitively expensive unless full advantage is taken of the possibilities of reducing both extent and cost by effectively incorporating and applying rehabilitation ideas and methods.

7. *Enlisting the support of both management and labor.* Although there are certain general areas of financial support, public service, and community encouragement in which the good offices of both labor and management people are needed for rehabilitation programs, the specific sphere in which no significant progress can be made without their help is that of the hiring and successful placement of the handicapped. Better methods of evaluating, testing, and training disabled

individuals in usable industrial skills can only be done with their help. The increasing age of our work force, and the prevalence of chronic illness or degenerative disease implicit in that aging, means greater need for effective re-placement of workers no longer able to perform physically strenuous jobs but still of real value to the employer if properly retrained, reoriented, and placed in different work. Union seniority rules, production costs, supposed insurance penalties, and threats of second injury or systemic breakdown are all barriers which can be broken down by careful and sincere management-labor discussion and action, perhaps by specific committees on employment, reemployment, or transfer of the handicapped worker.

8. *Improving communication and cooperation between agencies.* It is surprising how often a public or private agency rendering a supposed rehabilitation service in the community is almost insulated against knowledge of the complete community activity in the field or against any recognition of more than one specific disability. Every community must work diligently to overcome this barrier to effective integration of services. Central community committees or planning groups are an effective instrument in the common sharing of knowledge, personnel, and facilities to best advantage of all the agencies and all the disabled.

9. *Encouraging community acceptance of all the handicapped.* It is a common experience, even in a community which professes a well developed program for the disabled, to find that in the social and recreational opportunities of the community the handicapped person is not accepted. The result is a less than complete adjustment of the disabled individual. If the crippled child cannot join a Scout troop, if the Y.M.C.A. will not permit a teen-age polio victim in its pools, if a nursing home will not accept a blind person, if the spastic who can hold a job has to go home and stay there every night and week-end because of nonacceptance in various recreational or social groups and programs, rehabilitation in a community sense is something less than satisfactory. Rehabilitation is not just the job of the specialized agencies, it is the responsibility of all community groups.

10. *Maintaining flexibility of programs to meet changing disability needs.* As modern scientific and medical research gradually finds the way to isolate and combat the more serious of the crippling diseases, such as tuberculosis, poliomyelitis, and multiple sclerosis, there will be an increasing need for flexible community programs, facilities and services in rehabilitation. The disabling scourge of today may be the infrequent crippler of tomorrow. This is probably the best reason for comprehensive, multidisability services rather than those

restricted to only one kind of disease or condition. It is also important for the same reason that rehabilitation personnel be trained for and accept the responsibility for handling the general field of the handicapped rather than specializing in one variety of disability. Particularly vital is the need for more understanding of the mentally and emotionally handicapped and the practical possibilities for incorporating them in many of the same programs which have materially benefited the physically handicapped.

11. *Developing an improved public attitude toward the handicapped.* As schoolmates, friends, neighbors, fellow-employees, and members of churches, fraternal, or civic organizations, we reflect every day our sometimes unadmitted prejudices toward handicapped persons. Nothing can be more frustrating or defeating than to have a fine job of physical restoration, psychological adjustment and vocational training and placement followed by an outright refusal of fellow-employees to work beside a seriously handicapped individual. Again, this is an area in which public information at all levels, enlistment of the support of many community groups can accomplish wonders. The "Golden Rule" is an excellent working premise for all such efforts.

12. *Approving and supporting rehabilitation as an international force.* None of us is wise enough to accurately predict the forces for good or evil which will dominate the international scene in the years to come, but it is a safe guess that the measure of success with which the democratic forms of government and ways of life meet the test of human dignity and individual rights in all lands will lie, to some extent at least, in the initiative and understanding with which adequate programs for the complete rehabilitation of the world's disabled people are encouraged and developed. The appeal to human welfare is far stronger than political ideology, social theory, or economic assistance. Used wisely and sincerely, medical care and better rehabilitation could form a potent force for international security and mutual trust.

Rehabilitation is entering its golden age when it can truly become an accepted theory and practice of medical procedure, of social casework, of vocational education and counseling, of individual and group therapy, of hospital care, of management-labor concern, of agency planning, and of community understanding. The rehabilitation philosophy and method offer a way to overcome and control the legalistic maneuverings and financial rewards for disability. The concept will be fought tooth and nail by some elements, but the appeal of rehabilitation is basically the urge of mankind for a better world, for better individual sharing of rights and privileges. As both theory and practice, it can and must succeed in its endeavors, wherever those endeavors are both earnest and honest.

Jerome Pollack has said that

> Just as the Nineteenth Century came to preserve natural resources, so the conservation of human resources may become one of the keynotes of the Twentieth. Rehabilitation, as an affirmation of human worth, has an important place in this vital movement of our age.[2]

President Eisenhower, in his message to the Congress in January 1957, enunciated again the principles on which our republic was founded and with regard to which our national convictions have been enduringly strong. These were "a vigilant regard for human liberty, a wise concern for human welfare and a ceaseless effort for human progress." Nothing less than such principles and convictions should be the hallmark of those who labor in the cause of the handicapped. To the insistence that disability should not mean inability, that misfortune should not remove opportunity, we must all be whole-heartedly dedicated.

[2] Pollack, J., "Responsibility for Rehabilitation," *Best's Insurance News,* fire and casualty edition, **58**, No. 2, p. 28 (June 1957).

Bibliography

SINCE THERE ARE AT LEAST THREE OUTSTANDING bibliographical collections of rehabilitation literature, there is no attempt made in this book to include a full coverage of the field. Reference is made to the three principal sources of reference material, and the remainder is a limited listing of the more recent material as well as certain definitive data which were most helpful to the writer. Many of the works listed will necessarily constitute basic sources of information for all those interested in further exploration in the broader aspects of rehabilitation. No listing has been attempted of articles, pamphlets, or books which deal primarily with treatment methodology, equipment, special disability problems, or the more technical characteristics of the rehabilitation process. The majority of the material has a broad outlook toward the whole field or a major phase of rehabilitation activity.

Bibliographies

Graham, Earl C., and Marjorie M. Mullen, *Rehabilitation Literature, 1950–1955*, National Society for Crippled Children and Adults, McGraw-Hill Book Co., New York, 1956, 621 pages.

National Society for Crippled Children and Adults, *Bulletin on Current Literature* (now called *Rehabilitation Literature*), monthly publication, Chicago, 1940 to present.

Riviere, Maya, *Rehabilitation of the Handicapped—a Bibliography 1940–1946*, National Council on Rehabilitation, Livingston Press, New York, 1949, 2 Vols., 998 pages.

United Nations Social Reference Center, Division of Social Welfare, Department of Social Affairs, "Rehabilitation of the Handicapped," *Social Welfare Information Series*, ST/SOA/Ser. F/11.2, New York, September, 1953, 85 pages.

Administrative Aspects

Aitken, Alexander P., "Rehabilitation in Workmen's Compensation," *American Journal of Public Health*, 45, No. 7, pp. 880–884, July, 1955.

American Orthopedic Association, "Symposium on Crippled Children's Services" (Alfred R. Shands, Jr., Chairman), *J. Bone Joint Surg.*, 36A, No. 6, pp. 1259–1285, December, 1954.

American Public Welfare Association, "The Place of Rehabilitation in the Public Welfare Program," a statement of policy (reprint), Chicago, 1955.

Bamberger, Lisbeth, "Rehabilitation under Workmen's Compensation in California," *Ind. Med. Surg.*, 25, No. 2, pp. 62–72 (February, 1956).

Community Research Associates, *The Prevention and Control of Indigent Disability in Washington County, Maryland*, New York, 1954, 99 pages.

Covalt, Donald A., "Physical Medicine and Rehabilitation in Home Care Programs," *N. Y. State J. Med.*, 53, No. 14, pp. 1671–1673 (July 1953).

Dabelstein, Donald H., "Federal Support for Rehabilitation Research," *J. Rehabilitation*, XXIII, No. 2, pp. 4–6, 24–26 (March–April 1957).

Dawson, Marshall, "The Administration of Medical Care in the California Workmen's Compensation System," unpublished chapter in study prepared for Institute of Industrial Relations, University of California in Los Angeles, August 1954, 25 pages.

Dawson, Marshall, *The Development of Workmen's Compensation Claims Administration in the United States and Canada*, Bureau of Labor Standards, Washington, 1952, 39 pages.

Department of Education, Bureau of Vocational Rehabilitation, State of California, Sacramento:
"Disability and Dependency," Feb. 1956, 39 pages.
"A Study of Cases Closed in 1955–1956," Jan. 1957, 72 pages.
"A Study of Rejected Referrals," Apr. 1957, 28 pages.
"The Disabled Welfare Recipient," May 1957, 33 pages.

Federal Security Agency, Office of Vocational Rehabilitation, "Brass Tacks," Washington, 1949, 24 pages.

Galbraith, D. J., "Workmen's Compensation and Rehabilitation," *Am. J. Public Health*, 42, No. 8, pp. 963–966 (August, 1952).

Hellebrandt, Frances A., "Disability, Rehabilitation and the Law of Damages: Implications of Modern Rehabilitation Medicine," *Ind. Med. Surg.*, 22, No. 12, pp. 558–560 (December, 1953).

Kratz, John A., "Vocational Rehabilitation, Past, Present and Future in the United States," *Bull. Am. Rehabilitation Com.*, 2, No. 6, pp. 1–6 (May, 1954).

Pollack, Jerome, "Medical Care and Rehabilitation Under Workmen's Compensation—Present Status and Critique," Address before Medical Care and Industrial Hygiene Sections of American Public Health Association at 82nd Annual Meeting, Buffalo, October 13, 1954, 30 pages.

President's Committee on Veterans' Medical Services, Report to the President, Washington, 1950, 65 pages.

Rosner, S. Steven, "Workmen's Compensation and Cardiac Rehabilitation," *J. Rehabilitation*, XXI, No. 2, pp. 15–19 (March–April 1955).

Scheele, Leonard A., "New Partnerships in Rehabilitation and Public Health," *J. Rehabilitation*, XXI, No. 1, pp. 4–6, 14 (January–February, 1955).

Shimberg, Myra E., and Blauston, Miriam, "The Rehabilitation Program in A Public Welfare Agency," *Social Casework,* 36, No. 10, pp. 470–473 (December, 1955).

Somers, Herman M., and Somers, Anne R., *Workmen's Compensation: Prevention, Insurance and Rehabilitation of Occupational Disability,* John Wiley & Sons, New York, 1954, 341 pages.

Switzer, Mary E., "Ten Years of Rehabilitation Under Public Law 113," *J. Rehabilitation,* XX, No. 4, pp. 4–6, 26 (July–August, 1954).

U.S. Department of Health, Education and Welfare, "Training Grant Programs of the Office of Vocational Rehabilitation—Information Statement and Instructions for Preparing Application," Washington, March, 1956, 25 pages.

U.S. Department of Health, Education and Welfare, *Annual Reports*—Sections on Office of Vocational Rehabilitation, Washington, 1954, pp. 221–243; 1955, pp. 181–201.

U.S. Department of Health, Education and Welfare, *Working Together to Rehabilitate the Needy Disabled,* Washington, July, 1955, 26 pages.

Veterans Administration, Department of Medicine and Surgery, "Physical Medicine and Rehabilitation—Orientation Material," Washington, February 10, 1953, 12 pages.

Whitehouse, Frederick A., "Teamwork—Clinical Practice in Rehabilitation," *Exceptional Children,* 19, No. 4, pp. 143–153 (January, 1953).

Community Aspects

American Medical Association, Council on Medical Service, "The Key to Community Health," Chicago, 1955, 17 pages.

Bachmann, George, and Associates, *Health Resources in the United States: Personnel, Facilities and Services,* Brookings Institute, Washington, 1952, 344 pages.

Buell, Bradley and Associates, *Community Planning for Human Services,* Columbia University Press, New York, 1950, 464 pages.

Colcord, Joanna C., *Your Community—Its Provision for Health, Education, Safety and Welfare,* Russell Sage Foundation, New York, 1947, 263 pages.

Cumming, Elaine and John, *Closed Ranks—An Experiment in Mental Health,* Commonwealth Fund, Harvard University Press, Cambridge, 1957, 192 pages.

Girl Scouts of the U.S.A., *Working With the Handicapped—A Leader's Guide,* New York, 1954, 127 pages.

Gunn, Selskar M., and Platt, Philip S., *Voluntary Health Agencies—An Interpretive Study,* Ronald Press Co., New York, 1946, 264 pages.

Health and Welfare Federation of Allegheny County, "Survey of Handicapped Workers: Report of a Citizens' Committee," Pittsburgh, 1955, 97 pages.

Kaplan, Jerome, *A Social Program for Older Persons,* University of Minnesota Press, Minneapolis, 1953, 137 pages.

Littledale, Harold A., *Mastering Your Disability,* Rinehart, New York, 1952, 224 pages.

Pollack, Jerome, "Community Concern and Coordination for Rehabilitation," Keynote address to Pacific Regional Conference, San Francisco, March 6, 1957, 9 pages.

Robinson, Marion, O., "Prevention and Control of Indigent Disability," *J. Rehabilitation,* XXI, No. 4, pp. 6–8 (July–August, 1955).

Seidenfield, Morton A., "Building Public Understanding of Rehabilitation," *J. Rehabilitation,* XXII, No. 6, pp. 9–10, 14–15, 24–25 (Nov.–Dec., 1956).

Smith, J. Hank, and Porter, Edgar B., "Community Organization—A Plan of Action," *J. Rehabilitation*, **XIX**, No. 5, pp. 10–12 (Sept.–Oct., 1953).

Stearns, William F., "The Road to Integration," *J. Rehabilitation*, **XX**, No. 1, pp. 12–13, 18–19, 28 (Jan.–Feb. 1954).

Stearns, William F., "Integration of a Center Program with Community Agencies," *Arch. Phys. Med. Rehabilitation*, **37**, No. 7, pp. 413–415 (July 1956).

Warren, Roland L., *Studying Your Community*, Russell Sage Foundation, New York, 1955, 385 pages.

Wenkert, Walter, "Community Planning for Rehabilitation," *Am. J. Public Health*, **42**, No. 7, pp. 779–783 (July 1952).

Counseling Aspects

Bamber, Laurence, *Point the Way: Nine Steps in Counseling: A Handbook for Counselors*, St. Louis Chapter, American Red Cross, 1951, 39 pages.

Cannon, Ida M., *On the Social Frontier of Medicine*, Harvard University Press, Cambridge, 1952, 273 pages.

Clements, Stanley W., McGowan, John F., Johnston, L. T., and McCavitt, Martin E., "What Is A Rehabilitation Counselor," *J. Rehabilitation*, **XXIII**, No. 3, pp. 6–12 (May–June, 1957).

Devereaux, Jane, "Social Casework and Vocational Adjustment," *J. Rehabilitation*, **XXII**, No. 6, pp. 7–8, 22–23 (Nov.–Dec. 1956).

Elledge, Caroline H., *The Rehabilitation of the Patient—Social Casework in Medicine*, J. B. Lippincott Co., Philadelphia, 1948, 112 pages.

Federal Security Agency, Office of Vocational Rehabilitation, "Psychiatric Information for the Rehabilitation Worker," Rehabilitation Standards Memorandum No. 18, Washington, 1950, 74 pages.

Field, Minna, *Patients Are People: A Medical-Social Approach to Prolonged Illness*, Columbia University Press, New York, 1953, 244 pages.

Hahn, M. E., and MacLean, M. S., *Counseling Psychology*, McGraw-Hill, New York, 1955, 302 pages.

Lofquist, Lloyd H., *Vocational Counseling With the Physically Handicapped*, Appleton-Century-Crofts, New York, 1957, 384 pages.

National Foundation for Infantile Paralysis, "Report of a Conference on the Place of the Medical Social Worker in the Home Care of the Long-Term Patient," New York, 1955, 23 pages.

National Rehabilitation Association and National Vocational Guidance Association, "Rehabilitation Counselor Preparation," Washington, 1956, 78 pages.

Patterson, C. H., "Counselor or Coordinator," *J. Rehabilitation*, **XXIII**, No. 3, May–June, 1957, pp. 13–15.

Pepinski, Harold B. and Pauline N., *Counseling Theory and Practice*, Ronald Press, New York, 1954, 307 pages.

Pohlmann, Kenneth E., "Group Techniques in Rehabilitation Counseling," *J. Rehabilitation*, **XVII**, No. 4, July–August, 1951, pp. 7–9.

Sessions, Percy M., "Counseling Recovering Psychotics," *J. Rehabilitation*, **XXII**, No. 4, pp. 11–13, 30, 33 (July–August, 1956).

U.S. Department of Health, Education and Welfare, Office of Vocational Rehabilitation, "Methods and Standards for Guidance, Training and Placement: Proceedings of the Workshops of Guidance, Training and Placement Supervisors": *3rd Annual Workshop*, Rehab. Service Series No. 150, 1950, 104 pages.

4th Annual Workshop, Rehab. Service Series No. 161, 1951, 69 pages.

5th Annual Workshop, Rehab. Service Series No. 188, 1952, 3 parts.

U.S. Department of Health, Education and Welfare, Office of Vocational Rehabilitation, *Orientation Training for Vocational Rehabilitation Counselors—A Syllabus for Orientation Institutes,* Washington, October, 1955, 199 pages.

Warren, Sol L., "Internship Program for Rehabilitation Counselors," *J. Rehabilitation,* **XXIII,** No. 3, pp. 4–5, 20–22 (May–June, 1957).

Educational Aspects

Dolch, Edward W., *Helping Handicapped Children in School,* Garrard Press, Champaign, Ill., 1948, 349 pages.

Gorthy, Willis C., "Training Program for Rehabilitation Center Administrators," *Arch. Phys. Med. Rehabilitation,* **37,** No. 7, pp. 408–409 (July, 1956).

Heck, Arch O., *"The Education of Exceptional Children: Its Challenge to Teachers, Parents and Laymen,"* Second Edition, McGraw-Hill, New York, 1953, 513 pages.

Lee, John J., "The Role of the University in the Counselor Education Program," *J. Rehabilitation,* **XXI,** No. 5, pp. 4–5, 14 (Sept.–Oct., 1955).

Martin, Gordon M., "Educational Goals in Physical Medicine and Rehabilitation," *Arch. Phys. Med. Rehabilitation,* **37,** No. 10, pp. 597–603 (October, 1956).

New York City Board of Education, *Helping the Physically Limited Child,* New York, 1953, 211 pages.

Piersol, George M., "The Present Obligation of Physical Medicine and Rehabilitation," *J. Am. Med. Assoc.,* **147,** No. 12, pp. 1093–1096 (November 17, 1951).

Rusk, Howard A., "Physical Medicine and Rehabilitation: The Problems of Education," *Arch. Phys. Med. Rehabilitation,* **32,** No. 3, pp. 137–141 (March, 1951).

Wallin, J. E. W., *Children With Mental and Physical Handicaps,* Prentice-Hall, New York, 1949, 549 pages.

Facility Aspects

Allan, W. Scott, "Basic Planning for a Rehabilitation Center," *Performance,* President's Committee on Employment of the Physically Handicapped, Washington, April, 1954, pp. 3–5, 8.

Baruch Committee on Physical Medicine, "Report on A Community Rehabilitation Service and Center (Functional Plan)," New York, 1946, 24 pages.

Chenven, Harold, "The Mental Hygiene Team in a Rehabilitation Center," *J. Rehabilitation,* **XXII,** No. 4, pp. 9–10, 23–27 (July–August, 1956).

Conference of Rehabilitation Centers, Inc., "Proceedings—Annual Conferences and Workshops," 1952–1956 also "Proceedings of Institute on Rehabilitation Center Planning," February 25–March 1, 1957, Chicago.

Coulter, John S., "A Rehabilitation Center for the Injured Worker," *Arch. Phys. Therapy,* **XXV,** pp. 529–539, 570 (September, 1944).

Cronin, John W., and Galbraith, Thomas P., "Planning Multiple Disability Rehabilitation Facilities," *Hospitals,* (March 16, 1956).

Fortune, George J., "The Cleveland Hearing and Speech Center," *J. Rehabilitation,* **XIX,** No. 3, pp. 7–10 (May–June, 1955).

Gorthy, Willis C., "Rehabilitation's Hidden Dimension," *Arch. Phys. Med. Rehabilitation,* **38,** No. 2, pp. 95–100 (February, 1957).

Hochhauser, Edward, "The Sheltered Workshop in A Program for the Rehabilitation of the Chronically Ill," New York, 1951, 16 pages.

Hospitals, 29, No. 3, March 1955, entire issue devoted to planning and construction of hospital rehabilitation facilities.

Institute for the Crippled and Disabled, *Rehabilitation Trends–Midcentury to 1956,* New York, 1956, 96 pages.

Kendall, H. Worley, "Rehabilitation Unit," *Modern Hospital,* 78, No. 3, pp. 67–70, 118–122 (March 1952).

Liberty Mutual Insurance Co., "The Rehabilitation Centers," Boston, 1954, 16 pages.

National Committee on Sheltered Workshops and Homebound Programs, *Sheltered Workshops and Homebound Programs—A Handbook,* New York, 1952, 85 pages.

National Society for Crippled Children and Adults, Inc., "Proceedings—The Institute on Rehabilitation Centers," Chicago, June, 1955, 72 pages.

Park, Herbert W., et al, "Facts and Figures for a Rehabilitation Hospital," *Hospitals,* 26, No. 11, pp. 52–54 (November, 1952).

Pohlmann, Kenneth E., "Vocational Schools—A Community Resource for Rehabilitation," *J. Rehabilitation,* XX, No. 5, pp. 9–11 (Sept.–Oct. 1954).

Redkey, Henry, *Rehabilitation Centers in the United States,* National Society for Crippled Children and Adults and U.S. Department of Health, Education and Welfare, Office of Vocational Rehabilitation, Chicago, 1953, 128 pages.

Redkey, Henry, "The Community Rehabilitation Center," *J. Rehabilitation,* XX, No. 3, pp. 14–20, 29–30 (May–June, 1954).

Rusk, Howard A., "Rehabilitation in the Hospital," *Public Health Rep.,* 68, No. 3, pp. 281–285 (March, 1953).

Shands, A. R., Jr., "Diagnostic Clinic for Rehabilitation," *J. Am. Med. Assoc.,* 140, No. 11, pp. 937–940 (July 16, 1949).

Shepherd, Vivian, "Organization and Administration of a Community Rehabilitation Center," *Arch. Phys. Med. Rehabilitation,* 37, No. 8, pp. 473–476 (August, 1956).

Shover, Jayne, "Medical Relationships in A Rehabilitation Center," *J. Rehabilitation,* XX, No. 6, pp. 12–13, 36 (Nov.–Dec. 1954).

Switzer, Mary E. and McKneely, Thomas B., "Rehabilitation: A Challenge to the Voluntary General Hospital," *Hospital Prog.,* 32, No. 12, pp. 357–359 (Dec., 1951).

U.S. Department of Health, Education and Welfare, Office of Vocational Rehabilitation, *Rehabilitation Centers for Blind Persons,* Rehabilitation Service Series No. 380, Washington, 1957, 43 pages.

U.S. Department of Health, Education and Welfare, Office of Vocational Rehabilitation, *Workshops for the Disabled,* Rehabilitation Service Series No. 371, Washington, 1956, 167 pages.

White, Barbara, and Redkey, Henry, *The Prevocational Unit in a Rehabilitation Center,* U.S. Department of Health, Education and Welfare, Office of Vocational Rehabilitation, Washington, 1956, 22 pages.

Whitehouse, Frederick A., "The Rehabilitation Center—Some Aspects of a Philosophy," *American Journal of Occupational Therapy,* VII, No. 6, pp. 241–246, 270 (Nov.–Dec. 1953).

Yerby, Alonzo S., "Differential Use of Rehabilitation Facilities," *J. Rehabilitation,* XXII, No. 2, pp. 4–5, 15 (March–April 1956).

Yerby, Alonzo, S., "Planning the Rehabilitation Center," *J. Rehabilitation,* XXI, No. 4, pp. 13–15 (July–Aug. 1955).

General Aspects

Allan, W. Scott, "Rehabilitation—Challenge and Responsibility," *Am. Econ. Security*, **XIII**, No. 5, pp. 12–21 (Sept.–Oct. 1956).

Baruch Committee on Physical Medicine, *Annual Report for the Fiscal Year April 1, 1944, to March 31, 1945*, New York, 1945, 82 pages.

Belknap, Ivan, *Human Problems of a State Mental Hospital*, McGraw-Hill Book Co., New York, 1956, 277 pages.

Boas, Ernst P., *The Unseen Plague: Chronic Disease*, J. J. Augustin, New York, 1940, 121 pages.

Brophy, Thomas D., "Rehabilitation—A Challenge to Voluntary Effort," *The Crippled Child*, **34**, No. 5, pp. 4–6, 28 (Feb. 1957).

Commission on Chronic Illness, *Care of the Long-Term Patient*, Vol. II of *Chronic Illness in the United States*, Commonwealth Fund, Harvard University Press, Cambridge, 1956, 606 pages.

Dasco, Michael M., Novey, Josephine, and Kristeller, Edith L., *Survey of 95 Custodial Patients in a Municipal Hospital*, Monograph No. VII, Institute for Physical Medicine and Rehabilitation, New York University—Bellevue Medical Center, New York, 1954, 52 pages.

Davis, John E., *Principles and Practices of Rehabilitation*, Barnes, New York, 1943, 211 pages.

Donahue, Wilma (and others), *Rehabilitation of the Older Worker*, University of Michigan Press, Ann Arbor, 1953, 200 pages.

Elton, Frederic G., "Rehabilitation—The Place and Relationship of Services," *J. Am. Assoc. Ind. Nurses*, **4**, No. 3, pp. 6–14 (March 1956).

Ewing, Oscar R., "The Nation's Health—a Ten-Year Program," a report of the Federal Security Administrator to the President, Washington, September, 1948, 186 pages.

Frampton, Merle E., and Gall, Elena D., *Special Education for the Exceptional*, Porter-Sargent Publishing Co., Boston, 1955, 3 vols., 453, 677, and 710 pages, respectively.

Henry, Nelson B., editor, *The Education of Exceptional Children*, 49th Yearbook, Part II, National Society for the Study of Education, University of Chicago Press, Chicago, 1950.

Kessler, Henry H., *Rehabilitation of the Physically Handicapped*, Columbia University Press, New York, 1953, Revised Edition, 275 pages.

Kessler, Henry H., *The Principles and Practices of Rehabilitation*, Lea and Febiger, Philadelphia, 1950, 448 pages.

Mayo, Leonard W., "Synthesizing Forces for Rehabilitation," *The Crippled Child*, **34**, No. 4, pp. 4–5 (Dec. 1956).

New York Academy of Medicine, Committee on Public Health Relations, "Convalescence and Rehabilitation: Proceedings of the Conference," April 25–26, 1944, New York, 223 pages.

Pattison, Harry A., *The Handicapped and their Rehabilitation*, Charles C. Thomas, Springfield, Ill., 1957, 944 pages.

President's Commission on the Health Needs of the Nation, *Building America's Health*, 5 Vols.

Vol. I, *Findings and Recommendations*, 80 pages.

Vol. II, *America's Health Status, Needs and Resources*, 306 pages.

Vol. III, *America's Health Status, Needs and Resources—A Statistical Appendix;* 299 pages.

Vol. IV, *Financing a Health Program for America,* 363 pages.

Vol. V, *The People Speak—Excerpts from Regional Public Hearings on Health,* 521 pages.

Rusk, Howard A., "Recent Developments in Rehabilitation," *Am. Assoc. Ind. Nurses J.,* 5, No. 3, pp. 25–28 (March 1957).

Rusk, Howard A., and Taylor, Eugene J., *New Hope for the Handicapped,* Harper and Bros., New York, 1949, 231 pages.

Schwartz, Charlotte G., *Rehabilitation of Mental Hospital Patients,* U.S. Department of Health, Education and Welfare, Public Health Service, Public Health Monograph No. 17, Washington, 1953, 70 pages.

Soden, William H., editor, *Rehabilitation of the Handicapped: A Survey of Means and Methods,* Ronald Press, New York, 1949, 399 pages.

Switzer, Mary E., and Rusk, Howard A., *Doing Something for the Disabled,* Public Affairs Pamphlet No. 197, Public Affairs Committee, Inc., New York, 1953, 28 pages.

Upham, Frances, *A Dynamic Approach to Illness,* Family Service Association of America, New York, 1949, 200 pages.

U. S. Department of Health, Education and Welfare, "Study of the Homebound—Programs for Physically Handicapped Homebound Individuals," Report to the Congress, February 2, 1955, Washington, 68 pages.

Van Riper, Hart E., "Rehabilitation: A Prescription for Living," *Ill. Med. J.,* 102, No. 5, pp. 300–304 (Nov. 1952).

Whitehouse, Frederick A., "Habilitation—Concept and Process," *J. Rehabilitation,* XXIX, No. 2, pp. 3–7 (March–April 1953).

International Aspects

Amato, David, "Rehabilitation and the Democratic Process," *J. Rehabilitation,* XXII, No. 5, pp. 9–11 (Sept.–Oct. 1956).

International Society for the Welfare of Cripples, "Changing Attitudes Towards the Disabled," Proceedings of the Sixth World Congress, September, 1954, Central Council for the Care of Cripples, London, 1955, 287 pages.

Rusk, Howard A., "Rehabilitation: An International Problem," *Arch. Phys. Med. Rehabilitation,* 37, No. 3, pp. 135–137 (March 1956).

United Nations, Department of Social Affairs, *Services for the Physically Handicapped,* ST/SOA/Ser.P/1, November, 1953, 31 pages.

United Nations, Department of Social Affairs, *Modern Methods of Rehabilitation of the Adult Disabled,* ST/TAA/Ser.C/4, New York, November 25, 1952, 108 pages.

United Nations, Department of Social Affairs, *Rehabilitation of the Handicapped,* Social Welfare Information Series, Special Issue, ST/SOA/Ser.F/11:2, New York, September, 1953, 85 pages.

United Nations, Reprint from *United Nations Review,* "Living Whole Lives," New York, March 1956, 12 pages.

United Nations, *United Nations Conference of Experts on Physically Handicapped Children for Countries of Southeast Asia,* Jamshedpur, India, December, 1950, TAA Conference and Seminar Series No. 1, 60 pages.

Wilson, Donald V., "The Crippled," Reprint from *Social Work Year Book 1954,* International Society for the Welfare of Cripples, New York, 8 pages.

Insurance Aspects

Allan, W. Scott, "Industrial Accident Cases and the Community Rehabilitation Center, *Am. J. Occupational Therapy*, **IX**, No. 5, Part II, pp. 252–254 (Sept.–Oct. 1955).

Allan, W. Scott, "The Economics of Rehabilitation," *Tennessee Law Rev.*, **24**, No. 4, pp. 475–482 (June 1956).

Allan, W. Scott, "The Liberty Mutual Rehabilitation Program," *Arch. Phys. Med. Rehabilitation*, **37**, No. 7, pp. 405–407 (July 1956).

American Medical Association, Council on Medical Services, Council on Industrial Health and Committee on Medical Care for Industrial Workers, "A Survey of Union Health Centers," Chicago, 1954, 46 pages.

American Medical Association, Council on Medical Services, "Voluntary Prepayment Medical Benefit Plans," 1957 edition; also Charts and Graphs Supplement, Chicago, 1957, 167 pages.

Black, S. Bruce, *Free Institutions and the Quest for Security*, The Newcomen Society, Princeton University Press, Princeton, N. J., 1951, 28 pages.

Cooper, Richard B., "The Insurer's Role in Rehabilitation," *Ind. Med. Surgery*, **26**, No. 6, pp. 277–281 (June 1957).

Hanson, Stanwood L., "A Design for Effective Living," *Public Aid in Illinois*, **XXI**, No. 1, pp. 1–6 (Jan. 1954).

Hanson, Stanwood L., "Disabled Men Work Again," *Am. J. Public Health*, **42**, No. 7, pp. 787–790 (July 1952).

Hanson, Stanwood L., "Results of Rehabilitation in the Field of Workmen's Compensation," *J. Chronic Diseases*, **3**, No. 3, pp. 323–330 (March 1956).

Health Insurance Council, "The Contribution of Voluntary Health Insurance," reprinted from *J. Chronic Diseases*, 35 pages (1956).

Health Insurance Council, *The Health Insurance Story*, New York, 1956, 63 pages.

Hess, Arthur E., "Disability Insurance Provisions of the Social Security Act," *Ind. Med. Surgery*, **26**, No. 8, pp. 372–376 (Aug. 1957).

Institute for Crippled and Disabled, "Report of a Conference on Rehabilitation in Compensation Cases," A Panel Discussion and Demonstration, Jan. 16, 1952, New York, 53 pages.

Larson, Arthur, "Income Insurance and Labor Relations," Address to Economic Club of Chicago, May 19, 1954, 20 pages.

Miller, John H., "Health Insurance for Older Citizens," *Am. Econ. Security*, **XIII**, No. 6, pp. 17–24 (Nov.–Dec. 1956).

Miller, John H., "Meeting the Needs of the Disabled Worker," *Am. Econ. Security*, **XII**, No. 5, pp. 9–17 (Sept.–Oct. 1955).

Pollack, Jerome, "Major Medical Expense Insurance: An Evaluation," *Am. J. Public Health*, **47**, No. 3, pp. 322–334 (March 1957).

Reischl, Helen A., "Rehabilitation of the Injured Worker," *Nursing World*, **126**, No. 6, pp. 28–30, 43 (June 1952).

Research Council for Economic Security, *Disability Insurance, 1952: A Review of Disability Insurance Laws*, Publication No. 97, Chicago, 1953, 30 pages.

U. S. Chamber of Commerce, *Major Medical Expense Insurance*, Washington, February, 1956, 33 pages.

Wheatley, George M., "Voluntary Health Insurance—Progress and Problems," *New England J. Medicine*, **257**, No. 3, pp. 114–120 (July 18, 1957).

Legislative Aspects

Barrow, Roscoe L., and Fabing, Howard B., *Epilepsy and the Law*, Hoeber–Harper, New York, 1956, 177 pages.

Larson, Arthur, "Changing Concepts in Workmen's Compensation," Address before National Association of Claimants Compensation Attorneys, September 1, 1954, Boston, 21 pages.

Larson, Arthur, "The Model Workmen's Compensation Act," Address to the Sixth Annual Conference of Southern Association of Workmen's Compensation Administrators, Orlando, Fla., October 28, 1954, 11 pages.

New York State Joint Legislative Committee on Problems of the Aging, *Enriching the Years*, Legislative Document No. 32, Albany, N. Y., 1953, 199 pages.

New York State Joint Legislative Committee on Problems of the Aging, *Growing with the Years*, Legislative Document No. 32, Albany, N. Y., 1954, 159 pages.

U. S. Chamber of Commerce, *Analysis of Workmen's Compensation Laws*, Washington, 1956 (also 1957 Supplement), 56 pages.

U. S. Department of Health, Education and Welfare, Office of Vocational Rehabilitation, *New Hope for the Disabled* (VR-ISC-13), Washington, 1956, 23 pages.

U. S. Department of Labor, Bureau of Labor Standards, *Second Injury Funds— Standards and Patterns in State Legislation*, Bulletin 190, Washington, 1957, 61 pages.

U. S. Social Security Administration, Medical Advisory Committee, "Report and Recommendations of the O.A.S.I. Disability Freeze Provision," Washington, 1955, 10 pages.

Medical Aspects

Aitken, Alexander P., "The Need for Adequate Aftercare in Complete Rehabilitation of the Disabled," *Surgery, Gynecology Obstetrics*, **95**, pp. 317–320 (Sept. 1952).

Aitken, Alexander P., "The Case of the Injured Worker—Diagnosis and Treatment," *J. Rehabilitation*, **XVII**, No. 5 (Sept.–Oct. 1951).

Albee, Fred H., *A Surgeon's Fight to Rebuild Men*, Dutton, New York, 1943, 349 pages.

American Medical Association, *Handbook of Physical Medicine and Rehabilitation*, Blakiston Co., Philadelphia, 1950, 573 pages.

American Medical Association, *Medical Relations in Workmen's Compensation*, Chicago, 1955, 10 pages.

Boyd, Harold B., "Advances in Conquering Crippling," *The Crippled Child*, **34**, No. 1, pp. 4–6, 26 (June 1956).

Commerce and Industry Association of New York, Inc., *Medical Aspects of Workmen's Compensation*, New York, 1953, 104 pages.

Covalt, Donald A., "Dynamic Therapy in Chronic Disease," *J. Indiana State Med. Assoc.*, **43**, No. 1, pp. 17–20 (Jan. 1950).

Galdston, Iago', *The Meaning of Social Medicine*, Commonwealth Fund, Harvard University Press, Cambridge, 1951, 137 pages.

Hellerstein, Herman K., and Ford, Amasa B., "Rehabilitation of the Cardiac Patient," *J. Am. Med. Assoc.*, **164**, No. 3, pp. 225–231 (May 18, 1957).

Hoffman, J. L., "Rehabilitation Concepts in Mental Hospital Practice," *J. Rehabilitation*, **XXII**, No. 4, pp. 4–6, 16–19, 31 (July–Aug. 1956).

Hospital Association of Pennsylvania, Special Committee on Hospital Clinic Services, *Better Hospital Care for the Ambulant Patient,* Harrisburg, 1946, 184 pages.

Kessler, Henry H., *Low Back Pain in Industry,* Commerce and Industry Association of New York, Inc., New York, 1955, 227 pages.

Jones, Arthur C., "The Community Rehabilitation Center and the General Practitioner," *J. Am. Med. Assoc.,* 144, No. 12, pp. 994–995 (Nov. 18, 1950).

Krusen, Frank H., "New Frontiers in Rehabilitation," *The Crippled Child,* 30, No. 4, pp. 12–14 (Dec. 1950).

Krusen, Frank H., "Physical Rehabilitation for Industrial Diseases," *Brit. J. Phys. Med.,* pp. 220–224 (Oct. 1955).

Krusen, Frank H., "The Future of Physical Medicine," *J. Am. Med. Assoc.,* 125, pp. 1093–1097 (Aug. 19, 1944).

McCahan, Jermyn F., "Rehabilitation's Contribution to Industrial Health," *Am. Assoc. Ind. Nurses J.,* 5, No. 3, pp. 5–10 (March 1957).

McClellan, Walter S., *Physical Medicine and Rehabilitation for the Aged,* Charles C. Thomas, Springfield, Ill., 1951, 89 pages.

Neu, Harold N., "Rehabilitation: The Third Phase of Medical Care," *Nebraska State Med. J.,* 38, No. 9, pp. 315–320.

Rieke, Forrest E., "Doctor and Workmen's Compensation," *Ind. Med. Surgery,* 26, No. 1, pp. 9–22 (Jan. 1957).

Rowntree, Grady R., "The Physician, the Patient and the Community," *Ind. Med. Surgery,* 25, No. 9, pp. 433–434 (Sept. 1956).

Solomon, Walter M., "Progress in Physical Medicine and Rehabilitation," *J. Am. Med. Assoc.,* 156, No. 8, pp. 753–755 (Oct. 23, 1954).

Watkins, Arthur L., "Medical Progress—Physical Medicine and Rehabilitation," *New England J. Med.,* 255, No. 26, pp. 1233–1239.

Worden, Ralph E., "Responsibilities and Functions of Physicians in the Rehabilitation Center," *Arch. Phys. Med. Rehabilitation,* 37, No. 10, pp. 629–630 (Oct. 1956).

Personnel Aspects

Augustin, Dorothea C., and Ehmann, Janet A., "Employment Outlook for Physical Therapists: A Survey of Salary and Personnel Policies," *Arch. Phys. Med. Rehabilitation,* 38, No. 8, pp. 509–520 (Aug. 1957).

Miller, Leonard M., Garrett, James F., and Stewart, Nathaniel, "Opportunity: Rehabilitation Counseling," *Personnel Guidance J.,* 33, No. 8, pp. 444–447 (April 1955).

National Health Council, *Health Careers Guidebook,* New York, 1955, 153 pages.

National Society for Crippled Children and Adults, *Careers in Service to the Handicapped,* Chicago, 1952, 52 pages.

Office of Defense Mobilization, Health Resources Advisory Committee, *Mobilization and Health Manpower,* II, A Report of the Subcommittee on Paramedical Personnel in Rehabilitation and Care of the Chronically Ill, Washington, January, 1956, 87 pages.

Stearns, William F., "Effective Use of Rehabilitation Personnel," *J. Rehabilitation,* XXII, No. 3, pp. 4–5 (May–June 1956).

Psychological Aspects

Alger, Ian, and Rusk, Howard A., "The Rejection of Help by Some Disabled People," *Am. J. Med. Sci.*, **223**, pp. 106–112 (Jan. 1952).

Anastasi, Anna, *Psychological Testing*, MacMillan Co., New York, 1954, 682 pages.

Barker, Roger G., and Others, *Adjustment to Physical Handicap and Illness: A Survey of the Social Psychology of Physique and Disability*, Social Science Research Council, Bulletin 55, Revised 1956, New York, 440 pages.

Barnes, Robert H., "Psychological Problems in Physical Rehabilitation," *Am. J. Med. Sci.*, **223**, pp. 106–112 (Jan. 1952).

Garrett, James F., *Psychological Aspects of Physical Disability*, Federal Security Agency, Office of Vocational Rehabilitation, Rehabilitation Service Series No. 210, Washington, 1952, 195 pages.

George, Harlan E., "Psychological Problems in A Rehabilitation Center," *J. Rehabilitation*, **XXI**, No. 2, pp. 4–5, 12 (March–April 1955).

Grayson, Morris, and Others, *Psychiatric Aspects of Rehabilitation*, Institute of Physical Medicine and Rehabilitation, New York University—Bellevue Medical Center, Rehabilitation Monograph II, New York, 1952, 86 pages.

Grossman, Maurice, "Emotional Aspects of Rehabilitation," *Am. J. Psychiatry*, **109**, No. 11, pp. 849–852 (May 1953).

Nemiah, John C., "Contribution of Psychiatry to Research in Physical Medicine and Rehabilitation," *Arch. Phys. Med. Rehabilitation*, **37**, No. 6, pp. 341–344 (June 1956).

Nemiah, John C., "The Psychiatrist and Rehabilitation," *Arch. Phys. Med. Rehabilitation*, **38**, No. 3, pp. 143–147 (March 1957).

Phillips, E. Lakin, "The Problem of Motivation—Some Neglected Aspects," *J. Rehabilitation*, **XXIII**, No. 2, pp. 10–12 (March 1957).

Pitner, Rudolph, and Others, *The Psychology of the Physically Handicapped*, Appleton-Century-Crofts, New York, 1941.

Smith, Lillian, *The Journey*, World Publishing Co., Cleveland, 1954, 256 pages.

Super, Donald E., *Appraising Vocational Fitness by Means of Psychological Tests*, Harper Bros., New York, 1949, 727 pages.

Unterberger, Hilma, and Olshansky, Simon S., "Vocational Rehabilitation and the Psychotic Patient," *J. Rehabilitation*, **XXI**, No. 1, pp. 7–9 (Jan.–Feb. 1955).

Wilson, Arthus J., *Emotional Life of the Ill and Injured*, Social Science Publishers, New York, 1949, 416 pages.

Statistical Aspects

American Medical Association, *The Economic Position of Medical Care 1929–1953*, Bulletin 99, Chicago, 1955, 36 pages.

Britten, Rollo H., Collins, Selwyn D., and Fitzgerald, James S., "The National Health Survey: Some General Findings as to Disease, Accidents and Impairments in Urban Areas," Reprint No. 2143 from *Public Health Rep.*, **55**, No. 11, pp. 444–470 (March 15, 1940).

Federal Security Agency, Public Health Service, *The National Health Survey 1935–36: Scope, Method and Bibliography*, Public Health Service Publication No.

85, Washington, 1951, 67 pages; also Bulletins 1–11 in *Sickness* and in *Medical Care Series* and Bulletins 1–7 in *Hearing Study Series,* Washington, 1938.

Karpinos, Bernard D., "The Physically Handicapped," U. S. Public Health Service, *Public Health Rep.,* 58, No. 43, pp. 1573–1592 (Oct. 22, 1943).

McCoy, Georgia, and Rusk, Howard A., *An Evaluation of Rehabilitation,* Rehabilitation Monograph I, Institute of Physical Medicine and Rehabilitation, New York University, Bellevue Medical Center, New York, 1953, 87 pages.

National Health Education Committee, "Facts on the Major and Crippling Diseases in the United States Today: Heart Diseases, Cancer, Mental Illness, Arthritis, Blindness, Neurological Diseases and Other Health Problems," New York, 1955, various paging.

National Safety Council, *Accident Facts—1957 Edition,* Chicago, 1957, 96 pages.

Olshansky, Simon S., "The Labor Force Trend and Rehabilitation," *J. Rehabilitation,* XXII, No. 3, pp. 11–13, 15 (May–June 1956).

Social Planning Council of St. Louis, *Community Resources for Rehabilitation of the Disabled in St. Louis and St. Louis County,* St. Louis, 1952, 17 pages.

U. S. Department of Commerce, Bureau of the Census, *Statistical Abstract of the United States—1956,* 77th Edition, Washington, 1956, 1049 pages.

U. S. Department of Health, Education and Welfare, Office of Vocational Rehabilitation, *Number of Disabled Persons in Need of Vocational Rehabilitation,* Rehabilitation Service Series No. 274, Washington, June, 1954, 12 pages.

Whitten, E. B., "How Big Is the Rehabilitation Problem?" *J. Rehabilitation,* XXIII, No. 1, pp. 4–5, 16–21 (Jan.–Feb. 1957).

Woolsey, Theodore D., *Estimates of Disabling Illness Prevalence in the United States,* Federal Security Agency, Public Health Service, Public Health Monograph No. 4, Washington, 1952, 16 pages.

Therapy and Nursing Aspects

Appleby, Blanche, and Reilly, Genevieve, "Rehabilitation of the Severely Handicapped," *Trained Nurse,* 74, No. 5, pp. 235–239 (May 1950).

Bennett, Robert L., and Driver, Muriel T., "The Role of Occupational Therapy in Physical Rehabilitation," *J. Rehabilitation,* XXII, No. 2, pp. 11–14, 26–27 (March–April 1956).

Bogardus, Emory S., and Brethorst, Alice B., *Sociology Applied to Nursing,* Second Edition, W. B. Saunders, Philadelphia, 1945, 312 pages.

Gordon, Edward E., and Wellerson, Thelma L., "Does Occupational Therapy Meet the Demands of Total Rehabilitation?" *Am. J. Occupational Therapy,* 8, No. 6, pp. 238–240, 275–276 (Nov.–Dec. 1954).

Hartigan, Helen, "Nursing Responsibilities in Rehabilitation," *Nursing Outlook,* 2, No. 12, pp. 649–651 (Dec. 1954).

Ireland, Karl L., "Evaluating Work Behavior in Occupational Therapy," *J. Rehabilitation,* XXIII, No. 1, pp. 8–9, 25–28 (Jan.–Feb. 1957).

Morrissey, Alice B., *Rehabilitation Nursing,* G. P. Putnam's Sons, New York, 1951, 299 pages.

Odlum, Doris M., *Psychology, the Nurse and the Patient,* Philosophical Library, New York, 1954, 168 pages.

Schiffer, Doris M., "Liberty Mutual's Rehabilitation Program," *Am. J. Nursing,* 53, No. 7, pp. 834–837 (July 1953).

Stafford, George T., *Preventive and Corrective Physical Education*, Revised Edition, A. S. Barnes, New York, 1950, 312 pages.

Terry, Florence J., and Others, *Principles and Techniques of Rehabilitation Nursing*, C. V. Mosby Co., St. Louis, 1957, 345 pages.

West, Wilma, and McNary, Henrietta, "A Study of the Present and Potential Role of Occupational Therapy in Rehabilitation," *Am. J. Occupational Therapy*, **X**, No. 3, pp. 103–110, 131–132 (May–June 1956), and No. 4, pp. 150–156, 171–172 (July–Aug. 1956).

Willard, Helen S., and Spackman, Clare S., *Principles of Occupational Therapy*, 2nd Edition, J. B. Lippincott Co., Philadelphia, 1954, 376 pages.

Vocational Aspects

American Federation of Labor and Congress of Industrial Organizations, *Cooperation—the Key to Jobs for the Handicapped*, Publication No. 42, Washington, 1956, 10 pages.

American Museum of Safety and the Center for Safety Education, New York University, *Safety Training Digest—Industrial Rehabilitation*, New York, 1945, 91 pages.

American Mutual Liability Insurance Co., *Physical Abilities to Fit the Job*, Sanderson Bros. Inc., Boston, 1956, 145 pages.

Arthur, Julietta K., *How to Make a Home Business Pay*, Prentice-Hall, Inc., New York, 1949, 330 pages.

Barton, Everett H., "How to Get A Job," *The Crippled Child*, 33, No. 3, pp. 4–6 (Oct. 1955).

Bramblett, Earl R., "Problems of Management in the Placement of Handicapped Workers," *Arch. Phys. Med. Rehabilitation*, 37, No. 9, pp. 547–549 (Sept. 1956).

Breckenridge, Elizabeth L., *Effective Use of Older Workers*, Wilcox and Follett Co., Chicago, 1953, 224 pages.

Bridges, Clark D., *Job Placement of the Physically Handicapped*, McGraw-Hill, New York, 1946, 329 pages.

Canty, Thomas J., "Employment of the Amputee," *Performance*, President's Committee on the Employment of the Physically Handicapped, **II**, No. 4, pp. 1–2, 6–7 (Nov. 1951).

Elton, Frederic G., *Work Therapy*, American Rehabilitation Committee, Inc., New York, 1948, 30 pages.

Federal Security Agency, Office of Vocational Rehabilitation, *Vocational Rehabilitation of the Mentally Retarded*, Rehabilitation Service Series No. 123, Washington, 1950, 184 pages.

Gellman, William et al, *Adjusting People to Work*, Jewish Vocational Service and Employment Center, Chicago, 1956, 227 pages.

Hanman, Bert, *Physical Capacities and Job Placement*, Nordisk Rotogravyr, Stockholm (John DeGraff, Inc., New York), 1951, 167 pages.

Hirsch, Doris K., "A Work Trial Program for the Severely Handicapped," *J. Rehabilitation*, **XVI**, No. 6, pp. 3–6 (Nov.–Dec. 1950).

Irvin, E. A., "Industrial Placement of the Physically Handicapped," *Arch. Phys. Med. Rehabilitation*, 37, No. 10, pp. 622–626 (Oct. 1956).

Jansson, Kurt, "The Employment of Handicapped Workers in Industry," *Int. Labour Rev.*, 68, No. 2, 16 pages (Aug. 1953).

Marra, Joseph, Moore, Alice, and Young, Milton A., "Job Training for the Mentally Retarded," *J. Rehabilitation*, **XXIII**, No. 1, pp. 10–12, 29–30 (Jan.–Feb. 1957).

National Association of Manufacturers, *Guide for Employers in Hiring the Physically Handicapped*, New York, 1955, 31 pages.

National Association of Mutual Casualty Companies, *The Handicapped Man for the Job—The Job for the Handicapped Man*, Chicago, 1955, 15 pages.

National Research Council, *Rehabilitation: The Man and the Job*, Report of the Subcommittee on Rehabilitation of the Committee on Work in Industry, National Research Council Reprint and Circular Series No. 121, March 1945, Washington, 73 pages.

Odell, Charles E., "The Problem of Placement," *J. Rehabilitation*, **XXI**, No. 6, pp. 311–314 (Nov.–Dec. 1955).

Rudd, Jacob L., "Physical Medicine and Rehabilitation in the Member-Employee Program," *Arch. Phys. Med. Rehabilitation*, **38**, No. 8, pp. 505–508 (Aug. 1957).

Task Force on the Handicapped, Report to the Chairman of the Manpower Policy Committee, Office of Defense Mobilization, Washington, January 25, 1952, 89 pages.

U. S. Civil Service Commission, *Selective Placement of the Handicapped*, Washington, August, 1955, 13 pages.

U. S. Department of Labor, Bureau of Labor Statistics, *The Performance of Physically Impaired Workers in Manufacturing Industries*, Bulletin No. 923, Washington, 1948, 132 pages.

Usdane, William M., "Prevocational Evaluation Criteria for the Severely Handicapped," *Arch. Phys. Med. Rehabilitation*, **38**, No. 5, pp. 311–314 (May 1957).

Victorian Employers' Federation, *Employment of the Physically Handicapped: A Survey*, New South Wales, 1955, 37 pages.

Viscardi, Henry, Jr., "Return of the Disabled Worker," *Office Executive*, **30**, No. 11, pp. 7–10 (Nov. 1955).

Warren, Sol L., *Vocational Rehabilitation of the Tuberculous*, National Tuberculosis Association, New York, 1955, 193 pages.

Whitehouse, Frederick A., "Client Evaluation in the Habilitation Process," *J. Rehabilitation*, **XIX**, No. 6, pp. 4–6, 26–28 (Nov.–Dec. 1953).

Index of Names

Subject Index

243

Date Due